HEATH
Earth Science

Laboratory Investigations

Teacher's Annotated Edition

Author

Nancy Spaulding
Earth Science Teacher
Elmira Free Academy, Elmira, NY

Contributing Writer

Gabriele Reil
Environmental Studies Teacher
Chemistry Teacher
Moriarty High School, Moriarty, NM

Executive Editor: Ceanne P. Tzimopoulos
Supervising Editor: Christine H. Wang
Editorial Development:
Amy R. Pallant, Ann E. Bekebrede, Virginia A. Flook
Design Management and Cover Design: Lisa Fowler
Book Design and Development:
Reynolds Design & Management, Christine Reynolds
Production Coordinator: Maureen Bisso
Cover Photographs:
Spider Rock, Canyon de Chelly National Monument, Arizona, David Muench
Earth, © Telegraph Colour Library 199, FPG International

D.C. Heath and Company
Lexington, Massachusetts/Toronto, Ontario

Heath Earth Science Program

- Earth Science, Pupil's Edition
- Earth Science, Teacher's Annotated Edition
- Earth Science Laboratory Investigations, Pupil's Edition
- Earth Science Laboratory Investigations, Teacher's Annotated Edition
- Earth Science Overhead Transparencies
- Earth Science Study Guide
- Earth Science Study Guide Answer Key
- Earth Science Chapter Tests with Answers
- Earth Science Computer Test Bank; Apple, IBM, Macintosh
- Earth Science Computer Test Bank, Teacher's Guide
- Environmental Awareness Case Studies
- Computer Software:
  - Mountains and Crustal Movement
  - Dating and Geologic Time

Published simultaneously in Canada

Printed in the United States of America

International Standard Book Number: 0-669-26186-6

1 2 3 4 5 6 7 8 9 10 -BA- 99 98 97 96 95 94 93

Contents

To The Teacher

The activities in *Heath Earth Science Laboratory Investigations* are designed to give each student an opportunity to develop and use the basic science skills and concepts associated with earth science programs. In addition, students use related skills from other disciplines, such as English and mathematics.

The laboratory investigations in this manual are not intended to stand alone. They, along with the activities that appear within each chapter of the text, comprise the *Heath Earth Science* Laboratory Program. Both the lab investigations and the text activities complement the content in the text. However, the lab investigations are, in general, more involved than the text activities: more time will be needed for completion, more equipment may be necessary, and more deductive reasoning will be required on the part of the students. Students who perform both the text activities and the investigations in this booklet will benefit from the comprehensive hands-on approach of the *Heath Earth Science* Laboratory Program.

All of the laboratory investigations in this book are intended to be performed in class under your direct supervision and guidance. Investigations involving equipment must be preceded by a discussion of safety procedures.

The first two activities in the student manual are introductory exercises on laboratory safety and on the safe use of several scientific measuring instruments. The guidelines and safety equipment introduced in "Laboratory Safety" must be known and understood by each student before laboratory work begins. The instruments used in "Working in the Earth Science Laboratory" are fundamental to earth science, and will be used in other investigations throughout the year. These two activities serve as an introduction for those students who are not yet familiar with proper laboratory conduct and common laboratory instruments, and as a review for those who are.

Annotations within the pages of the Teacher's Annotated Edition provide suggestions on setting up and performing each investigation so that you can make the maximum use of laboratory time with your students. Data for typical results, sample calculations based on these data, and answers to Analysis and Conclusions questions are included with each investigation in the Teacher's Annotated Edition.

Do not let the length of the equipment list for a particular laboratory investigation deter you from attempting the activity with your students. Almost all of the equipment needed should be readily available to you. Some investigations will require advance preparation of equipment but, once constructed, the equipment can be stored away for future use, at which time no further advance preparation will be needed.

The following list summarizes some of the ways in which the investigations in this laboratory manual might be used most effectively:

1. The introductory investigations on safety and on the use of measuring tools should be done early in the school year. These investigations set the tone for good laboratory behavior and for the kind and level of work expected throughout the year.

2. Investigations may be used generally to extend and enrich students' classroom experiences; investigations may also be used specifically to develop an earth science curriculum with a strong emphasis on laboratory process.

3. For students who have difficulty learning by reading alone, the investigations can provide active experiences that reinforce the concepts developed in the text.

4. If time does not allow all students to perform all the investigations, some may be done as demonstrations by you or by selected groups of students.

Laboratory Safety

Laboratory safety can only be achieved by constant vigilance on the part of both teachers and students. The laboratory investigations in this laboratory manual do not expose students to any unreasonable hazards. Nevertheless, chemicals, cutting instruments, and hot objects are sometimes used; there is always a potential danger in the science laboratory. Unfortunately, even those activities that appear quite safe can, under certain circumstances, cause injury. Carelessness, inattentiveness, and other inappropriate behavior are potentially dangerous. Emphasize the need for careful behavior. Early in the school year, have students do the exercise entitled "Laboratory Safety" on pages 2–3 of this laboratory manual. Discuss the safety rules given in that investigation. In addition, spend class time reviewing the rules presented in *Safety in the Earth Science Laboratory* on pages xviii–xix in the text.

Safety Symbols

Throughout the investigations in this laboratory manual are a variety of safety symbols and **CAUTION** statements that relate to safe laboratory procedures. These symbols and their meanings are shown below. The symbols and **CAUTION** statements signal both teacher and student to take appropriate safety precautions. Remind students of the proper safety procedures at the beginning of each class in which there might be a risk of personal injury. Point out any symbols and **CAUTION** statements in the laboratory, explaining what is potentially dangerous about the procedures, and how to avoid risk. Throughout the lab period, remind students of the requirements for their safety.

Students must wear safety goggles and a lab apron. Investigation involves chemicals, hot materials, lab burners, or the possibility of broken glass.

Investigation involves handling irritating minerals or sediments. Students should wear plastic gloves to handle minerals and sediments.

Danger of cuts exists. Investigation involves scissors, wire cutters, pins, or other sharp instruments that must be handled with care.

Investigation involves hot plates, lab burners, lighted matches, or flammable liquids with explosive vapors.

Investigation involves chemicals that are poisonous. Students should avoid spills and avoid touching chemicals directly.

Investigation involves use of corrosive or irritating chemicals. In case of a spill, students should wash skin and clothes thoroughly with plenty of water.

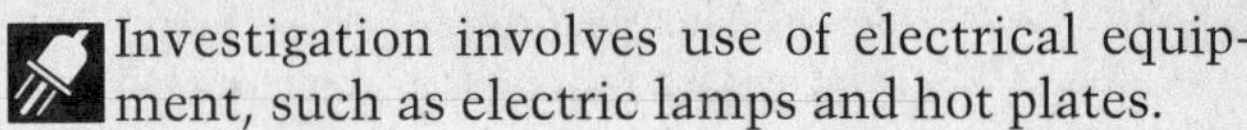
Investigation involves use of electrical equipment, such as electric lamps and hot plates.

The triangle alerts you and your students to additional, specific safety procedures in an investigation. Always discuss safety **CAUTIONS** with students before they begin work.

Using a Bunsen Burner

Although only one investigation in *Earth Science Laboratory Investigations* requires the use of Bunsen burners, many schools will use Bunsen burners as heat sources in the science laboratory. If you intend to use Bunsen burners, you and your students must be fully informed of all the necessary safety precautions.

1. Safety goggles and a laboratory apron must be worn whenever you work with a burner. Long hair must be tied back, and loose clothing must be confined.

2. Be sure you have an appropriate hose and that the hose does not have cracks or holes. Connect the hose securely to the burner and to the gas outlet.

3. a. If you are using a match to light the burner, light a match and then slowly open the gas outlet partway. Hold the lighted match near the top edge of the burner until the gas ignites; do not hold the match directly over the burner.

b. If you are using a flint burner lighter, turn the gas on first and then strike the lighter, holding it directly over the barrel of the burner.

4. If the flame goes out or you cannot light the burner, *immediately* turn off the gas outlet. If the flame roars or goes out, there is too much air. To decrease the air supply, turn the burner barrel clockwise. If the flame is yellow, there is not enough air; increase the air supply by turning the burner barrel counterclockwise. To adjust the size of the flame, use the gas-supply valve on the burner. The flame should be pale blue and burn quietly.

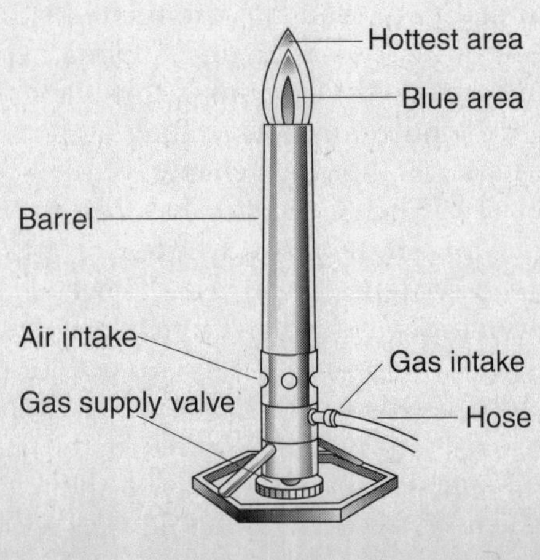

General Suggestions for a Safe Science Program

To ensure a safe environment in your classroom, the following safety suggestions have been prepared by the National Science Teachers Association and other safety consultants. Before starting any investigation, be sure to discuss the appropriate safety procedures with students.

1. Obtain a copy of the federal, state, and local regulations that relate to school safety, as well as a copy of your school district's policies and procedures.

2. Check your classroom on a regular basis to ensure that all possible safety precautions are being taken. Equipment and materials should be properly stored; hazardous materials should not be left exposed in the classroom. In addition, once a year conduct a "safety audit" to explore whether recommendations from recent safety audits have been implemented, whether safety rules have any significant gaps, and whether rules are enforced constructively.

3. Storage facilities should be locked at all times when not under direct supervision of a responsible person.

4. Before handling equipment and materials, thoroughly familiarize yourself with their possible hazards. Try out each investigation before assigning it to students.

5. Be extra cautious when dealing with fire, and instruct your students to take appropriate precautions. Familiarize yourself and your students with the school's fire regulations, evacuation procedures, and the location and use of the fire-fighting equipment in your laboratory.

6. Be prepared for accidental glass breakage—a normal and expected part of any laboratory procedure involving glassware. Care must be taken in cleaning up the glassware. Tell students to notify you whenever glass is broken. Immediate access to a small broom and dust pan can prevent accidents and save time and inconvenience when cleaning up broken glass.

7. Avoid using mercury thermometers. Whenever possible, use thermometers filled with colored alcohol, which is a far safer substance. If you must use a mercury thermometer, be sure you have a mercury spill cleanup kit available (such kits are available from science supply houses). Warn students that mercury is poisonous and it should **not** be touched directly with the hands under any circumstances. Further, mercury evaporates easily and its fumes are poisonous. Students must notify you immediately if a mercury thermometer breaks. They should not attempt to clean up either the broken glass or the spilled mercury themselves. Follow the instructions on the mercury spill cleanup kit. Never wash mercury down the drain.

8. All devices using 100-115 volt AC power should be equipped with three-wire cords and three-prong plugs. Each socket should be three-hole and protected with a ground-fault interrupter (GFI).

9. The size of the group working on an experiment should be limited to a number that can safely perform the activity without causing crowding, confusion, and accidents.

10. Student apparel should be appropriate to the activity. Remind your students to roll long sleeves above the wrist. Ties, coats, and bulky outerwear should be removed. Shoes that protect the foot should be worn, not sandals or shoes with openings over the toes. Long hair should be tied back during an activity, especially when an open flame is nearby.

11. Instruct students to wear safety goggles when using beakers, test tubes, thermometers and other glass apparatus and when working with dangerous chemicals, hot liquids, and other sources of splashes, spills, or spatterings.

12. Students should be instructed never to taste or touch substances in the science classroom. Students should also be instructed that it is unsafe to touch the face, mouth, eyes, and other parts of the body while they are working with chemical substances until they have thoroughly washed their hands.

13. Sufficient time should be planned for students to perform an activity. They should clean up and properly store the equipment and materials after use.

14. Although all of the activities in this laboratory manual involve standard equipment, you may find the need to modify the procedure to suit the equipment available to you, the needs of your students, or the needs of the curriculum you are following. Whenever such modifications are made, be sure that new hazards have not been introduced.

15. Dispose of dangerous waste chemicals and materials as prescribed by appropriate standards and the laws of your community. Provide separate waste receptacles for broken glass and waste paper.

16. In case of accidents, know your school's policy and procedures. Make accident reports promptly, accurately, and completely.

Student Injury or Illness

1. Do not move the student until the extent of the injury is determined.

2. Call the school nurse and render first aid. If the student isn't breathing, CPR (cardiopulmonary resuscitation) should be started. If there is significant bleeding, control it by applying pressure.

3. If the student is injured but ambulatory, do not allow him or her to walk to the nurse alone. Send along another student to be sure that the injured student arrives safely.

4. If the student has received a burn, first assess the extent of the burn. If the skin is severely burned, broken, or charred, prompt medical attention is needed to avoid infection. If the skin is not severely burned, immediate application of cold to the burn can help prevent tissue damage, pain, and blistering. Obtain an ice pack from the school nurse. Until the ice arrives, run cold water over the burn.

5. Expect to file a report on the incident leading up to the accident or illness.

Laboratory Investigations

Function of Laboratory Investigations

The laboratory investigations in *Earth Science Laboratory Investigations* are varied, but all have certain characteristics in common:

1. each investigation is relevant to the material being taught in the corresponding chapter of the text;

2. each investigation develops the students' laboratory skills;

3. the student makes observations and collects or analyzes data during each investigation;

4. the observations made during each investigation form a meaningful pattern.

The function of these laboratory investigations is to provide the students with observational experiences that are the direct result of their own work. These investigations have been designed for a typical secondary science classroom. The students are provided with complete and detailed directions for each laboratory procedure. In addition, the investigations are designed so that your time in the laboratory can be spent helping students, rather than preparing or attending to equipment, solutions, or other materials needed for the laboratory.

Format of Laboratory Investigations

Each laboratory investigation follows the same format.

1. The introductory paragraph provides background material for the investigation. In some labs, the introduction serves to remind students of relevant material in the text. In other labs, the introduction provides new information that goes beyond the text, but that is needed to successfully perform the activity.

2. The **Lab Skills and Objectives** of the laboratory are stated for the student in terms of the process skills they will utilize to successfully complete the laboratory investigation.

3. Next is a list of **Materials** needed for the laboratory activity. This list includes materials needed for one student or team to perform the investigation. When organizing materials for a given activity, adjust the quantities appropriately to meet the needs of your enrollment. (A Master Materials List of items and quantities needed to complete all investigations appears on pages T11–T15 of this book.)

4. In the section entitled **Procedure,** instructions are given for performing the investigation. The procedure is designed to be as simple and yet as complete as possible so that the students can successfully perform the investigation in a minimum of time. If the data collected by the students can best be summarized with a table, such a table is provided with the procedure.

5. Laboratory investigations end with the **Analysis and Conclusions** section, which includes questions to help the students interpret and understand the observations they have made.

The success of any laboratory exercise depends upon how well the class is prepared for the activity. Students should have an idea of what they are to do before they actually perform the activity; they should also know what kinds of safety procedures will be followed. Good pre-lab discussions will not only improve the quality of student work but will also enormously reduce the number of student questions you will be called upon to answer while the lab is in progress. As students perform the investigation, watch to see that each part of the procedure is being carried out correctly. After the investigation, conduct a post-lab discussion in which the students consider the implications of the laboratory data.

Function of Map Activities

The map activities in *Earth Science Laboratory Investigations* provide students opportunities to practice map reading and map interpretation skills. The map activities use the maps provided in the appendix of *Heath Earth Science.* Each map activity follows the same format as the Laboratory Investigations described above.

Introduction to Environmental and Inquiry Labs

Included with the investigations in this manual are Inquiry Labs and Environmental Labs. Both types of labs are designed to broaden the student's laboratory experience.

Inquiry Labs emphasize a more independent approach to laboratory work than the laboratory investigations. After completing one part of a laboratory investigation, students are asked to consider a similar or related problem. Students then have the opportunity to plan their own investigation using materials, methods, and hypotheses of their own choosing.

To prepare all groups of students for an inquiry approach to lab work, each Inquiry Lab in this manual begins with a traditional laboratory investigation which is then extended to include an independent student investigation. You may choose to use these extensions with your entire class or as an extra-credit project for those students with a particular interest in a topic or the scientific method.

Exposure to the inquiry approach to laboratory work will provide students with a realistic view of the scientific process. Instead of being told exactly what steps to take in an investigation, students will learn to utilize their own creative resources as they implement an experiment of their own design. The individual challenge presented by these inquiry labs is balanced by the satisfaction students gain in performing their own investigation.

Environmental Labs give students the opportunity to do more than just read about an environmental issue. Students work directly with actual materials and data to gain a greater appreciation of the processes involved in dealing with global environmental problems. By focusing attention on issues such as solar heating, soil salinization, acid rain, polluted water, and global warming, the environmental labs enhance the environmental awareness strand that runs throughout the *Heath Earth Science* program.

Laboratory Skills Development

The *Heath Earth Science* Laboratory Program consists of the investigations in this manual and the activities that appear within each chapter of the text. The strength of the laboratory program is in its emphasis on developing process skills important to the study of science. Process skills enable students to work effectively in a laboratory, to understand the implications of their observations, and to deal with the acquisition and use of numerical data and concepts.

In the chart below, process skills are listed with the investigations and text activities in which they are used. Process skills that are central to a lab are highlighted under the Lab Skills and Objectives section of each lab. Other process skills may also be used by students in completing a lab. The chart below is a compilation of *all* process skills used in the investigations and text activities of the laboratory program.

Process Skill	Investigations/Text Activities
Analyzing Data	**Investigations:** 1, 2, 4, 5A, 6A, 6B, 7C, 7D, 7E, 8, 10A, 11, 13A, 13B, 14, 15, 18, 21, 22, 23, 25, 26, 28A, 30, 31A, 31B, 33, 34 **Text Activities:** 1, 2, 4, 6, 7A, 14, 19, 21, 24, 25, 27, 28, 29, 33, 34
Applying a Strategy	**Investigations:** 5A, 6B, 7B, 8, 19, 20, 31A **Text Activities:** 2, 7A, 28
Calculating	**Investigations:** 2, 4, 8, 9A, 11, 13A, 17, 20, 22, 24, 25, 32 **Text Activities:** 2, 6, 7A, 7B, 8, 9, 14, 15, 18B, 21, 22, 23, 25, 27, 32, 34
Classifying	**Investigations:** 3, 4, 5A, 5B, 5C, 7C, 11, 13B, 14, 15, 16B, 21, 24, 25, 34 **Text Activities:** 4, 5, 33
Comparing and Contrasting	**Investigations:** 1, 2, 3, 5A, 6A, 6B, 7B, 7E, 8, 9A, 10A, 10B, 12, 13A, 13B, 14, 17, 19, 21, 23, 25, 26, 32, 34 **Text Activities:** 1, 4, 8, 9, 12, 13, 15, 19, 20, 22, 23, 24, 25, 26, 31
Constructing Tables and Graphs	**Investigations:** 2, 6A, 10A, 11, 14, 18, 19, 21, 22, 23, 25, 26, 30, 31A, 31B **Text Activities:** 1, 8, 11, 14, 15, 17, 18B, 22, 24, 25, 26, 33
Describing	**Investigations:** *LS-1, *LS-2, 1, 7A, 7D, 16B, 20, 27A, 28B **Text Activities:** 1, 6, 13, 20, 26
Determining Cause and Effect	**Investigations:** 6A, 6B, 9A, 9B, 10B, 11, 12, 14, 15, 16B, 17, 18, 19, 22, 26, 27A, 27B, 28A, 28B, 30, 31A, 31B, 33 **Text Activities:** 6, 7B, 8, 11, 12, 13, 17, 18A, 18B, 19, 20, 21, 24, 28, 30A, 30B, 31, 32
Determining Main Ideas	**Investigations:** 3, 4, 6A, 6B, 7B, 7D, 9A, 9B, 10A, 12, 13A, 18, 21, 22, 26, 27B, 28A, 28B, 30, 31A, 31B, 32, 34 **Text Activities:** 16A, 29
Forming Hypotheses	**Investigations:** 1, 8, 9A, 10A, 11, 19, 20, 27B, 31A **Text Activities:** 3, 29

(continued)

Process Skill	Investigations/Text Activities (continued)
Forming Models	**Investigations:** 3, 6A, 6B, 7A, 9B, 16A, 17, 19, 24, 27B, 32 **Text Activities:** 13, 27, 31
Interpreting Diagrams	**Investigations:** 1, 7A, 7B, 7C, 7D, 7E, 9A, 10B, 12, 13A, 13B, 15, 16B, 17, 21, 22, 23, 24, 25, 27B, 28A, 28B, 30, 31A, 34 **Text Activities:** 2, 5, 7A, 7B, 8, 9, 10, 11, 14, 15, 16A, 16B, 17, 18A, 18B, 19, 21, 22, 26, 30A, 30B, 31, 32
Measuring	**Investigations:** LS-2, 1, 2, 4, 5A, 6A, 6B, 7C, 7D, 8, 9A, 10A, 10B, 11, 13A, 16B, 17, 19, 20, 24, 25, 26, 27A, 30, 31A **Text Activities:** 1, 2, 3, 5, 28, 34
Observing	**Investigations:** LS-2, 1, 3, 4, 6A, 7E, 8, 9B, 10A, 12, 19, 20, 27A, 27B, 28B **Text Activities:** 3, 4, 6, 10, 13, 20, 27, 28
Predicting	**Investigations:** 8, 10A, 17, 18, 19, 20, 22, 31A, 34 **Text Activities:** 3, 6, 12, 24, 26, 28, 30A, 30B
Stating a Conclusion	**Investigations:** 9B, 10A, 15, 19, 20, 24, 26, 27A, 31B **Text Activities:** 7B, 13, 19, 25, 31, 33
Summarizing	**Investigations:** 9B, 10A, 17, 25, 26, 27A, 33 **Text Activities:** 16A, 16B, 18A
Verifying Results	**Investigations:** 2, 4, 5A, 17, 20, 24 **Text Activities:** 4

* LS-1 refers to Laboratory Skills 1, *Laboratory Safety;* LS-2 refers to Laboratory Skills 2, *Working in the Earth Science Laboratory.* LS-1 and LS-2 are introductory investigations that precede the Chapter 1 Investigation.

Evaluating Students' Laboratory Work

The preparation and presentation of laboratory activities is only a part of the job of a science teacher. The student laboratory work that results must be evaluated. When large numbers of students are involved, the amount of time spent in evaluation can be substantial. To reduce that time, *Heath Earth Science* offers the following suggestions.

For investigations involving the set-up, use, and collection of data from laboratory equipment, various studies have indicated that the written laboratory report may not adequately assess a student's work. Evaluations that include observations of student behavior during the investigation are better. To make such evaluations, prepare a list of evaluation criteria such as the those shown on the sample *Laboratory Skill Evaluation Sheet.* As you observe and evaluate students during the lab, make a point of helping each student strengthen his or her laboratory skills.

For labs involving calculations, student answers often fall within a range of values. If you make a list of answers within that range, you will not need to check every calculation on each individual lab report.

For written answers, scan for key words. Although students are instructed to answer questions in complete sentences, you may not need to read every word to determine whether an answer is correct. This does not mean that you should ignore spelling or other obvious errors—these, too, should be noted for the student.

For labs involving graphs or maps, a transparent sheet can save grading time. For orientation, mark on the sheet the outline of the graph or map. Then mark the locations of the points that the students should have plotted. Lay the transparent sheet over the student pages to easily and quickly check the accuracy of their plots.

Laboratory Skill Evaluation Sheet

Investigation *Passive and Active Solar Heating*

Date *10/12/93*

Laboratory Skill	*Student's Name*
Manipulation	
■ Sets up equipment properly	
■ Uses equipment correctly	
■ Handles equipment carefully	
Working Habits	
■ Keeps lab area organized and clean	
■ Observes safety regulations	
■ Follows laboratory directions	
Observation Skills	
■ Makes observations carefully	
■ Records observations immediately	
■ Records observations accurately	

Master Materials List

The materials list includes materials needed for one class of 24 students to complete all laboratory investigations in *Heath Earth Science Laboratory Investigations.* When ordering, adjust quantities for your enrollment. The investigations for which each material is needed are also listed. Addresses of science material suppliers follow the materials list.

Materials are listed in one of the following categories:

- **Equipment:** materials ordered through an equipment catalog and that do not need to be replaced each year
- **Supplies:** materials that are available locally or in the school, and/or materials that need to be replaced each year
- **Earth Science Specimens:** rock and mineral samples, fossils, and sediments
- **Chemicals:** compounds and solutions; some are available locally, others are ordered through a catalog

Materials such as tap water, paper towels, and other generally available consumables are not listed.

Materials List

Category	Material	Quantity	Chapter
Equipment	balance, triple beam	24	LS-2, 1, 2, 4, 5A, 6B, 8, 9B, 11, 17
	beaker		
	50-mL	48	1, 2, 8
	150-mL	24	6B
	250-mL	120	LS-2, 4, 7A, 9B, 26
	400-mL	72	8, 9A, 10A, 11, 12, 17, 19
	blow dryer	24	12
	bowl, shallow glass	24	27B
	brush, small scrubbing	12	27A
	brush, test-tube	24	9A
	Bunsen burner	24	6B
	burette clamp (or optical bench)	24	20
	C-clamp	24	4
	calculator	24	4, 14
	clamp, test-tube	24	9A
	compass, drawing	24	15, 24
	density kit: solids of different shapes, same material:		
	cube	24	2
	cylinder	24	2
	rectangular block	24	2
	drying oven	1	6B
	evaporating dish, 200-mL	24	6B
	eyedropper	24	1, 27A
	flashlight, narrow beam	24	27B
	flask, round bottom 250-mL	24	27B
	funnel, lab	24	9B
	goniometer, contact	24	3

Category	Material	Quantity	Chapter
Equipment (continued)	graduated cylinder		
	10-mL	24	1
	50-mL	12	27A
	100-mL	48	LS-2, 2, 5A, 6B, 8, 9A, 17
	1000-mL	24	10A
	hammer, or mallet	1	31A
	laboratory apron	24	6B, 27A
	lamp with 100 watt bulb	24	26
	lens holder	48	20
	lens, convex		
	focal length 5 to 10 cm	24	20
	focal length 20 to 40 cm	24	20
	magnifier (hand lens, magnifying glass)	24	1, 5A, 5B, 5C, 7C, 7D, 10B
	meterstick	24	LS-2, 10A, 20, 32
	petri dish	24	6B
	prism, glass	24	27B
	projector, slide	1	27B
	ring clamp	72	6B, 9B, 26
	ring stand	24	6B, 9A, 9B, 20, 26, 28B
	safety goggles	24 pair	1, 2, 6B, 8, 9A, 9B, 10, 11, 12, 17, 26, 27B
	screen holder, optical	24	20
	screening, or a strainer	24	8
	sieve set	24	10A, 11
	spatula	24	6B
	stereoscope	24	7E
	stirring rod	48	9B, 17
	stopper	24	27B
	tape measure, metric	1	31A
	thermometer, Celsius, plastic backed	72	LS-2, 6A, 19, 26, 31A
	timer, or stopwatch	24	LS-2, 9A, 10A, 19, 26
	tongs	24	6B, 27B
	tube, glass, 1 cm x 15 cm	24	9A
	watch glass	24	1
	wire mesh	24	6B
Supplies	adding machine tape	3 rolls	32
	alfalfa sprouts	3 pkg's	27A
	aluminum foil	1 roll	6A
	balloon, small	24	27B
	boards, 30 cm x 30 cm x 5 cm	48	16A
	bottle, plastic soft drink	24	9B
	box, large cardboard	24	12
	brick	24	6A
	candle	24	12
	cans, empty soup	72	26

Category	Material	Quantity	Chapter
Supplies (continued)	cardboard pieces	24	12, 19
	cardboard, white disks	24 pieces	28B
	cardboard, white, or screen	1 piece	27B
	chalk, colored	24 pieces	28B
	charcoal, aquarium	1 pkg	9B
	cheesecloth, 10-cm x 10-cm square	24 pieces	9B
	clay, modeling	48 sticks	7A, 16A, 17
	concrete	48 pieces	27A
	cup, paper	72	6A, 19
	cup, plastic or 150-mL beaker	144	27B
	drinking straw, plastic	24	17
	dust mask	24	12
	garlic powder	1 jar	9B
	gloves, plastic	72 pair	4, 10, 27A
	hole punch	24	6A
	index cards, 3 x 5	48	20
	jar, large glass	24	27B
	knife, plastic	24	16A
	matches, wooden	1 box	6B, 12, 27B
	metric ruler	24	2, 3, 6B, 7A, 7B, 9A, 13A, 17, 18, 19, 24, 27B, 30
	nail, or wooden stake	36	31A
	nail, steel	96	27A
	paint, dull black	2 liters	6A, 26
	paint, dull white	half liter	26
	paper clip	1 box	4, 12, 18, 19, 25
	paper clip, large	24	28B
	paper, construction	24 sheets	33
	paper, filter	48 sheets	9A, 9B
	paper, graph		
	1/4 inch grid	200 sheets	6A, 11, 18, 19, 22, 25, 26
	1- or 2-mm grid	24 sheets	1
	paper, tracing	100 sheets	7A, 18
	paper, unlined	96 sheets	7C, 24
	paper, waxed	1 roll	16A
	paste or glue	6 bottles	33
	pen, marking	24	17
	pencil, wax marking	24	6B, 7A, 8, 9A, 9B, 19, 27B, 31A
	pencils, colored	6 boxes	13A, 14, 23, 29, 30
	pin, straight	24	19
	plastic wrap	1 roll	6A
	protractor	24	3, 12, 14, 16B, 24, 25
	rubber band	24	4, 9B
	rubber cement	24 jars	6A
	sandpaper, coarse	24 sheets	5B
	scissors	24 pair	3, 6A, 9A, 16A, 17, 19, 27B, 31A, 33

Category	Material	Quantity	Chapter
Supplies (continued)	shoebox	24	6A, 16A
	shoebox, transparent plastic with lid	24	7A, 19
	steel wool	12 pieces	27A
	string	1 ball	4, 12, 28B, 31A
	tape, masking	6 rolls	3, 6A, 9A, 12, 16A, 19, 27B, 31A
	thread	1 spool	25
	toothpick	1 box	1, 7A
	vegetable oil, spray	1 can	17
	washer, large	120	28B
	washer, small, or nickel	240	LS-2

Earth Science Specimens

Category	Material	Quantity	Chapter
Minerals	calcite	24	4
	chalcopyrite	24	3, 4
	galena	24	4
	gypsum	24	3, 4
	halite	24	3
	magnetite	24	4
	pyrite	24	4
	quartz	24	3
	sulfur	24	3, 4
Fossils Plastic or natural	*Athyris*	2	34
	Exogyra	1	34
	Favosites	2	34
	Flexicalymene	1	34
	Gryphaea	1	34
	Hydnoceras	1	34
	Neospirifer	1	34
	Pentremites	2	34
	Phacops	1	34
	Phylloceras	2	34
	Terebratula	1	34
	Turritella	1	34
Rocks	andesite	24	14
	basalt	24	5A, 14
	chips, 2 kinds of rock	1 pkg of each	8
	chips, limestone	1 pkg	2, 8
	coal, bituminous	24	5B
	conglomerate	24	5B
	gabbro	24	5A

Category	Material	Quantity	Chapter
Rocks (continued)	gneiss	24	5C
	granite	24	5A, 12
	limestone, compact	24	5B
	limestone, shell	24	5B
	marble	24	5C
	obsidian	24	5A
	pumice	24	5A
	quartzite	24	5C
	rhyolite	24	5A, 14
	rock salt	24	5B
	sandstone	24	5B
	schist	24	5C
	scoria	24	5A
	shale	24	5B
	slate	24	5C
Sediments	clay (or silt)	1 pail	12, 9B
	glacial till	1 pail	11
	gravel	1 pail	12
	pebbles, small	1 pail	9B
	sand		
	coarse	1 pail	9A, 9B
	medium	1 pail	9A
	fine	1 pail	9A, 9B
	mixture of all three	1 pail	9A, 12, 16A
	sediment, unsorted	1 pail	10A, 6B
	soil, dry, local	1 pail	1, 26, 9B
	soil, potting	1 pail	27B
Chemicals	alum	120 g	9B
	sodium chloride (table salt)	870 g	6B, 17
	sulfuric acid, 0.1 *M*	2700 mL	27B
	vinegar	500 mL	8

Suppliers of Earth Science Materials

Carolina Biological Supply Company
2700 York Road
Burlington, NC 27215

Central Scientific Company
(CENCO)
11222 Melrose Avenue
Franklin Park, IL 60131
708-451-0150

Connecticut Valley Biological Supply
Company, Inc.
82 Valley Road
P.O. Box 326
Southampton, MA 01073

Crystal Productions
P.O. Box 2159
Glenvue, IL 60025

Delta Education, Inc.
P.O. Box 915
Hudson, NH 03051

Edmund Scientific Company
101 East Gloucester Pike
Barrington, NJ 08007

Fisher Scientific Company
Educational Materials Division
4901 West LeMoyne
Chicago, IL 60651
312-378-7770

Flinn Scientific, Inc.
131 Flinn Street
P.O. Box 219
Batavia, IL 60510

Frey Scientific Company
905 Hickory Lane
Mansfield, OH 44905
800-225-FREY

Hubbard Scientific Company
3101 Iris Avenue
Suite #215
Boulder, CO 80301

LaPine Scientific Company
13636 South Western Avenue
Blue Island, IL 60406

McKilligan Supply Corporation
435 Main Street
Johnson City, NY 13790

Nasco
901 Janesville Avenue
Fort Atkinson, WI 53538
or
Nasco West, Inc.
1524 Princeton Avenue
Modesto, CA 95352

Sargent-Welch Scientific Company
911 Commerce Court
Buffalo Grove, IL 60089
708-459-6225, 800-727-4368

Science Kit and Boreal Labs
777 East Park Drive
Tonawanda, NY 14150

Ward's Natural Science
Establishment, Inc.
East Coast Facility
5100 West Henrietta Road
P.O. Box 92912
Rochester, NY 14692-9012
716-359-2502, 800-962-2660
or
West Coast Facility
P.O. Box 5010
San Luis Obispo, CA 93403
800-872-7289

HEATH
Earth Science

Laboratory Investigations

Author

Nancy Spaulding
Earth Science Teacher
Elmira Free Academy, Elmira, NY

Contributing Writer

Gabriele Reil
Environmental Studies Teacher
Chemistry Teacher
Moriarty High School, Moriarty, NM

Executive Editor: Ceanne P. Tzimopoulos
Supervising Editor: Christine H. Wang
Editorial Development:
Amy R. Pallant, Ann E. Bekebrede, Virginia A. Flook
Design Management and Cover Design: Lisa Fowler
Book Design and Development:
Reynolds Design & Management, Christine Reynolds
Production Coordinator: Maureen Bisso
Cover Photographs:
Spider Rock, Canyon de Chelly National Monument, Arizona, David Muench
Earth, © Telegraph Colour Library 199, FPG International

D.C. Heath and Company
Lexington, Massachusetts/Toronto, Ontario

Heath Earth Science Program

Earth Science, Pupil's Edition

Earth Science, Teacher's Annotated Edition

Earth Science Laboratory Investigations,
Pupil's Edition

Earth Science Laboratory Investigations,
Teacher's Annotated Edition

Earth Science Overhead Transparencies

Earth Science Study Guide

Earth Science Study Guide Answer Key

Earth Science Chapter Tests with Answers

Earth Science Computer Test Bank;
Apple, IBM, Macintosh

Earth Science Computer Test Bank, Teacher's Guide

Environmental Awareness Case Studies

Computer Software:
Mountains and Crustal Movement
Dating and Geologic Time

Published simultaneously in Canada

Printed in the United States of America

International Standard Book Number: 0-669-26185-8

1 2 3 4 5 6 7 8 9 10 -BA- 99 98 97 96 95 94 93

Contents

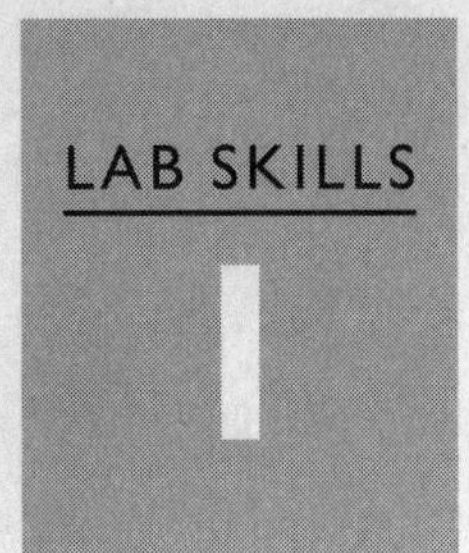

NAME ______________________

CLASS ____________ DATE ____________

LAB SKILLS

Laboratory Safety

Most observations and measurements needed for this laboratory manual can be done in a classroom laboratory. Almost all of them require some kind of laboratory equipment. As in any laboratory, some of that equipment can be dangerous if handled incorrectly. The classroom laboratory can be an enjoyable, exciting place to work but it can be dangerous if it is not approached with maturity and respect. Read and learn the safety rules below before you begin the laboratory work that is a vital and rewarding part of this course.

Lab Skills and Objectives

- To **describe** laboratory safety precautions
- To **identify** safety equipment in your earth science laboratory
- To **classify** laboratory behaviors as safe or unsafe

Safety Rules

1. Follow all instructions carefully. Use special care when you see the word **CAUTION.**

2. Familiarize yourself with the location of all safety equipment in your classroom laboratory.

3. Never eat, drink, or chew gum in a science laboratory.

4. Never run, push, throw objects, or engage in horseplay of any kind in the laboratory.

5. Report all accidents or injuries to your teacher immediately.

6. Use the equipment only as directed. Do not attempt to use equipment in unauthorized ways or perform unauthorized experiments.

7. Replace equipment where and as you found it. Dispose of used materials as your teacher instructs.

8. Keep your work area clean and uncluttered. Leave the area clean when you are through.

9. Dress properly for the laboratory:
   a. Don't wear loose-fitting sleeves or bulky outerwear.
   b. Wear shoes that cover the foot—not sandals. Tie back long hair.
   c. Wear safety goggles when using any glassware, chemicals, hot liquids, or burners, or when using a rock hammer.
   d. Wear a lab apron when working with chemicals or hot materials.

10. Be careful when using heat or fire:
   a. Never leave a hot plate, lit Bunsen burner, or other hot object unattended.
   b. Never reach over an exposed flame.
   c. Use tongs or pot holders to handle hot laboratory equipment.
   d. Use only Pyrex glassware for heating.
   e. Never point the mouth of a test tube towards anybody at any time.
   f. Set hot plates at the specified temperature, not at their maximum setting.

11. Use care working with chemicals:
   a. Never taste or touch substances in the laboratory without specific instructions.
   b. Never smell substances without specific instructions. Avoid inhaling fumes directly.
   c. Wash your hands with soap and water after using chemicals.
   d. Notify your teacher immediately of all spills.

12. Use care working with laboratory equipment:

a. Do not use chipped or cracked glassware.
b. When performing scratch or streak tests, place the glass plate or streak plate on a flat surface. Never do a scratch or streak test while holding the plate in your hand.
c. Never look directly at the sun. Damage to your eyes can occur.
d. Handle mineral and rock specimens with care. While many are tough, others are fragile. Do not test the strength of a mineral or rock unless directed to do so.
e. Never take equipment apart. Precision equipment can be ruined by tampering.
f. When electrical equipment is used, never touch the equipment with wet hands. Keep the work area around the equipment dry and free of flammable equipment. Never insert metal objects into power outlets.
g. Do not pick up broken glass with your bare hands. Use a dustpan and brush.
h. Use care in handling sharp equipment, such as drawing compasses.

Below is a Student Safety Contract that was developed by the National Science Teachers Association. Read the Safety Contract. Write your name in the first blank, then fill in the date and sign it.

I will:
- ☐ Follow all instructions given by my teacher
- ☐ Protect eyes, face, hands, and body while conducting laboratory activities
- ☐ Carry out good housekeeping practices
- ☐ Know the location of first-aid and fire-fighting equipment
- ☐ Conduct myself in a responsible manner at all times in the laboratory

I, ______________________, have read and agree to abide by the safety regulations as set forth above and also any additional printed instructions provided by my teacher and/or school district. I further agree to follow all other written and oral instructions given in class.

______________________ Date

______________________ Signature

Exercises

1. Divide the list of safety rules into things you should and should not do in the laboratory. Write these rules in your notebook.

2. You should be familiar with the use and location of all safety equipment in your earth science laboratory. Check off each of the items listed below that you can find and know how to use. If you cannot find an item or do not know how to use it, ask your teacher. On a separate sheet of paper, draw a map of your science laboratory room. Show the location of all safety equipment and exits. Keep your map in your notebook.

____ chemical spill kits
____ containers for broken glass
____ emergency eyewash
____ emergency gas shutoff
____ emergency shower
____ fire blanket
____ fire extinguisher
____ first-aid kit
____ room exits
____ sand bucket

3. Below are descriptions of student behavior in the laboratory. In the space following each description, write whether the behavior is *safe* or *unsafe*.

a. A student sniffed some ammonia to see if it had a strong smell. unsafe
b. Two students removed their safety goggles to see what they were heating. unsafe
c. A student went to get a brush and dustpan to pick up broken glass. safe
d. A student ate lunch in the laboratory. unsafe
e. A student picked up a beaker of hot water using two test-tube holders. unsafe
f. A group of students used Pyrex glassware to heat liquids. safe

LAB SKILLS

2

NAME ______________________

CLASS ______________ DATE ______________

LAB SKILLS

Working in the Earth Science Laboratory

Throughout your study of earth science, you will be using equipment to help observe and measure earth materials in the laboratory. In order to safely and effectively use laboratory equipment, you must first become familiar with its appearance and function. You must also practice its use. In Part A, you will observe and describe pieces of laboratory equipment common in the earth science laboratory. In Part B, you will make measurements using some of these pieces of equipment.

Five pieces of equipment commonly used in earth science laboratories are the metric ruler, triple-beam balance, graduated cylinder, thermometer, and stop watch. Each is used to obtain a different kind of measurement.

Length is measured with a metric ruler or meterstick. A meterstick is divided into 100 centimeters (cm). Each centimeter is divided into 10 parts, or 10 millimeters (mm). In this laboratory manual, you will often measure length to the nearest tenth of a centimeter, that is, to one of the ten divisions within the centimeter.

Mass is measured using a balance. A triple-beam balance is a common type of laboratory balance. It has a pan at one end and three beams, with riders, extending away from the pan and ending in a pointer. To find mass using a balance, place the object to be measured on the pan. Starting with the largest rider, move the riders away from the pan, one notch at a time, until the pan is balanced and the pointer is at zero. In the laboratories in this manual, you will often determine mass to the nearest tenth of a gram, that is, to the smallest division on the front beam of the balance (Figure 1).

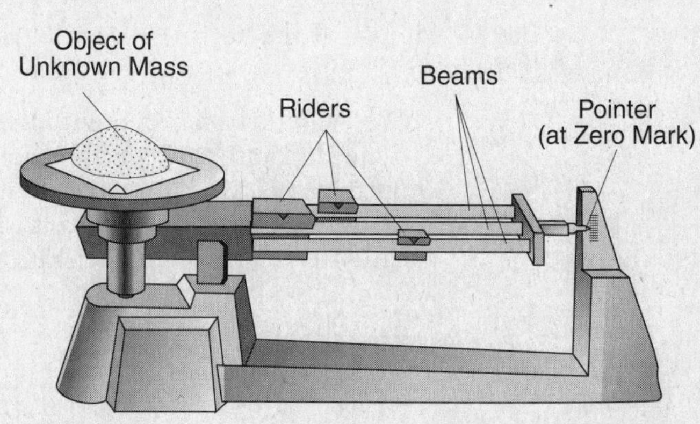

Figure 1

The volume of a liquid is measured with a graduated cylinder. Place the graduated cylinder on a level surface and pour in the liquid. Read the volume of the liquid with your eye at the level of the liquid surface. If the cylinder is made of glass, the surface of the liquid forms a curve, or *meniscus*. The volume of the liquid is read from the bottom of the meniscus (Figure 2).

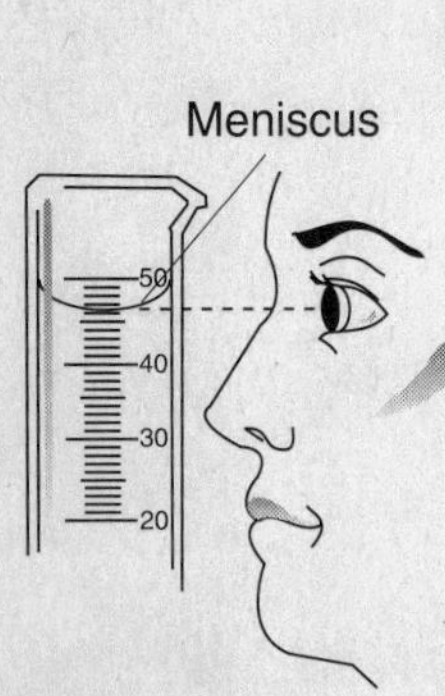

Figure 2

A graduated cylinder can also be used to find the volume of an object. Add water to the cylinder to a convenient level and note the volume. Carefully slide the object you wish to measure down the side of the cylinder and into the water. The change in water level is the volume of the object.

A stop watch is used to determine the duration of an event. Most stop watches have a button for starting and stopping the watch and another button for resetting the watch to zero. Some stop watches read to the nearest tenth of a second while others read to the nearest hundredth.

A thermometer is used to measure temperature. Laboratory thermometers, unlike thermometers you may use at home, are not shaken down before they are used. When measuring temperature, allow the thermometer to stabilize (stop changing) before taking the reading. Read the level of the liquid in the thermometer at eye level.

2 NAME ______________ CLASS ______________ DATE ______________

Lab Skills and Objectives

- To **observe** and **describe** the appearance and function of various pieces of laboratory equipment
- To **measure** quantities through the manipulation of laboratory equipment

Materials

- triple-beam balance
- meterstick
- safety goggles
- 100-mL graduated cylinder
- 150-mL or larger beaker
- thermometer
- stop watch
- 10 nickels
- water
- paper towels

Procedure

Part A

The pictures in Figure 3 represent some of the pieces of equipment that will be needed for the investigations in this course. Observe each of the items pictured in Figure 3. Try to match each item with any real objects on display in your laboratory. Then, based on the appearance of the laboratory equipment, answer Analysis and Conclusions questions 1–4. Students will become better acquainted with laboratory equipment if you can display some examples during Part A.

Figure 3

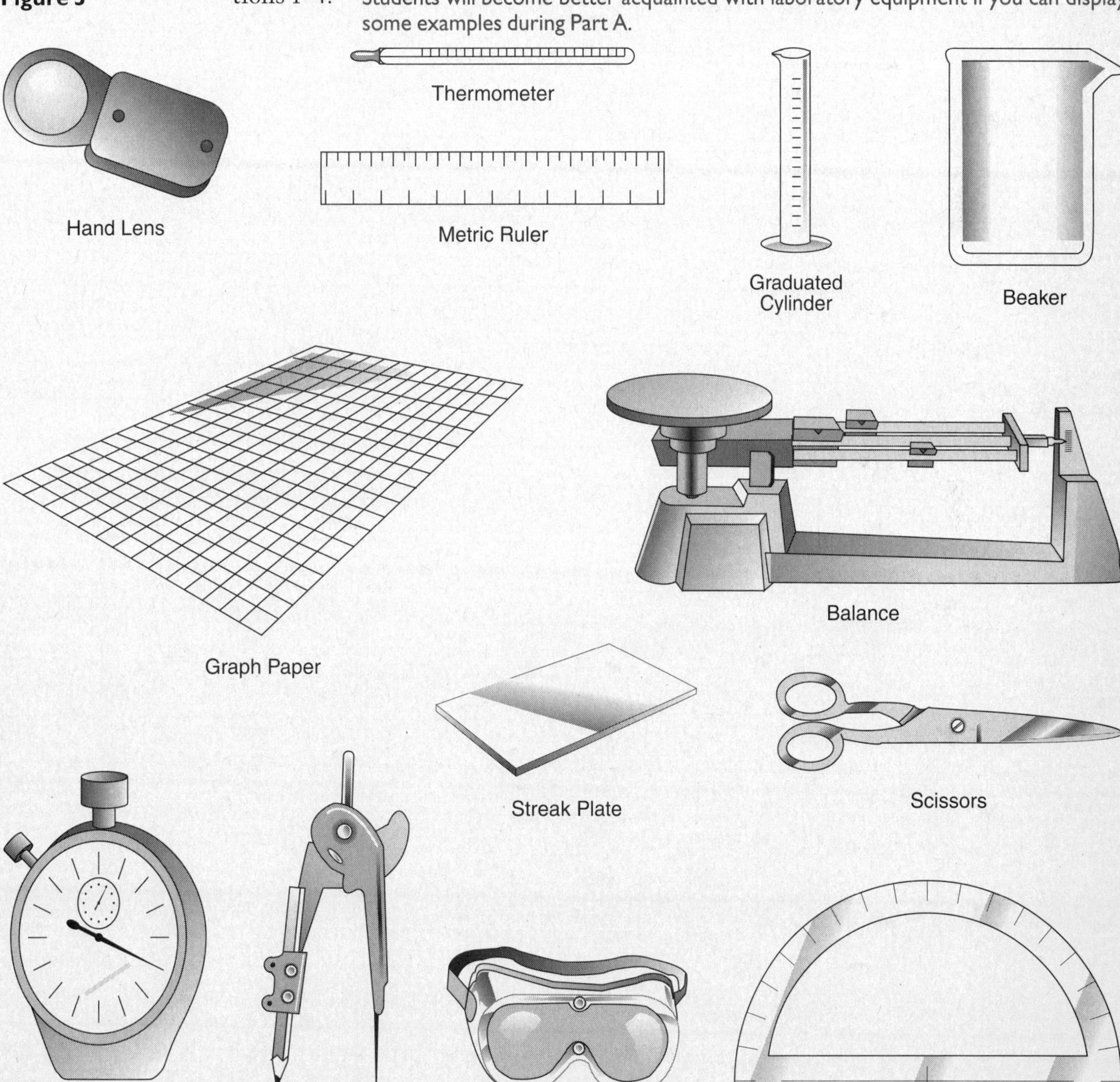

Part B

1. Use the edge of the meterstick to align 10 nickels in an even row. Use the meterstick to determine the length of the row of nickels, to the nearest tenth of a centimeter. Record your answer in the table in Figure 4.

2. Check to see that the triple-beam balance is in balance. To do this, slide all of the riders to their zero points. The pointer should swing freely and should point to the zero mark.

3. Place the 10 nickels on the pan of the balance. This will cause the pointer to move to the top of its scale. Move the rider for the largest unit one notch at a time. Be sure the rider slips squarely into the notches. After the pointer swings to the bottom of the scale, move the rider back one notch. Repeat this procedure with the rider for the smaller units. Slide the smallest rider until the pointer points to zero. Read the mass of the 10 nickels on the balance to the nearest tenth of a gram. Record the mass in Figure 4.

4. **CAUTION: Put on your safety goggles.** Place between 50 and 60 mL of water in the graduated cylinder. Read the level of the water in the cylinder and record the volume in Figure 4. Carefully slide the 10 nickels, one at a time, down the side of the cylinder and into the water (Figure 5). Read and record the new water level. Subtract the initial volume from the final volume to find the volume of the nickels. Record the volume in Figure 4. Pour the water from the cylinder into the beaker and carefully remove the nickels. Place the wet nickels on a paper towel.

5. Learn and practice how to start, stop, and reset your stop watch.

Students should drop the nickels carefully and at a reasonable rate. This is not a race.

6. Refill the graduated cylinder with water to the 100-mL mark. With the help of a partner, determine the time needed to carefully drop the 10 nickels, one nickel at a time, into the water. Start the stop watch when the first nickel breaks the meniscus. Stop the stop watch when the last nickel reaches the bottom of the graduated cylinder. Read the stop watch to its most accurate decimal place and record in Figure 4.

Always use alcohol thermometers, if available.

7. Determine the temperature of the water in the cylinder. Leave the thermometer bulb below the surface of the water while you read the temperature. Avoid letting the thermometer touch the sides and bottom of the graduated cylinder. **CAUTION: If a thermometer should break, notify your teacher immediately. The liquid inside may be mercury, a poisonous substance.** Read the thermometer to the nearest whole degree and record in Figure 4.

8. Answer Analysis and Conclusions questions 5–8.

Data Table	
Length of 10 nickels (cm)	21.0
Mass of nickels (g)	49.8
Original level of water in cylinder (mL)	74.0
Final level of water in cylinder (mL)	79.8
Volume of 10 nickels (mL)	5.8
Time for 10 nickels to fall (seconds)	10.8
Temperature of water (°C)	25

Figure 4

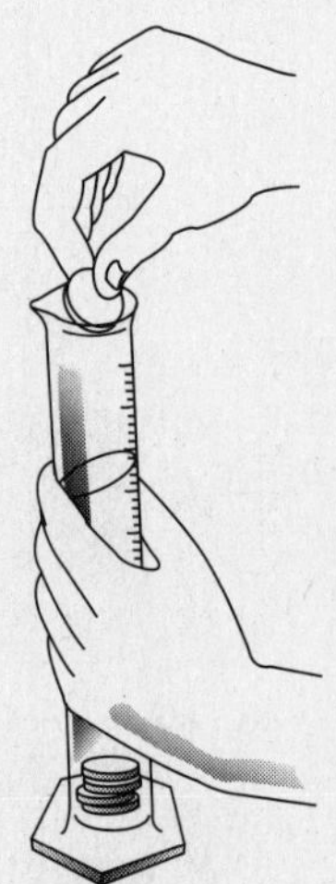

Figure 5

Analysis and Conclusions

1. Which pieces of laboratory equipment would be useful for pouring liquids? How can you tell?

The beaker and graduated cylinder; both have pouring spouts.

2. Which pieces of equipment are measuring devices? How can you tell?

The triple-beam balance, metric ruler, thermometer, stop watch, and graduated cylinder; all have marks and/or number values to indicate different amounts.

3. Which piece of equipment will protect your eyes from splashes of liquid, shattered glass, and flying chips of rock?

Safety goggles will protect the eyes.

4. Which pieces of equipment will most likely involve using paper and/or a pencil?

graph paper, drawing compass, protractor, and scissors

5. Write the name of the scientific instrument that would be used to determine each of the following.

a. temperature of a liquid — thermometer

b. mass of an object — triple-beam balance

c. duration of an event — stop watch

d. length of an object — meterstick or metric ruler

e. volume of a liquid — graduated cylinder

6. The rate at which one nickel fell through the water could be determined if the distance the nickel fell and the time needed for the nickel to fall were known. What instruments would be needed to determine the rate of a falling nickel? What would each instrument be used to measure?

A meterstick or metric ruler would be needed to measure the distance the nickel falls. A stop watch would be needed to find the duration of the fall.

7. The *temperature gradient* is the change in temperature over a specific distance. What instruments would be needed to find the temperature gradient between the floor and ceiling in your classroom? What would each instrument be used to measure?

A meterstick would be needed to find the distance between the floor and the ceiling of the room. A thermometer would be needed to find the temperature at the floor and at the ceiling.

8. A kilogram of rocks and a kilogram of feathers have the same mass, but the rocks take up less space. The rocks are said to be more dense than the feathers. *Density* is the ratio of the mass of an object to its volume. What instruments would be needed to determine the density of a small pebble? What would each instrument be used to measure?

The mass of the pebble would be measured with a triple-beam balance. The volume could be found by measuring a change in water level in a graduated cylinder after the pebble is added to it.

NAME ____________________

CLASS ____________ DATE ____________

LAB INVESTIGATION

Observations of a Sample of Earth Material

Making observations is a fundamental part of the study of any science. An **observation** is any information gained directly by using your senses. Everyone makes observations based on what they see, smell, taste, and touch. In this laboratory, you will take note of the way in which you use your senses to make observations. Scientists also use **instruments** to extend their senses. Instruments make it possible for you to use your senses to their full advantage and to quantify your observations with measurements. Scientists also record their observations by taking notes and making sketches.

Lab Skills and Objectives

- To **observe** and **describe** a sample of soil
- To **measure** and **record** data about the soil sample
- To **hypothesize** about the source of the soil sample
- To **compare** and **contrast** individual soil measurements with class measurements

Materials

- safety goggles
- 20 to 30 g of dry soil
- magnifying glass or hand lens
- graph paper, ruled with 1- or 2-mm spacing
- balance
- 10-mL graduated cylinder
- toothpick
- watch glass
- 2 50-mL beakers
- eyedropper

If 10-mL graduated cylinders are not available, use test tubes calibrated to read 10 mL.

Procedure

1. **Put on your safety goggles.** Fill a 50-mL beaker with soil provided by your teacher.

2. Place about one fourth of the soil sample on the watch glass. Use the magnifier to carefully examine the different particles that make up the soil sample. Describe the appearance of the soil in Analysis and Conclusions question 1.

Have a large pail or other container filled with soil available for students to scoop a soil sample with a 50-mL beaker.

3. Place a small portion of the soil in the palm of your hand. Rub the soil between your fingers. Is the soil moist or dry, gritty or smooth? Are the particles loose or difficult to separate? Record observations in Analysis and Conclusions question 2.

4. Fill about half of the second 50-mL beaker with water. Using the eyedropper, add one drop of water at a time to the soil on the watch glass. Observe how the sample changes and any odor it emits. Record this information in Analysis and Conclusions questions 3 and 4.

5. Measure the size of each grid square on your graph paper so that you can use the paper to determine the size of the soil particles. Spread about one fourth of the dry soil sample on the graph paper so that the lines on the paper are visible through the sample. Break up any soil clumps into individual grains. Using the magnifier, estimate the size range of the soil particles and record them in Analysis and Conclusions question 5.

6. In Analysis and Conclusions question 6, draw a sketch of the soil as it appears when magnified on the graph paper. Include any identifiable particles such as organic matter, oddly-shaped grains, or particles that seem to be made of combined materials.

Have students write the mass of 1 mL of soil on the blackboard so that they can compare results.

7. Use the balance to find the mass of the soil remaining in the beaker. First, determine the mass of an empty 10-mL graduated cylinder. Record all measurements in Figure 1.1. Carefully fill the cylinder to the 10-mL mark with dry soil. Press the soil into the cylinder as compactly as possible using the eraser end of a pencil. Determine the mass of the cylinder and the soil. Compute the mass of 1 mL of soil from the mass of 10 mL of soil.

Data Table			
Mass of Empty Graduated Cylinder	Mass of Cylinder + 10 mL of Soil (g)	Mass of 10 mL of Soil (g)	Mass of 1 mL of Soil (g)

Figure 1.1

Analysis and Conclusions

1. What is the general appearance (color, how loose or compact it is, kind of particles, and so forth) of the original soil sample?
Answers will depend on the soil used, but color, type of particles within the soil and unique features should be noted.

2. What does the sample feel like? Describe it in as much detail as possible.
Answers will vary. Soils with a large amount of clay tend to form smooth, hard clumps. Those with more sand are loose and gritty. Organic matter also affects the texture.

3. Was there any change in the soil as water was added?
Answers will vary. Most soils become darker when wet. Clay-rich soils become muddy. Very sandy soils appear like wet beach sand. Organic matter may float.

4. Describe any odor given off by the wet soil.
Answers will vary. An earthy odor will be apparent in clay-rich soils. Organic materials produce a number of different odors ranging from pungent to rotten.

5. What is the range in size of the individual particles (not soil clumps) in the soil?
Answers will vary. Silt- and clay-size particles are too small to be measured, even with a magnifier. Sand ranges in size from 0.06 to 2 mm, so larger sand grains should be seen. Pebbles are larger than 2 mm.

6. How does the soil appear when magnified? On a separate piece of paper, draw a sketch of your observations. Sketches will vary.

7. Based on your observations, where do you think the soil sample came from? Explain.
Answers will vary but should suggest deductive reasoning.

8. What senses did you use in doing this laboratory? Give an example for each sense.
Sight was used to determine the appearance of the soil, to study the effect of water on the soil, to determine particle sizes, and to make a sketch. Touch was used to determine how the soil felt. Smell was used to detect the soil's odor.

9. What senses did you not use?
The senses of taste and hearing were not used.

10. What instruments did you use to extend your senses?
Instruments included the magnifier, the balance, and any quantified measuring tool such as the graph paper, graduated cylinder, ruler, and beakers.

CHAPTER 2

NAME ______________________

CLASS ____________ DATE ____________

LAB INVESTIGATION

The Density of Earth Materials

Density measures the amount of earth material (mass) in a given space (volume). The density of any earth material is the ratio of its mass to its volume, expressed as $D = m/V$.

In this lab, you will determine the density of two kinds of solids: those with regular geometric shapes (such as cubes or rectangular blocks) and those with irregular shapes. The mass of both kinds of solids is determined by using a balance. The volume of a regular solid can be determined by first measuring its dimensions and then calculating its volume using the geometric formulas in Figure 2.1. Most earth materials are irregular-shaped solids whose volumes are determined by the amount of water they displace when submerged.

Even careful measurements of density contain some error. The **percent error** is the amount by which any measurement differs from the accepted value. Percent error is determined by using the following formula.

$$\text{Percent error} = \frac{\text{difference between measured and accepted value}}{\text{accepted value}} \times 100$$

Lab Skills and Objectives

- To **measure** the mass and volume of several objects
- To **compute** and **compare** the density of these objects
- To **compare** computed values with accepted values
- To **graph** and **interpret** data

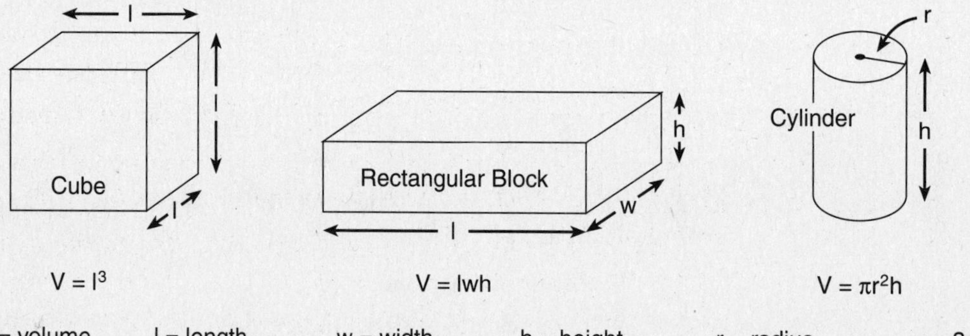

Figure 2.1 V = volume l = length w = width h = height r = radius $\pi = 3.14$

Different-shaped objects can be used; however, the three objects must be made of the same material.

Materials

- cube
- rectangular block
- cylinder
- balance
- metric ruler
- safety goggles
- 100-mL graduated cylinder
- 50-mL beaker
- wet limestone chips
- paper towels

Better results are obtained if the limestone chips are soaked overnight before the day of the lab.

Procedure

Part A Finding the Density of Regular Solids

Record all measurements and calculations in procedure steps 1–7 in the Density Chart for Regular Solids (Figure 2.2).

1. Determine and record the mass of the cube to the nearest tenth of a gram.

2. Using the metric ruler, measure and record the dimensions of the cube.

3. Using the formula in Figure 2.1, compute and record the volume of the cube.

4. Use the mass and volume of the cube to compute its density.

5. Repeat procedure steps 1–4 using the rectangular block.

6. Repeat procedure steps 1–4 using the cylinder.

7. From your teacher, obtain the accepted value for the density of each of the three objects. Use this value to calculate the percent error for each.

The densities of aluminum and steel are about 2.7 g/cm³ and 7.8 g/cm³. Any student calculation within 10 percent of the accepted density value should be considered correct.

Figure 2.2

Density Chart for Regular Solids*

Object	Mass (g)	Length (cm)	Width (cm)	Height (cm)	Volume (cm³)	Density (g/cm³)	Percent Error
cube			X	X			
block							
cylinder		Radius (cm)	X				

* Round off all values to the nearest tenth of a unit.

Part B Finding the Density of Irregular Solids

Record all measurements and calculations from procedure steps 8–17 in the Density Chart for Irregular Solids (Figure 2.3).

8. **Put on your safety goggles.** Pour 50 to 60 mL of water into a 100-mL graduated cylinder. Record the volume of the water in the cylinder. Leave the water in the cylinder.

9. Use the balance to determine and record the mass of the cylinder plus water.

10. Use a 50-mL beaker to obtain a sample of wet limestone chips. Take five chips out and blot them with a paper towel. Slide the chips into the cylinder, being careful not to splash any water. Record the volume of water plus chips. Leave the chips in the cylinder.

11. Subtract the original volume to determine the amount by which the volume changed when you added the five chips. Record this amount as the volume of the five chips.

12. Use the balance to find the mass of the cylinder containing water plus five chips.

13. Subtract the mass of the cylinder plus water from the mass of the cylinder plus water plus five chips. Record your result as the mass of the five chips.

14. Use the formula D = m/V to determine the density of the five limestone chips. Record the density.

15. Take five more chips and blot them with a towel. Repeat procedure steps 11–15 using a total of ten chips. Then repeat, using totals of 15 and 20 chips. Record each set of data.

16. Plot the data for the mass and volume of the chips on the graph in Figure 2.4. Draw a straight line on the graph that comes as close as possible to most of the points.

Density Chart for Irregular Solids*

Solid	Mass Cylinder + Water (g)	Mass Cylinder, Water, + Chips (g)	Mass Chips (g)	Volume Water (mL)	Volume Water + Chips (mL)	Volume Chips (mL)	Density Chips (g/mL)
5 chips	144.8**	151.2	6.4	56.0	58.2	2.2	2.9
10 chips	144.8	163.3	18.5	56.0	62.9	6.9	2.7
15 chips	144.8	179.4	34.6	56.0	68.9	12.9	2.7
20 chips	144.8	198.8	54.0	56.0	76.9	20.9	2.6

Figure 2.3

Round off values to the nearest tenth of a unit. **Sample data

Students may need help in drawing a graph line when they know only the density of the material. If necessary, illustrate the connection between the density, the slope of the line (m/V), and specific points along that line.

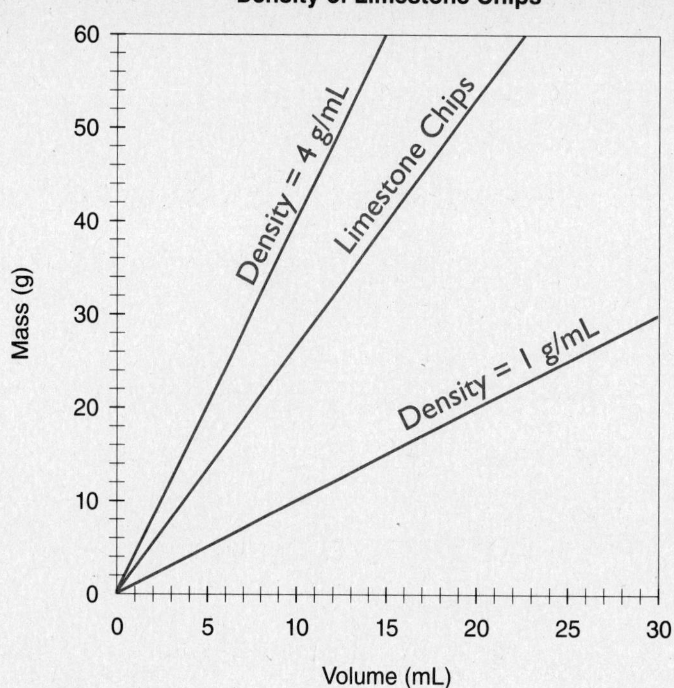

Figure 2.4

Analysis and Conclusions

1. Why are the densities of the three different-shaped objects approximately the same?

Their densities are the same because all three objects are made of the same material.

2. If the block were cut into two pieces, what would be the density of each piece? Why?

The density of each piece would be the same as the density of the original piece because the material is still the same.

3. What happened to the mass and the volume of the chips as the number increased?

As the number of chips increased, both the mass and volume of the chips increased.

4. Why do the points on the graph (Figure 2.4) nearly form a straight line? What does that say about the ratio of mass to volume? (Hint: Note that the slope of your line equals the density.)

All the limestone chips are made of the same material with the same density, so they have the same ratio of mass to volume. Therefore, the graph is a straight line.

5. On the graph, draw and label a line for a material with a density of 1.0 g/mL (slope equals m/V or 1.0 g/mL). Where is this line relative to the line for the chips? Explain.

The line representing a material with a density of 1.0 g/mL is below (or to the right of) the limestone line because the material is less dense than the limestone chips.

6. On the graph, draw and label a line for a material with a density of 4.0 g/mL. Where is this line located relative to the line for the limestone chips? Explain why.

The line representing a material with a density of 4.0 g/mL is above (or to the left of) the limestone line because the material is more dense than the limestone chips.

NAME ______________________

CLASS ______________ DATE ______________

LAB INVESTIGATION

Crystals and Crystal Systems

In nature, every crystal is formed from the regular, repeating arrangement of the atoms from which it is made. As beautiful and varied as they seem, all crystal shapes belong to one of six crystal systems. The crystal systems are defined by the dimensions (length, width, and height) of imaginary axes inside the crystal and by the angles at which these axes meet. (See Figure 3.14 on page 39 of your text.) In this lab, you will construct models of crystals from several crystal systems. You will then observe several actual minerals and compare your crystal models to the crystals in the minerals.

Lab Skills and Objectives

- To **form models** of crystals
- To **classify** the models and the actual crystals by their crystal systems
- To **evaluate** mineral system identification

Materials

- photocopy of Figure 3.3
- scissors
- pencil or pen
- straightedge
- tape or glue stick
- protractor
- Figure 3.14 on page 39 of your text
- several numbered mineral crystals
- contact goniometer

The minerals only need to be identified by number. (Mineral identification is covered in Chapter 4.) Use halite, sulfur, chalcopyrite, quartz, and gypsum in order to include five of the six different mineral systems. Select samples that have clear crystal shapes.

Procedure

Copy the models in Figure 3.1 onto heavy-weight colored paper. If a copy machine is not available, have students trace the model onto a separate sheet of paper before cutting out. Then students can paste their tracing onto heavier weight paper.

Part A

1. Obtain a photocopy from your teacher of the crystal models shown in Figure 3.3.

2. With scissors, carefully cut out Model A along the solid lines. Do not cut along the dashed lines. **CAUTION: Use scissors with care. The points and the edges are sharp.**

3. With a pen or pencil and a straightedge, draw along the dashed lines of Model A. This will enable the paper to fold more easily. Then fold along the dashed lines. Paste or tape together with the tabs inside the figure.

4. Cut out and construct each of the remaining crystal shapes from Figure 3.3. As with Model A, cut along the solid lines and fold along the dashed lines. Paste or tape each model together.

5. Place each model on the table so that the longest dimension is vertical (if possible). Recall that the axes of a crystal are perpendicular to the crystal faces and intersect in the center of the crystal. Looking down on the top surface of each model, imagine that you can see the horizontal axes as they intersect inside the models. Draw in the horizontal axes on the top surface of each model.

6. With a protractor, measure and label the angles of intersection of the horizontal axes for each model. Answer Analysis and Conclusions questions 1–5.

Goniometer

Crystal

Figure 3.1
The internal angle between the axes is measured as 40°. (The angle between the faces of the crystal is measured as 140°.)

The goniometer, if read as shown, measures the internal angle of the axes. The angle between the faces is 180°–40° or 140°.

Part B

7. Look carefully at each of the numbered mineral specimens. For each specimen, try to compare its length, width, and height. If possible, use a goniometer as shown in Figure 3.1 to measure the angle at which these axes meet. Determine the crystal system to which each belongs. Use the table in Figure 3.2 to summarize your observations. Answer Analysis and Conclusions questions 6–8.

Mineral Dimensions

Mineral Number	Description of Dimensions	Axial Angles	Crystal System
1			
2			
3			
4			
5			

Figure 3.2

Analysis and Conclusions

1. Position Model A so that its longest axis is vertical. How do the other two axes compare in size with each other? At what angle do the axes meet?

The other two axes are the same size; 90°.

2. Read the description for the tetragonal system in Figure 3.14 on page 39 of your text. Does Model A represent a tetragonal crystal? Explain how you know.

Yes. In the tetragonal system, the length and the width are the same, the height is different, and all three axes meet at right angles.

3. Describe the dimensions and the angles of intersection of the axes in Model B. To what crystal system does Model B belong?

The three dimensions are all different, but the axes all meet at right angles. The model represents an orthorhombic crystal.

4. Describe the dimensions and the angles of intersection of the axes in Model C. To what crystal system does Model C belong?

All three axes are different lengths. Two axes meet at right angles. The model represents a monoclinic crystal.

5. Position Model D so that its longest dimension is vertical. How many vertical faces does Model D have? How many horizontal axes does Model D have? At what angle do the axes intersect? To what crystal system does Model D belong?

six vertical faces; three horizontal axes; 60°. The model represents a hexagonal crystal.

6. Compare each actual mineral to the model that represents the same system. What are some differences between the model and the actual mineral. In what way do the differences make crystal system identification for actual minerals more difficult?

Answers will depend on the actual crystals used. Some likely answers are that the actual mineral samples do not have complete crystal surfaces and that the actual minerals may be formed from closely packed crystals. Both factors make identification difficult.

7. What factors can prevent crystals from forming with all faces visible?

There must be enough room for crystals to grow. With many crystals packed closely together in a mineral, the growth of adjacent crystals interferes with the growth of others.

8. Why can a protractor be used to measure the axial angles for the models but not for the actual minerals?

Since the models are large and have smooth top surfaces, the axes can be drawn and measured. It is unlikely that this would be possible with the actual samples.

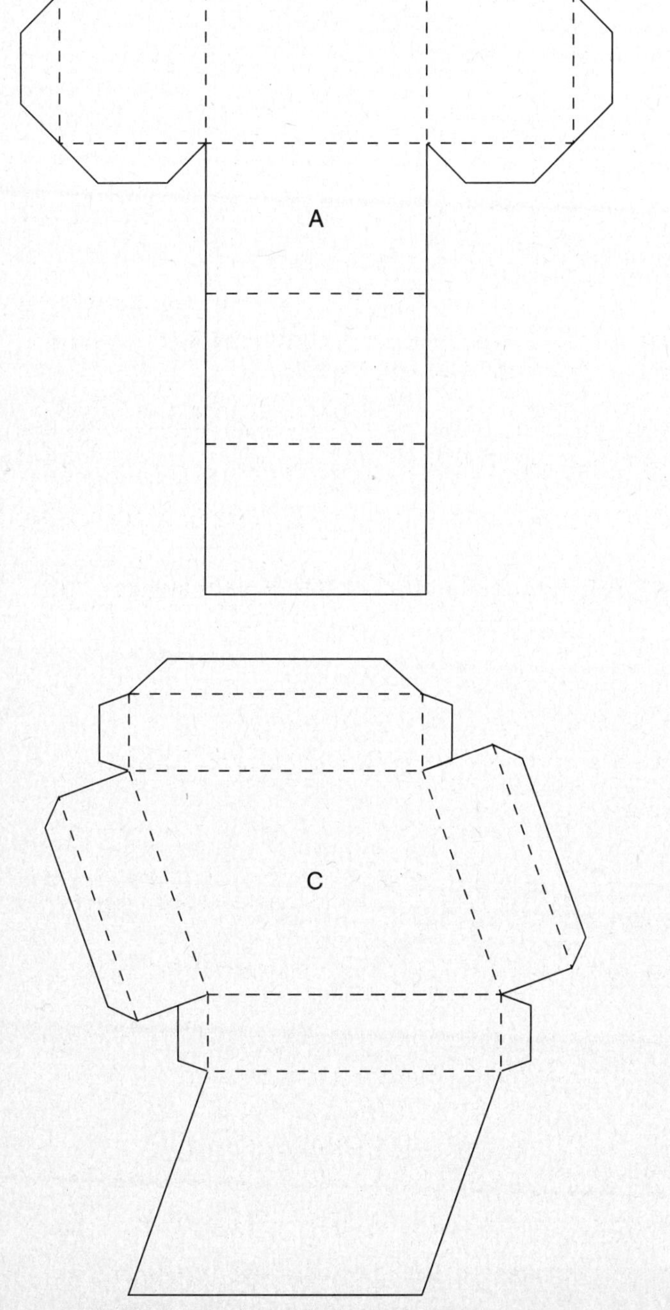

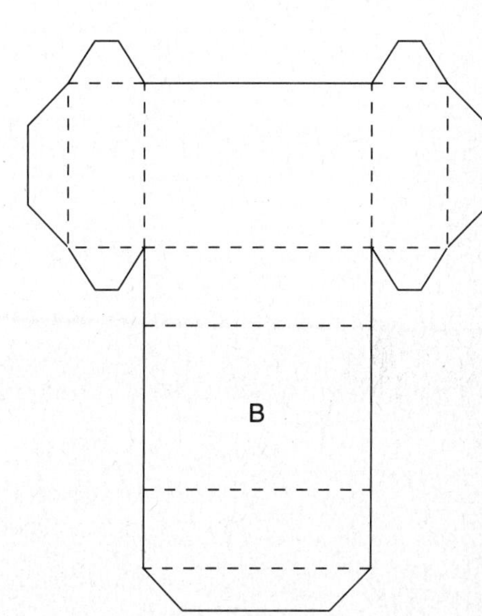

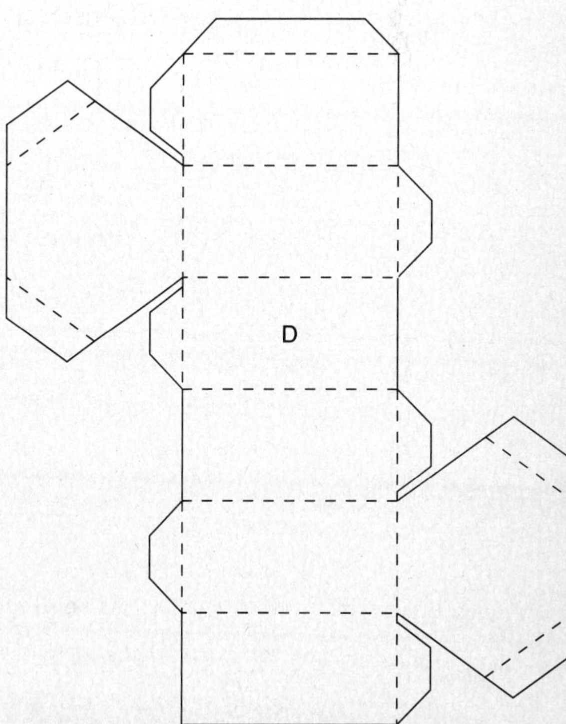

Figure 3.3

NAME ______________________

CLASS ____________ DATE ____________

LAB INVESTIGATION

Specific Gravity and Mineral Identification

When identifying minerals, sometimes visual inspection and simple tests such as streak, cleavage, and hardness are not enough to distinguish one mineral from another. For example, albite and oligoclase, both plagioclase feldspars (see page 54 of your text), are similar in appearance and most other properties. One property that does slightly differ between these two minerals is specific gravity: 2.62 for albite and 2.65 for oligoclase. Careful measurements of the specific gravity of each mineral would make it possible to tell the two apart with confidence.

The value for specific gravity is a ratio, or a comparison, of the weight of the mineral to the weight of an equal volume of water. A sample of albite, for example, would weigh 2.62 times as much as an equal volume of water.

In this activity, you will determine the specific gravities of three unnamed minerals and then use your values to identify each mineral.

Lab Skills and Objectives

- To **measure** data and **calculate** the specific gravity of several minerals
- To **identify** minerals using their specific gravities

Materials

- mineral kit containing 3 unnamed minerals
- triple-beam balance
- C-clamp
- 250-mL beaker
- water
- string (8–10 cm)
- paper clip
- plastic gloves
- rubber band
- calculator
- Properties of Some Common Minerals, Appendix A, pages 644–645 of your text

Inform students that one of their minerals (galena) contains lead. Students should wear plastic gloves and avoid putting their hands near their mouth, nose, and ears. Afterwards, make sure students wash their hands and scrub under their nails with soap and water.

Prepare the mineral kits ahead using *only* the minerals listed in Figure 4.3. Larger specimens will yield more accurate results. Retain a record of which minerals are in each numbered kit.

A spring scale, such as the one illustrated in Figure 4.6 on page 50 of the text, can be used in place of the balance. However, the results will be less accurate.

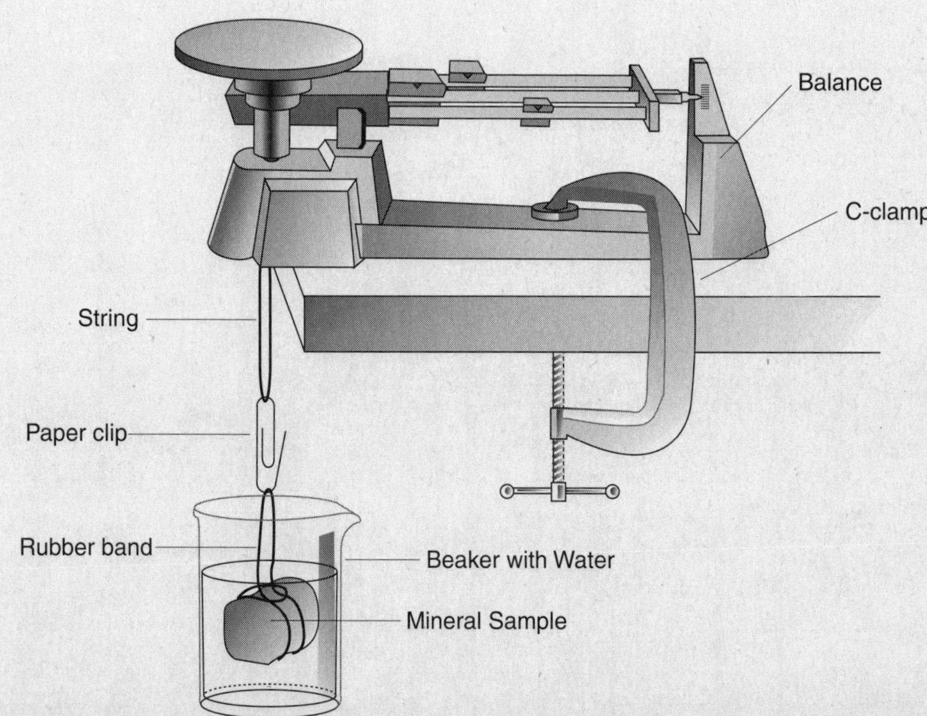

Figure 4.1

Procedure

1. Record the number of your mineral kit in the space provided in Figure 4.2.

2. Set the balance on the lab table so the pan is just hanging over the edge of the table. Be careful to keep most of the weight of the balance on the table so that the balance does not fall off. Attach the balance to the tabletop with a C-clamp.

If students are using a balance with a suspended pan (or, a high-form balance), students can remove the pan, hang the mineral from the beam, place the beaker on the tabletop, and adjust the length of the string so that the mineral will be submerged at the proper depth in the beaker of water.

3. Look under the balance and locate the metal piece that comes down from the pan. Attach a loop of string to this metal piece. Tie the string securely so that the loop of string hangs below the balance.

4. **CAUTION: Put on your plastic gloves.** Place your first mineral sample on the rubber band. Loop one end of the rubber band through the other end. Carefully tighten the rubber band around the mineral.

Figure 4.2

Data Table			
Mineral Kit Number:	**Mineral 1**	**Mineral 2**	**Mineral 3**
Mass in Air (g)*			
Mass in Water (g)*			
Loss of Mass in Water (g)			
Specific Gravity (calculated)			
Name of Mineral			
Specific Gravity (accepted value)			
Deviation from Accepted Value			

* Round off values to the nearest tenth.

5. **CAUTION: The ends of the paper clip may be sharp.** Make a hook out of a paper clip and attach it to the free loop of the rubber band. Hook the other end of the paper clip to the loop of string suspended from the balance pan. Your mineral sample should now hang freely from the bottom of the balance pan as shown in Figure 4.1.

Explain to students the difference between mass and weight. Results will be the same using mass or weight since specific gravity is a ratio in which the units cancel. If you wish to determine the weight of a mineral sample, convert the mass to Newtons by multiplying the mass in kilograms by the value for g, the gravitational field strength. At the surface of Earth, g = 9.8 Newtons/kilogram.

6. Adjust the balance and record the measurement in Figure 4.2 as *Mass in Air.* (For the purposes of this experiment, you can use mass instead of weight for determining specific gravity.)

7. Fill a 250-mL beaker with approximately 150 mL of water. Leaving the mineral attached to the balance, raise the beaker of water under the mineral until the mineral is totally submerged in the water. Do not allow the mineral to rest on the bottom of the beaker. Again adjust the balance and record the measurement in Figure 4.2 as *Mass in Water.*

8. Find the difference between the mass in water and the mass in air and record your result in Figure 4.2 as *Loss of Mass in Water.* Use the formula below to calculate the specific gravity of your mineral sample.

$$\text{Specific Gravity} = \frac{\text{mass of sample in air}}{\text{loss of mass in water}} \times 100\%$$

9. Repeat procedure steps 4–8 for the other two minerals in your kit. Record your results in Figure 4.2.

10. After returning the minerals to the kit, scrub your hands and clean under your fingernails with soap and water.

Specific Gravities of Selected Minerals	
Mineral	**Specific Gravity**
Sulfur	2.1
Gypsum	2.3
Calcite	2.7
Chalcopyrite	4.2
Pyrite	5.0
Magnetite	5.2
Galena	7.5

Figure 4.3

11. Use the values for specific gravity in Figure 4.3 to identify each of your mineral samples. Select the mineral from the table whose specific gravity is closest to your calculated value for each mineral. Record the mineral names and the actual values for specific gravity in Figure 4.2. (If you are unable to identify a mineral from its specific gravity alone, the table *Properties of Some Common Minerals* in Appendix A on pages 644–645 of your text may be helpful.)

12. Use the formula below to determine the percentage by which your values for specific gravity deviate from the accepted values.

$$\text{Deviation} = \frac{\text{difference between your value and accepted value}}{\text{accepted value}} \times 100\%$$

Analysis and Conclusions

1. Were you able to identify any of the minerals in your mineral kit by inspection before determining their specific gravities? If so, explain what tests you used in their identification.

Some minerals may be recognizable to students based on color, luster, or crystal shape.

2. From your results, were you able to use specific gravity alone in identifying the minerals in your kit?

With accurate measurements and pure samples, identification should be possible.

Explain to students that *sources of error* in an experiment refer to errors that are inherent to the design of and/or materials used in the experiment and not necessarily mistakes that may or may not have been made.

3. What sources of error in the experiment might account for any deviations from the accepted value of specific gravity for each mineral?

Sources of error include measurement error, the fact that a portion of the rubber band is submerged along with the mineral, and an impure mineral sample.

4. (a) Which minerals in Figure 4.3 are nonmetallic?

sulfur, gypsum, and calcite

(b) Which minerals are metallic.

chalcopyrite, pyrite, magnetite, and galena

(c) In general, how do the specific gravities of nonmetallic minerals differ from those of metallic minerals?

In general, metallic minerals have higher specific gravities than nonmetallic minerals.

5. When identifying a valuable gemstone, why is specific gravity more likely to be used than mineral tests such as streak or hardness?

Testing for either streak or hardness would damage the mineral. This method would leave it wet but unharmed.

6. Why can't the procedure for this investigation be used to find the specific gravity of halite?

Halite dissolves in water.

7. Imagine you are holding a sample of sulfur in one hand and an equal-sized sample of galena in the other hand. Use the table in Figure 4.2 to determine which will feel heavier. Explain your answer by using the words *specific gravity* in your response.

The galena feels heavier because it has a higher specific gravity.

8. Explain how a liquid with a specific gravity of 5.1 can be used to distinguish pyrite from magnetite.

Since pyrite has a lower specific gravity than the liquid, it will float. Magnetite has a higher specific gravity than the liquid and will sink.

CHAPTER
5A

NAME ______________________

CLASS ____________ DATE ____________

INQUIRY LAB

A Study of Igneous Rocks

In this lab you will classify igneous rocks on the basis of two observable features: color and texture. In general, igneous rocks are categorized as either *light-colored* or *dark-colored*. Igneous rocks have three basic textures. A coarse-grained igneous rock is composed of crystals that are large enough to be seen with the unaided eye. A fine-grained igneous rock consists of mineral crystals that are too small to be seen with the unaided eye. A rock with a glassy texture contains no crystals.

Lab Skills and Objectives

- To **classify** and **identify** several igneous rocks
- To **compare** the densities of light-colored and dark-colored igneous rocks

Materials

- igneous rock specimens, including basalt, gabbro, granite, obsidian, pumice, rhyolite, and scoria
- hand lens or magnifying glass
- 100-mL graduated cylinder
- balance
- notebook paper

Procedure

1. Sort the igneous rocks into two groups by color.

2. Sort the rocks in each color group into three texture groups.

3. Using the Summary Table: Common Igneous Rocks on page 68 of your textbook, write the name of each igneous rock (listed under Materials) in the correct location on the chart in Figure 5.1. (For the purposes of this laboratory, ignore the category of medium-colored rocks in the Summary Table.) Then on notebook paper, draw a chart identical to Figure 5.1 but make the boxes large enough to place the rock specimens in them. Place each rock in the appropriate box. Use this chart to answer Analysis and Conclusions questions 1–6.

Students who have completed Lab Investigation 2 on page 10, may outline the method given for determining the densities of irregular solids in Part B. A suitable data table is given in Figure 2.3. An alternative procedure for determining the densities involves massing the rock sample directly on the balance and then determining the volume by displacement of water.

4. Design a procedure that you could use to determine the densities of granite and gabbro. After you have written the steps in your procedure, use a separate sheet of paper to create a table on which you can record your data.

1. Fill a graduated cylinder with enough water to cover the rock. Measure and record the volume.
2. Determine and record the mass of the cylinder and water.
3. Slide the rock into the water. Measure and record the mass of the cylinder, water, and rock.
4. Measure and record the volume of the water and rock in the cylinder.
5. Determine the mass and volume of the rock by subtraction.
6. Use the formula D = m/V to calculate the density.

5. Ask your teacher to check your procedure. Then use your procedure to find the densities of granite and gabbro. Answer Analysis and Conclusions questions 7–9.

Data Table		
	Color	
Texture	Light-colored	Dark-colored
glassy	pumice, obsidian	scoria
fine-grained	rhyolite	basalt
coarse-grained	granite	gabbro

Figure 5.1

Analysis and Conclusions

1. Using a hand lens or magnifying glass, look carefully at the mineral grains in the specimen of granite. What minerals occur in granite?

Quartz, feldspar, and biotite are readily identifiable. Other minerals that may be present include amphibole (hornblende), pyroxene, muscovite, and pyrite.

2. What minerals would you expect to occur in rhyolite? Explain your answer.

Rhyolite should contain the same minerals as a granite (quartz, feldspar, and biotite) because rhyolite is really fine-grained granite.

3. What minerals can you identify in the specimen of gabbro?

Gabbro contains feldspar and augite. Olivine, hornblende, and biotite may also be present.

4. What minerals would you expect to occur in basalt? Explain your answer.

Basalt should contain the same minerals as gabbro (feldspar and augite) because basalt is fine-grained gabbro.

5. Based on its color and texture, where would you place obsidian on the chart? Based on the information in the Summary Table in your textbook, where would you place obsidian on the chart? Explain why your second classification is the correct answer.

Obsidian is dark in color. Based on its appearance, obsidian would be placed with the dark-colored, glassy-textured rocks. However, it should be placed with the light-colored, glassy-textured rocks because its composition is like that of a granite.

6. Compare the pumice and scoria. Why are the holes in the scoria larger than the holes in the pumice? (Hint: Gas bubbles can move more easily in thin lava than in thick lava.)

The mafic lavas that form scoria are more fluid than the felsic lavas that form pumice. More fluid lava enables small bubbles to join together and form larger bubbles before the lava solidifies.

7. Which rock is more dense, gabbro or granite?

Gabbro is more dense.

8. How is the density of rhyolite likely to compare with the density of basalt? Why?

Rhyolite should be less dense than basalt because granite is less dense than gabbro.

9. The average density of granite is 2.6 g/mL. Using the formula in Laboratory 2, calculate the percent of error of your density value for granite. Write the formula and show all work.

$$\text{percent error} = \frac{\text{difference between measured and accepted value}}{\text{accepted value}} \times 100$$

NAME ______________________

CLASS ______________ DATE ______________

LAB INVESTIGATION

A Study of Sedimentary Rocks

Sedimentary rocks are classified into three groups: clastic, chemical, and organic. **Clastic** sedimentary rocks are formed from bits and pieces of other rocks. In some clastic rocks, the original pieces are easily seen. **Chemical** sedimentary rocks are formed by chemical activity such as precipitation in fresh water or seawater. These rocks are usually fine textured. **Organic** sedimentary rocks form from the remains of plants or animals. Fossils of the original plant or animal may still be seen in some organic sedimentary rocks.

Lab Skills and Objectives

- To **classify** and **identify** several sedimentary rocks

Materials

- set of sedimentary rock specimens, including conglomerate, sandstone, shale, shell limestone, compact limestone, coal, and rock salt
- hand lens or magnifying glass   Use a bituminous coal specimen.
- notebook paper
- coarse sandpaper

Procedure

1. Carefully examine the set of sedimentary rock specimens. Using the Summary Table: Common Sedimentary Rocks on page 74 of your textbook, write the name of each sedimentary rock (listed under Materials) in the correct location on the chart in Figure 5.1.

2. On notebook paper, draw an identical chart with boxes large enough for you to place the rock specimens in. Place each rock in the box that matches its description.

Data Table

Clastic	Chemical	Organic
sand and gravel cemented together, resembles concrete conglomerate	microscopic grains of calcite, gray or tan in color, dense compact limestone	rock made from plant remains coal
cemented sand grains (usually quartz), gritty feel sandstone	natural form of salt, salty taste rock salt	skeletons and shells of sea animals shell limestone
compact mud, earthy odor, usually easily broken shale		

Figure 5.1

 NAME ______________ CLASS ______________ DATE ______________

Analysis and Conclusions

1. How are the particles that make up the conglomerate different from the particles in the sandstone or in the shale?

The particles in the conglomerate are, in general, larger than those of the sandstone or of the shale.

2. Look carefully at the largest grains in the conglomerate specimen. Of what mineral are they composed?

The mineral is most likely to be quartz.

3. Using a hand lens or magnifying glass, examine a piece of sandpaper and the sandstone specimen. Why does the sandstone feel like sandpaper?

Sandpaper is sand grains cemented to paper and sandstone is sand grains cemented together.

4. Of what mineral or minerals is the sandstone made?

It is mostly quartz, but students may also be able to identify feldspar and mica. Other mineral grains present in the sandstone will probably be too small for students to identify.

5. In what way is the overall appearance of the shale different from that of the conglomerate and the sandstone?

Shale will generally appear to be of a smaller grain size, more layered, and of a different color.

Students should not do the chemical test involving hydrochloric acid. The test may be done as a demonstration.

CAUTION: Wear safety goggles and a lab apron when working with hydrochloric acid.

6. What chemical test could be used to identify both of the limestones you examined? Explain your answer.

Both limestones should react to dilute hydrochloric acid because both contain the mineral calcite, which bubbles in acid.

7. How do the two limestone specimens differ in appearance?

The shell limestone contains fossils and the compact limestone appears massive.

8. Examine the particles that make up the shell limestone. Are they whole or in fragments? Name any particles that you can recognize.

The limestone may include fragments or whole pieces of clams, mussels, corals, and so forth.

9. Is rock salt different from the mineral halite? Explain your answer.

Halite is the name given to the mineral; rock salt is the name given to the rock made from halite.

10. What is the overall color of the coal? Is its surface shiny or dull? Are any fossils visible?

The coal will most likely be black and shiny. Plant fossils, such as fern imprints, may be present.

11. Why are fossils rare in conglomerates?

Conglomerates consist of coarse particles deposited in rough water where fossil materials are likely to be destroyed.

NAME ____________________

CLASS ____________ DATE ____________

LAB INVESTIGATION

A Study of Metamorphic Rocks

In general, metamorphic rocks can be placed into one of two texture categories: foliated and nonfoliated. **Foliated** (or banded) metamorphic rocks have a layered appearance. Gneiss, schist, and slate are examples of foliated rocks. **Nonfoliated** metamorphic rocks are generally massive with no apparent layering. Quartzite and marble are examples of nonfoliated rocks.

Lab Skills and Objectives

- To **classify** and **identify** several metamorphic rocks

Materials

- set of metamorphic rock specimens, including gneiss, schist, slate, quartzite, and marble
- hand lens or magnifying glass
- notebook paper

Procedure

1. Carefully examine the set of the metamorphic rock specimens and separate those that appear foliated from those that appear nonfoliated.
2. Using the information in Chapter 5 of your textbook, write the name of each metamorphic rock (listed under Materials) in the correct location on the chart in Figure 5.1.
3. On notebook paper, draw an identical chart with boxes large enough for you to place the rock specimens in. Place each rock in the box that matches its description.

Data Table

Foliated	Nonfoliated
coarse grains, light and dark bands gneiss	hard, dense, crystalline, fused quartz grains quartzite
thin and parallel bands with wavy, uneven surfaces schist	crystalline, visible crystals of calcite, often white or gray marble
red, gray, green, or purple, very fine grained, splits into smooth, flat layers slate	

Figure 5.1

5C NAME ______ CLASS ______ DATE ______

Analysis and Conclusions

1. Note the light and dark bands in gneiss. Using a hand lens, try to identify quartz, feldspar, and either mica or hornblende in the bands. Which minerals make up the light bands and which ones make up the dark bands?

Quartz and feldspar occur as light bands. Hornblende and mica occur as dark bands.

2. Many gneisses are believed to have formed from granites. Compare the minerals that occur in gneiss with those that occur in granite. (Refer to your work in *A Study of Igneous Rocks* on pages 20 and 21 of this booklet.)

Gneiss and granite contain the same minerals, including quartz, feldspar, mica, and hornblende.

3. How is gneiss different in appearance from granite?

The minerals in gneiss are arranged in bands while those in granite are randomly arranged.

4. Look at the specimen of schist. How do the color and thickness of its mineral bands compare with those in the specimen of gneiss?

Both rocks have alternating light and dark bands, but the bands are thinner in the schist.

5. Mica schist is the most common kind of schist. In it, the flakes of mica are all parallel and easily seen. Is your specimen a mica schist? Why or why not?

Students should be able to support their answer by identifying the kind of mica present or by discussing the lack of mica in their specimens.

6. What sedimentary rock does slate most closely resemble? (Refer to your work in *A Study of Sedimentary Rocks* on pages 22 and 23 of this booklet.)

Slate most closely resembles shale.

7. How is the texture of marble different from the texture of quartzite?

Marble is usually coarser in texture.

8. How could mineral hardness be used to tell quartzite from marble?

Quartzite is harder than marble because it contains quartz, which is harder than the calcite in marble.

Students should not do the chemical test involving hydrochloric acid. The test may be done as a demonstration.

CAUTION: Wear safety goggles and a lab apron when working with hydrochloric acid.

9. How could dilute hydrochloric acid be used to tell quartzite from marble?

The calcite in marble will bubble in dilute hydrochloric acid. The quartz in quartzite will not react.

10. Excluding marble and quartzite, what general properties of appearance can be used to determine whether a rock is metamorphic, igneous, or sedimentary?

In general, a crystalline rock that lacks banding or foliation is igneous. A foliated, crystalline rock is metamorphic. A noncrystalline rock consisting of cemented grains is sedimentary.

NAME ______________________________

CLASS ______________ DATE ______________

Passive and Active Solar Heating

When the sun's energy is used for heating buildings, two kinds of solar collectors are used. One is a *passive solar collector* that uses the building itself to collect and store heat. The other is an *active solar collector* that consists of a system for collecting heat, a heat storage area, and ducts for moving heat in the building. The two collectors absorb and release heat at different rates. In this experiment, you will construct models of passive and active solar collectors and observe the differences between them.

Lab Skills and Objectives

- To **construct** models of a passive solar collector and an active solar collector
- To **compare** the operation and effectiveness of solar collectors

Materials

- 2 shoe boxes of the same size
- 1 brick
- 2 thermometers
- 1 sheet of aluminum foil
- 2 paper cups
- 2 pieces of plastic wrap
- masking tape
- black paint
- rubber cement
- 1 sheet of graph paper
- scissors
- hole punch

Use water-base latex paint only. In using rubber cement, be sure that students follow the precautions described on the label.

Procedure

Figure 6.1

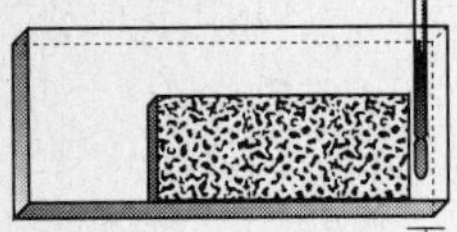

1. To construct a passive solar collector, use rubber cement to glue a brick to the bottom of a shoe box. Place the brick 1 cm from the end of the box as shown in Figure 6.1. Paint the inside of the box and the brick with black paint. Cover the top of the box with a piece of plastic wrap. Tape the plastic to the outside of the box using strips of masking tape.

2. Use a hole punch to make a hole in the side of the shoe box just large enough to slide a thermometer through it. Position the hole so that the bulb of the thermometer can be centered in the 1 cm space between the box and the brick. Use masking tape to secure the thermometer at the hole and to prevent air from escaping. See Figure 6.1.

Use nonmercury thermometers.

Figure 6.2

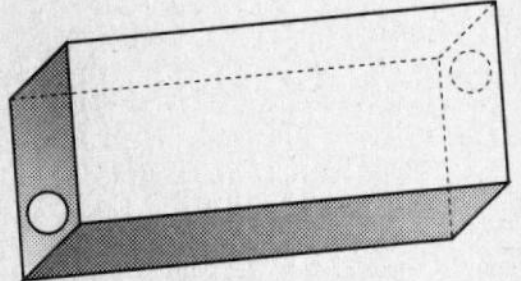

3. **CAUTION: Scissors are sharp. Handle them with care.** Construct an active solar collector by using the open end of a paper cup to trace two circles diagonally opposite each other on the outside of the second shoe box. The circles should be in the bottom corners of the short sides of the box as shown in Figure 6.2. Cut out the two circles with a scissors.

The holes in the shoebox could be made in advance if students are likely to have difficulty cutting them.

4. Use the bottom of a paper cup to make flaps that can be opened and closed. Cut around the bottoms of the cups but leave one eighth of the circumference still attached.

Figure 6.3

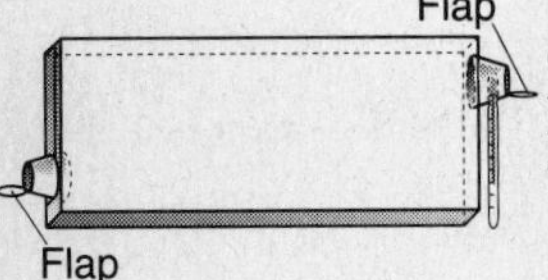

5. From the inside of the box, insert the narrow end of a cup into one of the holes. Pull gently until the lip of the cup is even with the side of the box. Tape the cup in place. Repeat the procedure for the second cup.

6. Punch a hole in the side of one of the paper cups at the point at which it joins the box. Insert a thermometer and position the bulb of the thermometer in the center of the cup. Tape the thermometer to the outside of the box. Make sure that you can read the entire thermometer scale.

7. Line the sides of the box with aluminum foil and glue the foil in place. Cut the foil from the holes in the box. Paint the bottom of the box black. Cover the top of the box with plastic wrap and tape the plastic to the outside of the box.

If this investigation must be done on a cloudy day, incandescent lamps such as those used in Lab Investigation 26, page 112, can be used. Connect the lamps to curcuits with ground-fault interrupters.

8. Place the collectors in full sunlight. Tilt each collector so that it faces the sun. The collectors will be at the correct angle when a pencil held perpendicular to the plastic cover has no shadow. Prop the collectors with books and allow them to heat for 3 minutes.

9. Read the temperatures on both thermometers and open the flaps on the active solar collector. Record the temperatures in the data table. For the next 16 minutes, read and record the temperatures on both thermometers every 2 minutes.

10. Remove the collectors from the sunlight. As the collectors cool, read and record the temperatures every 2 minutes for 16 minutes.

11. Make a graph of your data by plotting time on the x-axis and temperature on the y-axis. Begin numbering the y-axis with the lowest temperature you recorded. Use two different colors to plot the data for the two collectors.

Data Table

	Heating Phase									Cooling Phase							
Minutes	0	2	4	6	8	10	12	14	16	18	20	22	24	26	28	30	32
Temperature (°C), Passive Collector																	
Temperature (°C), Active Collector																	

Figure 6.4

Analysis and Conclusions

Describe for students a typical active solar collector consisting of water circulating in rooftop pipes and conducted through pipes to a storage area inside the building. Point out the high capacity of water to absorb heat.

1. Which collector reached the higher temperature? active

Which collector stayed warm longer? passive

2. If you were building a passive solar heated house, what features would you include in the design to help the house hold heat?

masses of brick or stone, barrels of water, well-insulated walls

3. There are three parts of an active solar collector. Which one is missing in the model you built? Explain why the missing part is needed.

the storage area; Heat that is absorbed during the day must be retained for release during the night.

4. Your collectors were painted black. Design an experiment that determines whether black is the most efficient color.

Set out several passive collectors, each painted a different color. One collector should be black. Allow the collectors to absorb heat for the same period of time. The highest temperature will be reached by the collector painted with the color that is most efficient in absorbing heat.

5. Compare the use of solar energy for heating with the burning of fuels such as coal, oil, and gas. What environmental benefits are there in the use of solar energy?

Solar energy does not release pollutants into the air. It does not require that land be torn up in strip mining or that environmentally sensitive places be drilled for oil.

6. Do you think it would be wise to invest in research to improve the efficiency and reliability of solar energy? Explain your answer.

Since coal, oil, and gas supplies are rapidly being used up, solar energy may be an important source of energy in the future.

NAME ______________________

CLASS ______________ DATE ______________

Salinization of Soils

When you eat fresh vegetables in winter, you are benefit from the irrigation of crops that are grown in hot, dry climates. Crops are sometimes irrigated with mineral-laden water from a river or a well. The dissolved minerals in the water can cause a crust to form as water evaporates from the surface of the soil. You will make a model of a salt crust.

Lab Skills and Objectives

- To **model** and **observe** salinization
- To **measure** the thickness and mass of salt crust
- To **measure** the amount of dissolved and suspended solids in a river water sample

Materials

- safety goggles
- lab apron
- balance
- half of a petri dish
- 100-mL graduated cylinder
- 150-mL beaker
- drying oven
- soil (sand and clay or bricklaying sand)
- 30 g salt
- balance
- wax pencil
- spatula
- metric ruler
- tongs
- paper towels

Procedure

More than one lab period is required. The crust in Part A requires one or more days to dry. Have students work in pairs.

Part A

1. **Put on your safety goggles and lab apron.** Fill a petri dish almost to the top with a soil sample.

2. Use a wax pencil to write your name on the side of the petri dish.

3. Measure 30 g of salt into a beaker. Add 60 mL of tap water to the beaker. With a stirring rod, stir the salt solution until all of the salt is dissolved.

4. Pour the salt solution slowly over the soil. The soil should be completely covered with water. You are modeling flood irrigation in which the soil is covered and saturated with water.

5. Put the petri dish in a drying oven set at 110°C. Allow the soil samples to dry.

If a drying oven is not available, the soil samples can be dried for a longer time at room temperature.

Day 2

6. **Put on your safety goggles and lab apron.** Using tongs, remove the soil sample from the drying oven and allow it to cool. Write your observations of the contents of the petri dish in the data table.

7. When the soil sample has cooled, use a spatula to lift the crust off the soil.

8. Obtain the mass of a piece of smooth paper just large enough to hold the crust. Record the mass in the data table.

9. Transfer all pieces of crust onto the paper. Use your metric ruler to measure the thickness of the crust and record the thickness in the data table.

10. Measure the mass of the crust and the paper. Record the mass in the data table. Calculate the mass of the crust and record this in the data table.

11. Place soil and crust samples in a trash basket. Wash beakers and evaporating dishes with soap to remove all residue. Rinse and dry them.

Data Table			
Part A		**Part B**	
Mass of paper + crust		Identity of water sample	
Mass of paper		Mass of evaporating dish + dried solids	
Mass of crust		Mass of evaporating dish	
Thickness of the crust		Mass of dried solids	
Observations of crust			

Figure 6.1

Analysis and Conclusions

1. Compare the mass of the crust in Part A with the mass of salt that you dissolved in the water in procedure step 3. Account for any difference in the two masses.

Answers will vary. The crust should be heavier than the mass of the dissolved salt because the salt combines with soil particles to form the crust.

2. The heat of the oven models the heat of the sun on the surface of the soil. How does heat on the soil surface cause the crust to form at the surface?

Wicking causes the water to rise to the surface carrying the salt with it.

3. Would an equally thick crust form on a field if the soil was porous and irrigation water could drain away?

No, water seeps away into the groundwater carrying minerals with it.

4. From your observations of the crust, explain why a lettuce seed germinating underneath the crust would have a difficult time breaking through.

The crust was very uniform and not easily broken. There would be little opportunity for a seedling to break through.

Students should not undertake any experimental procedures without your approval.

5. Over 30 % of irrigated agricultural land has been salinized. Design an experiment that will test how salts can be flushed out of a damaged soil.

Student should design an experiment that soaks the soil to dissolve the salts and drains the salt water away from the bottom.

NAME ______________________

CLASS ____________ DATE ____________

LAB INVESTIGATION

Mapping a "Mountain"

Mapmakers use different methods to represent the shape of the land surface on maps. The most common method uses lines called **contours,** which are drawn to connect points at the same elevation above sea level. The maps on which contour lines appear are called **contour maps** or **topographic maps.**

Lab Skills and Objectives

- To **describe** the shape of a land surface using a contour map

Materials

Contour model kits, available from science supply houses, can be used if you would prefer not to construct clay mountains.

- modeling clay
- transparent plastic shoebox and lid
- toothpick
- marking pencil
- metric ruler
- tracing paper
- pencil
- 250-mL beaker
- water

In the absence of a transparent plastic lid, sheets of clear, thick acetate or plastic can be used.

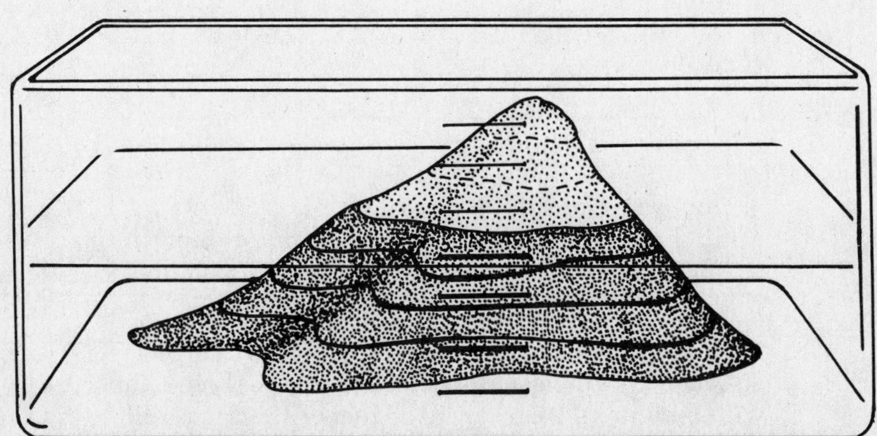

Figure 7.1

Procedure

1. Use the metric ruler and the marking pencil to mark off 1-cm intervals on the outside of the plastic shoebox from the bottom to the top, as indicated in Figure 7.1.

2. Use the modeling clay to make a cone-shaped "mountain" no more than 8 cm high. Make sure that the base of the mountain is large enough to almost cover the base of the shoebox yet small enough to fit into the box. Make one side of the cone steeper than the other. Include a river valley or ravine running down the gentler side (see Figure 7.1).

3. Place the mountain in the shoebox. Fill a beaker with water and carefully pour the water into the box up to the level of the first centimeter mark.

4. With the end of a toothpick, draw a line in the clay all around the mountain at exactly the water level.

5. Add more water to the shoebox until the next centimeter mark is reached and draw a line around the mountain at that exact water level.

6. Repeat procedure step 5 at each marked level until the top of the mountain is reached.

7. Carefully pour all water from the shoebox. Place the lid on the box.

8. Looking straight down through the clear lid, trace a line with the marking pencil on the lid to represent the base of the mountain. Then draw lines on the lid, tracing each of the marked levels on the mountain. (Hint: Tracing is easier if you close one eye.)

9. Using tracing paper and a pencil, transfer the lines you have drawn from the lid onto the paper.

10. Label the line drawn for the base of the mountain "0" for sea level. Then label the elevation of each of the other lines 1, 2, 3, and so forth. Complete your map by adding a scale, the contour interval, the name of the person who prepared the map, a map title, and the date.

Analysis and Conclusions

1. Select any line drawn around the mountain on your map. What is true of the elevation of every point along this line?

The elevation of every point along the line is the same.

2. Each line drawn on your map should be a closed loop. Explain why.

Each line on the map represents a line (or water level) that went completely around the mountain. Therefore each line on the map should be closed.

3. Why is the line around the base of your mountain a contour line?

This line is also a line of equal elevation.

4. What is the difference in elevation between the highest and lowest contour lines?

Answers will vary, but should be less than 8 cm.

5. What is the elevation of the highest contour line on your map? Is this the elevation of the mountaintop? Explain your answer.

Answers will vary. Since the mountaintop is an isolated point, it can never be on a contour line.

6. On which side of the mountain are the contour lines closer together?

The contour lines are closer together on the steeply sloping side.

7. Contour lines that cross valleys or ravines bend out of line with the rest of each contour loop. Do your contour lines bend upstream or downstream when they cross the valley or ravine?

Contour lines bend upstream.

ENVIRONMENTAL CONNECTIONS

Suppose that you are to guide a group of people on a hike to the top a mountain. The hikers you will lead have never before climbed a mountain. They are all healthy and energetic, but many in the group are concerned about whether they can make it to the summit. A topographic map of the mountain shows a number of hiking trails. Explain how you would use the map to select the best trail for this inexperienced group. How could the map help you give advice on what clothing to wear and what supplies to carry?

NAME ______________________

CLASS ______________ DATE ______________

CHAPTER

7B

Map Legends and Symbols

A map legend, or key, is an explanatory list of information appearing along the borders of a map. Legends may include the title, the scale, the compass directions, the contour interval, the symbols, when the map was prepared and by whom, the type of map projection used, the datum (the zero-elevation point), and the location of the mapped area relative to other places.

Color, shading, and texture are often used to represent particular regions (countries, states, climatic zones) or the distribution of features (rock types, elevation, population). Pictures, geometrics, lines, numbers, and letters are also used as symbols. They represent natural features (rivers, natural resources, vegetation) or structures (cities, buildings, roads).

Imagine that a friend gives you a map of his distant hometown and county. On your way to school, everything but the map legend is destroyed in the rain. The legend includes the information provided in Figure 7.1.

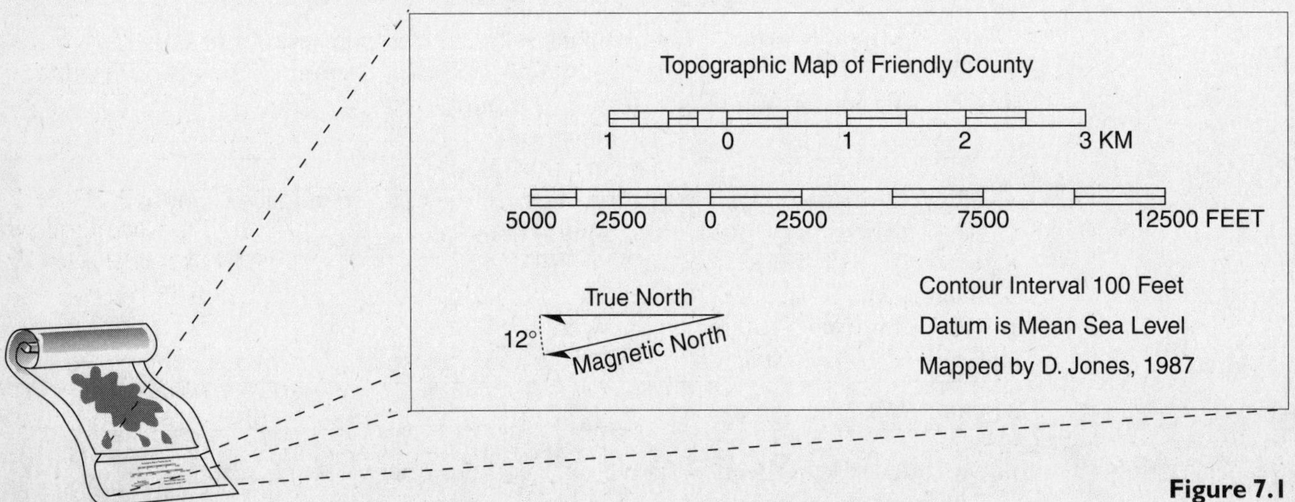

Figure 7.1

Map Skills and Objectives

- To **recognize** and **use** map legends and symbols in reading maps

Materials

- Topographic Map Symbols, Appendix B, Map Atlas, pages 666–667 of your text
- metric ruler

Procedure

1. Determine the name of your friend's home county.

Friendly County

2. Find out which direction on the map is east (up, down, right, or left).

up

3. If your friend's school is located in the lower right corner of the map, in what section of the county (in terms of compass direction) is it located?

southwest section

4. What is the map scale? State the scale verbally and numerically. (Hint: To get the numerical representative fraction, first determine the metric verbal scale. Then calculate the number of units of length on Earth equal to one of the same units on the map.)

I cm equals 0.5 km; I:50 000 or I/50 000

Analysis and Conclusions

1. You discover a map of the same county drawn at a scale of 1:24 000. Which of the two is the larger-scale map?

1:24 000

Assume that the map legend also includes a table of map symbols exactly like the one on pages 666–667 of your text. Use this table to answer questions 2 and 3.

2. What color is used to represent your friend's house?

black

the forest in his backyard?

green

his favorite fishing pond?

blue

3. Name three occupations your friend could pursue in his county. Explain your answer.

The map symbols suggest these occupations: teacher (school), clergyman (church), engineer (railroad), construction worker (buildings, bridges), fruit farmer (orchard), miner (quarry), and so forth.

4. Your friend's house and his neighbor's house are 1500 feet apart. They occur on two adjacent contour lines on the map. What is the difference in elevation between the two houses?

100 feet

Your friend's school is 2400 feet from his house. It occurs on a depression contour, and there is a second depression contour between the school and the house. Does your friend have a steeper walk to his school or to his neighbor's house? Explain your answer.

to his neighbor's house; The slope to the house is 0.07, the slope to the school is 0.04.

5. What is the magnetic declination for the mapped area?

12°

6. Compare the legends of the ten maps in Appendix B on pages 650–664 of your text. Of those with scales, which is the largest-scale map? Which is the smallest-scale map? How are compass directions represented? What types of symbols are used? Name two maps that use the same symbol to represent two different features.

Geologic Map: Flaming Gorge, UT; Physical United States; north arrow and lines of latitude and longitude; Symbols vary. The same colors and lines are used to represent different things on different maps.

NAME ______________________

CLASS ______________ DATE ______________

MAP ACTIVITY

Reading a Topographic Map

Topographic maps show the shape of Earth's surface by means of contour lines. **Contour lines** are lines that connect points that are at the same elevation above sea level.

Map Skills and Objectives

- to **use map symbols** and **interpret** a topographic map

Materials

- Topographic Map, Harrisburg, PA, Appendix B, page 652 of your text
- Topographic Map Symbols, Appendix B, pages 666–667 of your text
- 2 sheets of white paper
- magnifying glass or hand lens

Procedure

1. Figure 7.1 is a topographic map of an area along a seacoast. The map includes each of the following topographic features:

C	cliff	A	ocean
D	rock quarry (man-made basin)	G	island
B	river	E	steep quarry wall
F	mountain peak		

Complete the numbering of contour lines in Figure 7.1 by using a contour interval of ten feet. Label each contour at the break in the line, as shown for the zero- and ten-foot contours. Then identify each topographic feature on the map and write its corresponding letter in the space provided above.

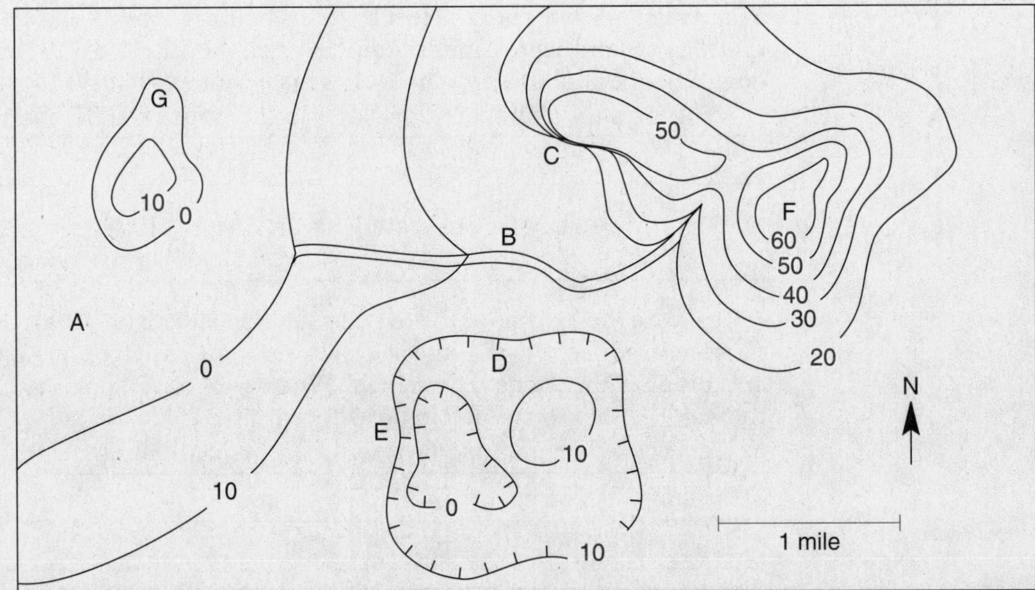

Figure 7.1

2. Locate Fishing Creek (south of Cove Mountain) on the Harrisburg map in your text. (A magnifying glass may make reading the map easier.) In what direction does the creek flow? How can you tell?

northeast or east; The contour lines bend toward the southwest or west, indicating the upstream direction.

3. Locate the Susquehanna River, which flows through the Appalachian Mountains. In the Harrisburg area, the Appalachian Mountains consist of ridges and valleys. How can you distinguish ridges and valleys on the map?

Valleys are shown by contour lines that are farther apart and that represent lower elevations. Ridges are shown by contour lines that are close together or that form closed circles and that represent higher elevations.

4. Locate the east bank of the Susquehanna River at the point at which the river enters the map and at the point at which it leaves the map. Line up the straight edge of a sheet of paper with these two points. Mark the position of the two points on the paper. Hold the marked edge along the map scale and use the scale like a ruler to measure the distance between the two marks. What is the straight-line distance (in miles) between the two points on the river?

approximately 6.5 miles

5. What is the actual distance, measured along the east bank of the river, between the two points in procedure step 4? Think of the east bank as a series of connecting, zigzag segments. Line up a straight edge of the paper with the bank where the river enters the map. Mark the beginning and end of the first zigzag segment. Pivot your paper on the second mark so that the edge of the paper lines up with the second zigzag segment. Mark the end of this segment. Continue pivoting the paper and marking each segment until you have a series of marks representing bends in the riverbank. Hold the paper along the map scale and determine the distance between the first and last marks.

approximately 8.2 miles; Answers will vary.

Analysis and Conclusions

1. Describe the shape and the orientation of the ridges and the valleys.

The ridges and the valleys are long and narrow. They parallel each other and are oriented approximately northeast-southwest.

2. Using the ridges on the Harrisburg map as examples, how would you define the term ridge?

a mountain that is long and narrow with sharp peaks and steep sides

3. You are driving north on highway 225 from the point at which it crosses Clark Creek to where it crosses the Appalachian Trail. What is the straight-line distance (in miles) of your trip?

approximately 1.7 miles

What distance will your car's odometer measure for your trip?

approximatlely 2.5 miles; Answers will vary.

4. The relief of the mapped landscape is the result of millions of years of erosion by the wind and the rain. Which features on the map consist of rocks that were the most resistant to this erosion? Which features consist of rocks that were the least resistant to erosion?

ridges; valleys

CHAPTER 7D

NAME ____________________

CLASS ____________ DATE ____________

Drawing Profiles

While a topographic map shows features, contours, and distances, it is still just a flat model of a given area. When a more detailed portrayal of the elevations and the features across the map is required, a profile is made. In this activity, you will use a topographic map to help create several profiles of regions surrounding Monadnock Mountain located in southern New Hampshire.

Map Skills and Objectives

- To **construct a profile** of an area on a topographic map
- To **interpret** features on the profile
- To **evaluate** vertical exaggeration on the profile

Figure 7.1

Materials

- Topographic Map: Monadnock, NH, Appendix B, page 650 of your text
- Topographic Map Symbols, Appendix B, pages 666–667 of your text
- two strips of white paper, 2 × 7 cm and 2 × 12 cm
- magnifying glass or hand lens

Procedure

1. Locate Fern Hill on the Monadnock, NH, map on page 650 of your text. An enlarged and rotated map of the hill is shown in Figure 7.1.

2. Begin a profile of Fern Hill by laying a strip of paper, 2 × 7 cm, along line A-B on the enlarged map. Mark and label the position of points A and B on the paper strip. At each point where a contour line crosses line A-B, mark the contour's position on the edge of the paper strip and label the elevation. (If necessary, refer to the Monadnock Mountain map.)

3. When you have marked all the contour lines, tape your paper strip to the graph so that it becomes your horizontal axis. Plot the elevation of each mark according to the vertical axis. Connect the points with a smooth curve. Answer Analysis and Conclusions questions 1 and 2.

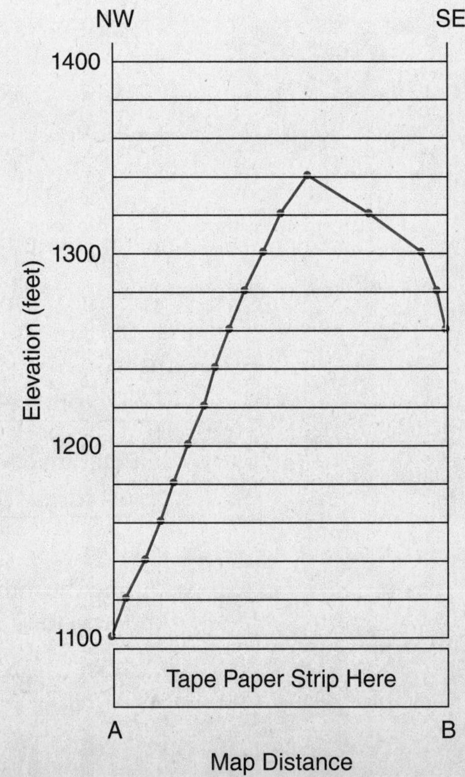

4. Locate Monadnock Mountain and Spaulding Hill on the map in your text. To construct a profile of the landscape between these two features, lay a paper strip, 2 × 12 cm, on the map so that one edge of the strip forms a line connecting the distance check point on the top of Monadnock Mountain and the last "l" in "Spaulding Hill."

5. Profile the area between these two points by using the method outlined in Procedure step 2. Be sure to include the position of any contour lines, streams, marshes, roads, and spot elevations that your line crosses. The following suggestions will help you with your profile.

a. Use a magnifying glass when contour lines are close together and index contours are difficult to trace.

b. Locate the road that parallels Gleason Brook. Profile only the index contours to the south of the road and profile all contour lines to the north of the road.

c. Remember that you can estimate the elevation of features located between two contour lines.

6. Draw your profile on the graph provided in Figure 7.2 with the northwest to the left and the southeast to the right. The vertical exaggeration is ¼ inch equals 100 feet. Answer Analysis and Conclusions questions 3–8.

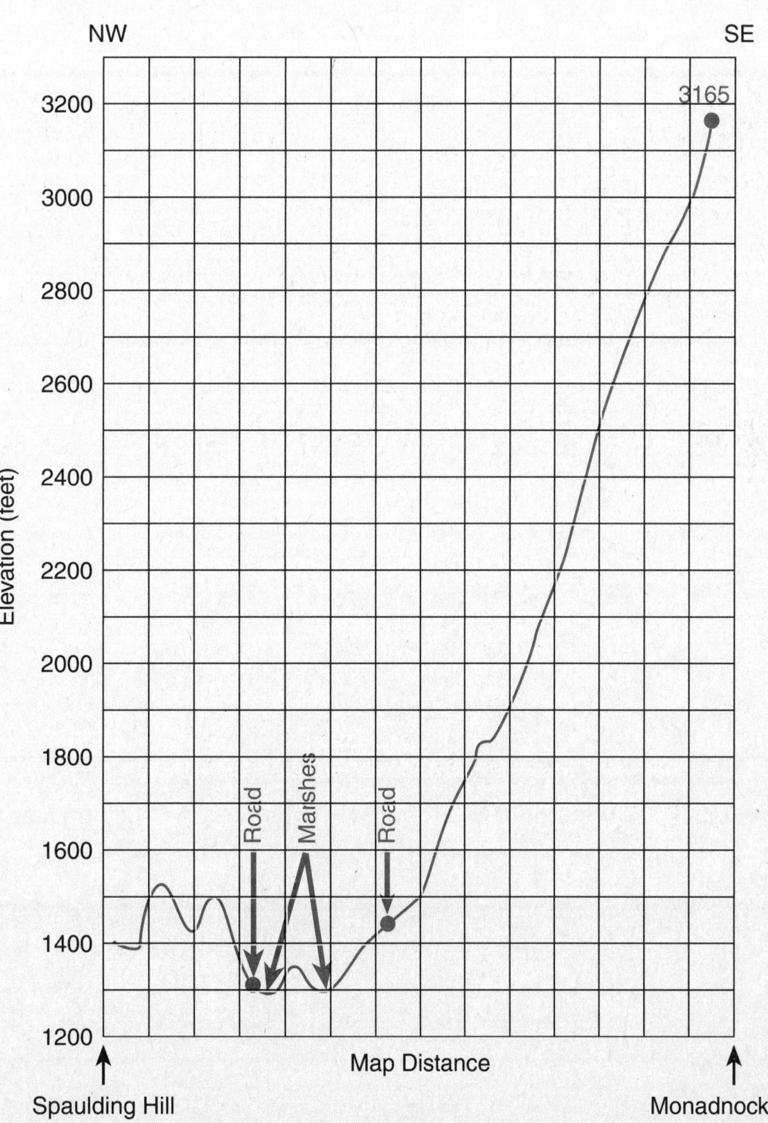

Figure 7.2

7D NAME ______ CLASS ______ DATE ______

Analysis and Conclusions

1. Which side of Fern Hill has a more even, continuous slope, the northwest or the southeast? State two ways in which you can tell.

northwest; On this side, the profile shows a more even slope, and the map shows contours that are more evenly spaced.

2. The scale along the vertical axis of the graph has been stretched out, or exaggerated, in comparison to the horizontal map scale. How would the profile look different if you had used a vertical scale equal to the horizontal scale?

The relief would be less apparent.

3. Describe the shape of the landscape in your profile in Figure 7.2.

The landscape begins with a valley in the northwest, then two small hills, then two small marshes separated by a low hill, and then a steady incline to the top of Monadnock Mountain to the southeast.

4. How many roads does your profile line cross?

two

5. Which road is more likely to flood during the wet season? Explain why.

The road north of the marsh is more likely to flood because it is adjacent to and at the same elevation as the marsh.

6. Locate the spot elevation of 1449 feet at the base of Farmers Trail. Why are such spot elevations needed in addition to contour lines?

Elevations between contour lines can only be estimated because contour lines only give exact elevations for multiples of 20 feet.

7. If a spot elevation was not provided, what would be the *most accurate* assessment you could make for the elevation of the spot in question 6?

greater than 1440 feet but less than 1460 feet

8. (a) Locate Bigelow Hill. The peak of the hill is encircled by what contour line?

1680-foot contour

(b) What can you say about the elevation of the area inside that circle?

equal to or greater than 1680 feet but less than 1700 feet

CHAPTER

7E

NAME ______________________

CLASS ____________ DATE ____________

Comparing Topographic Maps and Stereophotos

Aerial photographs are valuable tools for drawing and interpreting topographic maps. The two aerial photographs on page 651 of your text represent a narrow section of the Monadnock map on page 650. These two photographs are called **stereophotos,** or a **stereo pair.** Notice that the two images overlap. When viewed through a **stereoscope,** the stereophotos give a three-dimensional view of the area of overlap.

Map Skills and Objectives

- To **observe** and **interpret** stereophotos
- To **compare** and **contrast** topographic maps and stereophotos

Materials

- Topographic Map: Monadnock, NH, Appendix B, page 650 of your text
- Stereophotos: Monadnock, NH, Appendix B, page 651 of your text
- stereoscope

Procedure

1. Observe the differences between forested areas and water on the Monadnock map and the aerial photographs. Answer Analysis and Conclusions question 1.

2. Cover the top photograph with a blank sheet of paper. Locate Thorndike Pond on both the map and the photograph and observe its size and orientation on each. Answer Analysis and Conclusions questions 2–4.

3. Follow the directions on page 651 of your text for setting up the stereoscope. The three-dimensional image you see is an exaggeration of the actual profile. Locate Stanley Brook near Thorndike Pond. Answer Analysis and Conclusions questions 5 and 6.

Analysis and Conclusions

1. How do you tell the difference between the forested areas and the water on the map? How do you tell the difference between the two on the photos?

On the map, the forested areas are green, and the water is blue. On the photos, the forested areas are light and grainy, and the water is dark and smooth.

2. Are the map and the photo oriented the same way? Which direction is north?

yes; North is up on both.

3. From viewing Thorndike Pond, which has a larger scale—the map or the photo?

Since the pond is smaller on the map, the scale must be larger on the photo.

4. Are the following map features inside or outside the area in the photograph?

Gilson Pond ___inside___, Highway 124 ___outside___, Fasset Brook ___inside___

5. Compare the way relief is shown on the map and the stereophotos.

Relief is shown by contour lines on the map but actually appears in three dimensions on the stereophotos.

6. Describe how Stanley Brook and the surrounding area appear when viewed through the stereoscope.

Stanley Brook flows along a wavy line through a wide, flat marsh. On either side of the marsh, the land rises, forming low hills.

NAME ______________________

CLASS ____________ DATE ____________

INQUIRY LAB

Weathering of Rock Materials

Ice wedging and carbonation are two examples of weathering processes. **Ice wedging** is a physical weathering process that occurs because water expands as it freezes. **Carbonation** is a chemical weathering process and is the dissolving of a rock in carbonic acid.

Lab Skills and Objectives

- To **observe** and **measure** some effects of chemical weathering on rock samples

Materials

- safety goggles
- limestone chips
- 2 other kinds of rock chips
- water
- vinegar
- balance
- 50-mL beaker
- 3 400-mL beakers
- paper towels
- 100-mL graduated cylinder
- screening or a strainer
- marking pencil

Use any other kinds of rock chips of a size comparable to the limestone chips. Wash and completely dry all chips before using.

Procedure

Procedure steps 1–3 should be completed one day before the other procedures

1. **Put on your safety goggles.** In a 50-mL beaker obtain a sample of the limestone chips and measure out 45 to 55 g of the chips. Record the type of chips and their mass in Items 1 and 2 of the data table (Figure 8.1).

2. Place the chips in a 400-mL beaker. Pour 100 mL of water on them and label the beaker with your name and the type of chips.

3. Repeat procedure steps 1 and 2 for the two other chip samples.Allow the three samples to stand undisturbed overnight.

4. The next day carefully pour the water from each sample of chips. Use the screening or a strainer to prevent the chips from being poured out with the water.

5. Use a paper towel to blot any excess water off the chips. Determine the mass of each sample of towel-dried chips. Record these masses in Item 3 of the table.

6. Calculate and record the amount (indicating positive or negative) by which each of the chip samples changed in mass after standing in water (Item 4).

7. Calculate the percentage by which each chip sample changed in mass as indicated in Item 5 of the table. Record this value as positive or negative.

8. Return the chips to their three beakers. Pour 100 mL of vinegar on each of the samples of chips and observe any reaction. Allow the samples to stand undisturbed for 10 minutes.

9. After 10 minutes, use the strainer and pour the vinegar from each sample. Rinse each sample thoroughly with water. Towel-dry each sample.

10. Determine the mass of each of the chip samples. Record the data in Item 6 of the table.

11. As indicated in Item 7 of the table, determine and record the amount (indicating positive or negative) by which each of the chip samples changed in mass while standing in vinegar.

12. Determine the percentage by which each chip sample changed in mass while standing in vinegar as indicated in Item 8 of the table. Record this value as positive or negative.

13. Answer Analysis and Conclusions questions 1–6 before continuing.

14. Write an explanation of how time affects the weathering of limestone by carbonation.

Student procedures should involve placing a massed sample of limestone in vinegar and massing it at regular intervals—for example, every day for a week. If time and materials are available, you may want students to carry out their procedures.

15. Discuss your hypothesis with other members of your class. Then on a separate sheet of paper, write out the steps in an experimental procedure you might do to test whether your explanation is correct.

Figure 8.1

Data Table			
1. Type of Chips	Limestone	Sandy Shale	Sandstone
2. Original Mass of Dry Chips* (g)	50.0**	50.0	50.0
3. Mass of Chips after Standing in Water (g)	50.2	50.6	53.1
4. Change in Mass after Standing in Water (g) (Item 3 – Item 2)	+0.2	+0.6	+3.1
5. Percent Change = $\frac{\text{Change in Mass (Item 4)}}{\text{Original Mass (Item 1)}} \times 100$	+0.4%	+1.2%	+6.2%
6. Mass of Chips after Standing in Vinegar (g)	49.1	50.6	53.1
7. Change in Mass after Standing in Vinegar (Item 6 – Item 3)	–1.1	0	0
8. Percent Change = $\frac{\text{Change in Mass (Item 7)}}{\text{Wet Mass (Item 3)}} \times 100$	–2.2%	0%	0%

* Record all values to the nearest tenth of a gram. ** Sample data

Analysis and Conclusions

1. Which chip sample had the greatest increase in mass after standing in water? What property must the chip material have in order to show the greatest increase in mass?

Answers will vary depending upon the kinds of chips used. The material must have pore spaces that filled with water.

2. According to your textbook, under what conditions does ice wedging occur?

Ice wedging occurs when water enters pores or cracks in a rock and then freezes and thaws.

3. As represented by the chip samples, which kind of rock would weather most by ice wedging? Why?

The sample that gained the most mass should weather most by ice wedging because it has the most pores for holding the most water.

4. Which chip material had the greatest decrease in mass after standing in vinegar?

limestone

5. Carefully compare the appearance of the chips in question 4 with the appearance of the same kind of untreated fresh chips. Is there any difference?

The edges of the vinegar-treated chips are slightly more rounded.

6. Refer to the photograph of a statue on page 137 of your textbook. How are the results of this experiment related to the condition of the statue? What naturally occurring acid is responsible for the damage shown? (See Topic 4, Chapter 8 in your textbook.)

The statue has been weathered by the action of acids in rain. The natural acid is carbonic acid, but other acids are present in rainwater due to air pollutants.

ENVIRONMENTAL **CONNECTIONS**

How acidic is the water in your environment? You can test water samples for acidity by using pH test paper. The pH of an acid is a number from 0 to 7. A solution with a pH of 7 is neutral. Pure water is neutral. If a water sample has a pH between 0 and 7, the sample contains one or more substance that makes it acidic. The lower the pH the higher the level of acidity.

- Collect samples of water from as many sources as possible: your faucett at home, rainwater, melted snow, ponds, rivers, streams, runoff, wells, or springs. Label each sample and its source.
- Test each sample with pH paper. Test the vinegar that you used in your experiment. Record your results in a table.
- Mix small portions of each water sample with a pinch of chalk dust (a substance related to limestone). Retest the samples with pH paper. Record the results and share the data with your class.

1. Lakes and ponds with pH values below 6 have been found to suffer environmental damage. If one or more of your pH values is 6 or below, brainstorm with your classmates what might be possible causes.

2. How might the presence of limestone rocks around a pond or stream affect the pH of the water? How could limestone be used to revive a pond that was suffering the effects of acid rain?

NAME ______________________

CLASS ____________ DATE ____________

CHAPTER

9A

Porosity, Permeability, and Capillarity

The pore space, or **porosity,** of a rock or sediment is the amount of the material that is open space. The **permeability** is the rate at which water or other fluids will pass though these open spaces. **Capillarity** is the rate at which water is pulled upward from the water table into pore spaces by capillary action. In general, particles with larger pore spaces have better permeability and poorer capillarity.

Lab Skills and Objectives

- To **measure** and **compare** the porosity, permeability, and capillarity of several particle sizes

If a sieve kit with #6, #20, #40, and #100 screens is used to separate particle sizes, do not use the sizes that are retained on the #6 screen or that pass through the #100 screen. The largest size has instant permeability; the smallest size has no permeability.

Materials

- safety goggles
- coarse sand, medium sand, fine sand, mixture of all three
- 2 100-mL clear graduated cylinders
- watch with second hand
- 2 400-mL beakers
- test-tube brush
- paper towels
- masking tape
- scissors
- glass tube, 1 cm × 15 cm
- filter paper
- marking pencil
- metric ruler
- test-tube clamp
- ring stand

If you choose to have students work in groups, have each group of students be responsible for just one particle size and then have them share their data.

Procedure

Part A Porosity and Permeability

1. Put on your safety goggles.

2. Use one of the beakers to obtain a sample of one of the four sand samples assigned to you by your teacher.

You may need to show students this technique.

3. Fold a piece of filter paper in half and then fold it in half again so that it forms a cone. With scissors, cut off the pointed end and open the paper so that it forms a funnel. Use it to fill one of the graduated cylinders to the 50-mL level with the sand (Figure 9.1). Gently tap the cylinder to settle the particles.

4. Fill the other graduated cylinder to the 50-mL level with water.

5. *Read all of this procedure step before starting it.* The 50 mL of water is to be poured gently but quickly by one student into the cylinder containing 50 mL of sand. The time needed for the water to reach the bottom of the cylinder is to be measured by another student. Determine the time between the instant the water is poured into the cylinder and the instant the first drop of water reaches the bottom of the cylinder. This time indicates the permeability of the sample. Record the time in Figure 9.2.

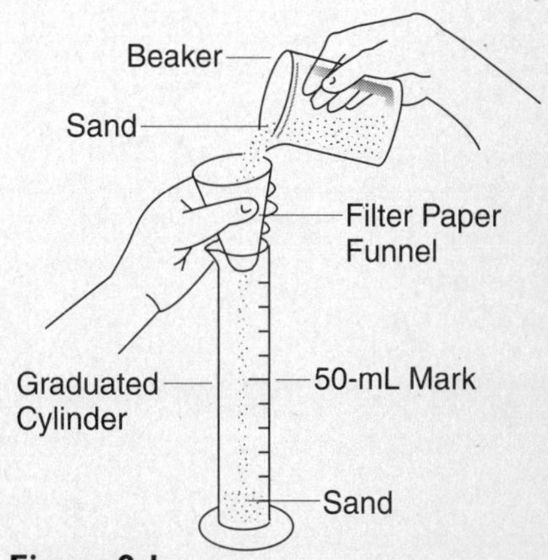

Figure 9.1
Pour 50 mL of particles into the graduated cylinder.

Data Table				
	Coarse Sand	**Medium Sand**	**Fine Sand**	**Mixed Sizes**
Time for Water to Reach Cylinder Bottom(s)	10*	60	135	186
Volume of Water + Sediment (mL)	79.6	80.1	81.1	85.0
Volume of Pore Space (mL) = 100 mL – (Volume of Water and Sediment)	20.4	19.9	18.9	15.0
Porosity (percent) = $\frac{\text{Volume of Pore Spaces}}{\text{50 mL}} \times 100$	40.8%	39.8%	37.8%	30.0%
Time for Water to Rise to 4-cm Level (s)	39	32	22	32

Figure 9.2

*Sample data

6. When the water has completely wet all of the particles in the graduated cylinder, tap the cylinder gently to remove any air bubbles left between the particles.

7. Read the level of the water in the cylinder to the nearest tenth of a milliliter. When you added water to the sediment, any pore space in the sediment was replaced by water. The water level is the volume of the water plus the sediment alone (no pore space). Record this volume in Figure 9.2.

Be sure to have pails or other containers into which students can pour their wet sediments. Some water in the pail will facilitate removal of difficult particles from the graduated cylinder.

8. To obtain a value for the porosity of the sample, first subtract the volume of water plus sediment from the original volume of dry sediment plus pore space plus water (100 mL). This gives you the volume of the pore spaces. Record this volume in Figure 9.2. To determine the percent porosity of the original dry sample, divide the volume of the pore space by the volume of dry sediment plus pore space (50 mL) and multiply by 100. Record the porosity in Figure 9.2.

9. Place the used, wet sample in the container supplied by your teacher for particles of that size. *Do not pour particles into the sink.* Wash out the graduated cylinder. Wrap a piece of paper towel around a test tube brush and dry the inside of the cylinder completely.

Part B Capillarity

10. Fill the second beaker with water.

Make sure the ends of the glass tubes are fire polished and have no sharp edges.

11. Obtain a hollow glass tube. Using a metric ruler and a marking pencil, draw a line completely around the tube about 4 cm from one end.

12. Using the same end of the tube as a guide, trace the circular outline on a piece of filter paper. Then draw a freehand circle around the first circle, but about 1 cm larger all the way around. With scissors, cut out the larger circle. Tape the filter paper to the end of the tube on which you drew the 4-cm line, sealing off the open end completely. Be careful not to cover any part of the line with tape.

13. Holding your hand over the end with the filter paper, fill the tube to a depth of about 10 cm with one of the four sand samples assigned to you by your teacher.

14. Clamp the tube to a ring stand. Place the beaker of water on the base of the ring stand below the tube (Figure 9.3).

15. *Read all of this procedure before you start.* You will place the end of the tube with the filter paper just below the surface of the water in the beaker. Determine the elapsed time between the instant that the tube is placed in the water and the instant that the first drop of water rises through the tube and reaches the 4-cm line. This time is an indication of the capillarity of the particles. Record this value in Figure 9.2.

16. Hold your tube above the container designated by your teacher for particles of this size and remove the filter paper and tape. Pour the wet sample into the container. Wash and completely dry the glass tube.

17. Have four groups who recorded data for the different particle sizes write their data for Parts A and B on the chalkboard. Record this information in Figure 9.2.

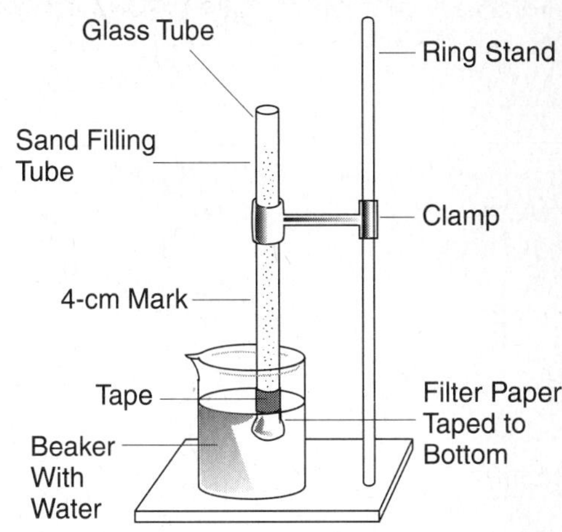

Figure 9.3
Place the bottom of the tube just below the water level.

Analysis and Conclusions

1. The graduated cylinders in procedure steps 3 and 4 of Part A held 50 mL of sediment and 50 mL of water. Why wasn't the final volume of water and sediment 100 mL? Where did the water go?

Some of the water filled the pore spaces in the sediment.

2. For which sample was the water level in the graduated cylinder (volume of water plus sediment) highest? Why?

The water level should have been highest on the mixed-size sample. The reason is that small particles were already filling some of the pore spaces.

3. How is the difference between the final volume and the initial 100-mL volume related to the porosity of each sample?

The difference indicates the porosity.

4. Which sand size (coarse, medium, or fine) has the greatest permeability? What is the evidence for your answer?

The coarse sand has the greatest permeability; water passed through it fastest.

5. Why does the mixture of sand sizes have the poorest permeability?

The mixed sample had the least amount of pore space and therefore the least amount of space for water to pass through.

6. Once a sample is wet, a film called **capillary water** surrounds each particle. What effect would capillary water have on the permeability of a sample? Why?

The capillary water will reduce the size of the pore space and thereby reduce the rate at which water can pass through the material. Therefore, capillary water will decrease the permeability of a substance.

Explain that the large number of tiny spaces in the fine sand are equal in volume to the smaller number of larger spaces in the coarse sand. This is a fundamental concept relative to the porosity of a sediment.

7. Look at your values for the porosity of the coarse, medium, and fine sands. What is the average of your three values? (The average equals the sum of the three porosity values divided by three.) Are all three values within 10 percent of this average? If differences within 10 percent are ignored, how do your values for the porosity of these three samples compare?

The porosity of these samples should be essentially the same.

8. Which particle size has the best capillarity? What is the evidence for your answer?

Fine sand has the best capillarity. The evidence is that its water level rose to the 4-cm mark in the shortest time.

These conclusions apply only to rocks made of spherical particles, not to rocks made of flakelike particles.

9. Which should be more permeable, sandstone or siltstone? Why? Which should have better capillarity? Why?

Sandstone, being made of sand-size particles, should be more permeable because it has larger pore spaces. Siltstone is composed of silt-size particles and should have better capillarity because it has smaller pore spaces.

ENVIRONMENTAL **CONNECTIONS**

Water that you use every day may be drawn from an aquifer that is fed by rain and snow. Although groundwater supplies are large and renewable, aquifers can be depleted as demand for water grows. Groundwater also can become polluted. Buried toxic materials or the residues of fertilizers and pesticides can seep into groundwater making it unsuitable for drinking.

- Wetlands are areas that are covered by shallow water for at least part of each year. Fresh water wetlands allow surface water to seep into the water table. Unfortunately, many wetlands have been drained for agriculture or for commercial or residential development. Explain how building a shopping mall on a wetland can reduce the volume of water entering an aquifer.
- Disposal of trash is a complex modern problem. One method of disposal is the sanitary landfill, the modern version of a dump. Today the location of a landfill is carefully choosen to reduce the hazard of pollution. Use what you have learned in Chapter 9 and in this experiment to list the qualities a sanitary landfill site must have if groundwater is to be protected.

NAME ____________________

CLASS ____________ DATE ____________

ENVIRONMENTAL LAB

Cleaning Polluted Water

In many communities, wastewater from houses is treated to remove pollutants before the water is released to the environment. How are pollutants removed from water? In this activity, you will investigate several methods of cleaning polluted water.

Lab Skills and Objectives

- To **observe** the results of three treatment methods for wastewater
- To **evaluate** the effectiveness and limitation of wastewater treatment methods

Materials

Obtain one 1-L plastic beverage bottle for each student group. **CAUTION: Use care in cutting the plastic.** With a sharp knife, cut away the bottom of each bottle. The remaining bottle should be about 20 cm long from mouth to cut edge. Put waterproof tape over the sharp cut edges.

- safety goggles
- plastic soft drink bottle with bottom removed
- 5 250-mL beakers
- 2 stirring rods
- rubber band
- wax pencil
- 10-cm × 10-cm square of cheesecloth
- filter paper
- ring stand and ring
- lab funnel
- balance
- metric ruler
- small pebbles
- coarse sand
- fine sand
- "polluted" water
- alum
- aquarium charcoal

Procedure

Prepare "polluted" water by mixing a few handfuls of rich soil and grass clippings into 3 L of tap water. If the soil contains little clay, add some. If you have soft water, add some baking soda to make the water alkaline. Add garlic powder until the water has a strong smell. Add food coloring to give it an unusual color. The food coloring represents bacteria and heavy metals that pass through the treatment in this activity. Do not allow students to drink any of the water samples.

Alum is potassium aluminum sulfate. Alum reacts with minerals in alkaline water to produce a jelly-like "floc."

1. **Put on your safety goggles.** Label a 250-mL beaker *Control.* Label a second beaker *Treated.*

2. **CAUTION: Do not taste any of the water samples.** To each beaker add about 200 mL of "polluted" water. Observe the properties of the water. Properties include color, smell, clarity, and the presence of visible solids. Record your observations in the data table.

3. Use the balance to obtain 5 g of alum and add it to the beaker marked *Treated.* Using a different stirring rod for each beaker, stir the contents of each beaker for about one minute. Allow the water in both beakers to settle for 15 minutes. Continue with procedure steps 4–7 while you are waiting for the water to settle.

4. Cover the mouth of the soft drink bottle with cheesecloth. Use a rubber band to hold the cloth in place.

5. Set up a ring stand and ring. Set the bottle, neck down, in the ring as shown in Figure 9.1. Place a 250-mL beaker under the mouth of the bottle.

6. Construct a filtering system by filling the neck of the bottle with small pebbles. Add coarse sand to make a layer about 4 cm deep on top of the pebbles. Add fine sand to make a layer about 4 cm deep on top of the coarse sand.

7. Clean the sand filter by gently pouring tap water through it until the water coming out of the filter runs clear. Empty, clean, and replace the beaker below the filter.

8. After the *control* and *treated* waters have settled, observe the properties of both samples and record your observations in the data table.

9. Pour the treated water through the sand filter. Observe the water that comes through the filter and record your observations in the data table.

If you are not going to use the sand filters, allow the alum treatment to continue overnight.

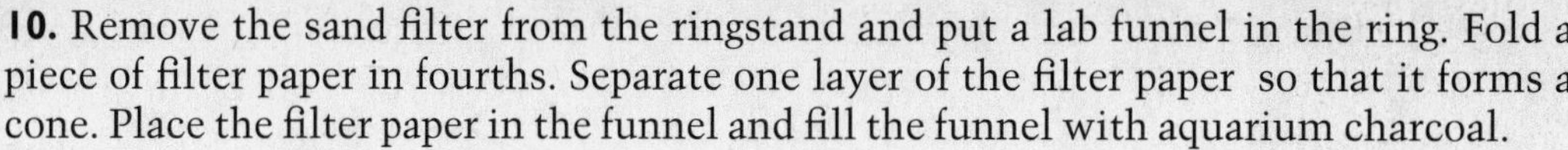

Wash the aquarium charcoal in a sieve to remove dust that might discolor water. Provide large containers in which students can place the wet contents of the sand filters. The sand and pebbles can later be rinsed and sieved.

10. Remove the sand filter from the ringstand and put a lab funnel in the ring. Fold a piece of filter paper in fourths. Separate one layer of the filter paper so that it forms a cone. Place the filter paper in the funnel and fill the funnel with aquarium charcoal.

11. Place a clean 250-mL beaker under the funnel. Gently pour the sand-filtered liquid through the charcoal.

12. Place another clean beaker under the funnel and pour the filtered water through the filter again. Observe the filtered water. Record your observations.

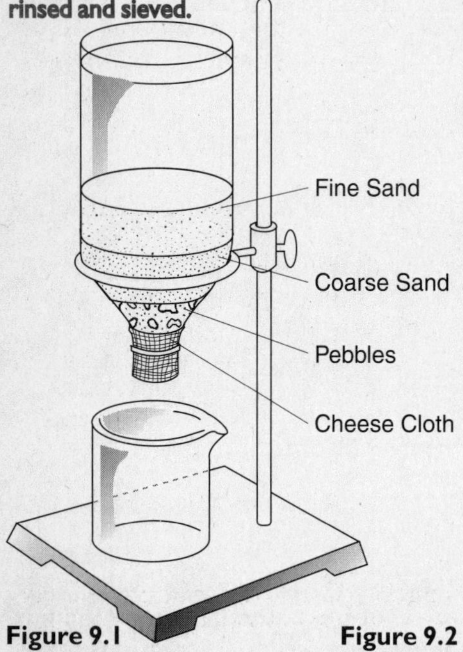

Figure 9.1 Figure 9.2

Data Table

Sample	Color	Smell	Clear or Cloudy?	Presence of Visible Solids
"Polluted" water (step 2)				
Control water after settling (step 8)				
Treated water after treatment with alum and settling (step 8)				
Treated water after passing through sand filter (step 9)				
Treated water after passing through charcoal filter twice				

Analysis and Conclusions

1. After which stages did the appearance of the water change the most?

after the settling with alum or after the sand filter

2. After which stage did the smell of the water change the most?

after the charcoal filter

3. Is the water that passed through the charcoal completely clean? Give evidence for your answer.

No; the water is still colored.

4. Which types of pollutants may still remain in the water, even though they are not visible?

bacteria, viruses, some toxic chemicals

5. Earth's water supply is constantly recycled. Explain how murky water standing in wetlands, such as marshes and bogs, is in the process of purification.

The water is slowly filtering through layers of sand and gravel similar to the filters used in this lab.

6. Boston harbor is now being cleaned up after years of being used as a dump for raw sewage. Explain how the quality of life for people and other living creatures can be affected by dumping untreated sewage into the ocean.

Beaches may be polluted. Shellfish may no longer be edible. Odors may make boating unpleasant and swimming dangerous. Species of animals may be destroyed.

NAME ______________________________

CLASS ____________ DATE ____________

CHAPTER 10A

Particle Size and Settling Rate

A number of different factors determine the rate at which a particle settles in water. One factor is particle shape. In general, spherical particles settle more rapidly than flat or disk-shaped particles. Particle size and particle density are also factors that can determine settling rate. In Part A of this laboratory, you will write an hypothesis about the relationship between particle size and settling rate. Then you will test your hypothesis by performing an experiment. In Part B, you will design an experiment to determine the relationship between particle density and settling rate.

Lab Skills and Objectives

- To **observe, measure,** and **compare** the settling rates of several particle sizes
- To **design an experiment** to investigate settling rates of several particle densities

Materials

- safety goggles
- sediment sample
- large beaker
- sieve set, consisting of 4 screen sizes (#6, #20, #40, and #100, or similar)
- 1000-mL graduated cylinder
- water
- timer or stopwatch
- meter stick
- plastic gloves

Any appropriate container can be used, but the particles should be able to fall at least 30 cm.

Procedure

Part A

1. Think about how a particle's size would affect its settling rate. Will the rate for a large particle be greater or less than the rate for a small particle? Write an hypothesis on how particle size will affect settling rate. On what do you base your hypothesis?

Accept any reasonable answers.

____

2. **Put on your safety goggles and plastic gloves.**

3. Use a large beaker to obtain a sediment sample.

4. Stack the sieves in order of screen size, with the smallest mesh on the bottom (above the pan) and the largest mesh on the top.

5. Pour a sample of the sediment onto the top screen. Place the lid on the sieve set. Shake the sieves for at least one minute to sift the sample through the screens. Carefully separate the sieves and pan. Answer Analysis and Conclusions questions 1 and 2.

Information regarding sieve numbers and mesh sizes appears with Lab Investigation 11.

6. Fill the graduated cylinder with water to within 1 cm of the top (this should be *above* the 1000-mL level).

7. Starting with the particles on the top (largest mesh) sieve, select a few particles. A small pinch should be right. Hold the particles just *below* the surface of the water. Then release the particles by rubbing your thumb and index finger together. Measure the time from the instant the fastest-falling particle passes the 1000-mL line until it reaches the bottom of the cylinder. Record the time on the data table (Figure 10.1). (Hints on procedure: You must hold the particles below the surface of the water, because small particles may not be heavy enough to break through the water surface. Practice your technique of dropping and timing the particles several times before you start collecting data.)

Encourage students to make several trials before they start to record data.

8. Repeat procedure step 7 until you have obtained five good time measurements for the sample in the top sieve.

9. Repeat procedure steps 7 and 8 for each sieve and in the pan below the sieves. Record all your data in Figure 10.1. Answer Analysis and Conclusions questions 3 and 4.

10. Determine the average settling time for each particle size by finding the sum of the times for each sieve and dividing the sum by 5. Answer Analysis and Conclusions question 5.

11. Measure the distance from the 1000-mL line to the bottom of the cylinder. Record this measurement in the space provided below Figure 10.1.

12. Using each of the values for average time, calculate the average speed (in centimeters per second) at which the particles fell. Round each answer to the nearest tenth and record your calculations in Figure 10.1. Answer Analysis and Conclusions questions 6–10.

13. Wash your hands with soap and water.

Data Table							
Sieve	**Trial 1**	**Trial 2**	**Trial 3**	**Trial 4**	**Trial 5**	**Average Time (Seconds)**	**Settling Speed (cm/s)**
top sieve							
second sieve							
third sieve							
bottom sieve							
pan							

Figure 10.1 Distance from 1000-mL level to bottom of graduated cylinder = ______________ cm

If there is time and the necessary materials are available, have students perform their experiments. Be sure to review each student's procedure for safety before they proceed.

Part B

14. On a separate sheet of paper, design an experiment that investigates the relationship between particle density and settling rate. Include a hypothesis and a list of materials needed to test your hypothesis. Write out each procedure step for your experiment. Be sure to include a data table to record your results. After completing your experimental design, answer Analysis and Conclusions questions 11–14.

Student's answers will vary. Materials should include at least three sediment samples of varying density, a large beaker, one sieve of any size, a graduated cylinder, water, a timer or stopwatch, and a meter stick. Accept any reasonable experimental design.

Analysis and Conclusions

1. How does the sieve set separate the particles by size?
Each screen allows smaller particles to pass through and retains larger particles.

2. Where in the sieve set were the largest particles retained? The smallest?
The largest particles were retained on the top sieve; the smallest in the pan.

3. Was it difficult to measure the settling time for the particles from the pan? Why?
The particles are so small that they are difficult to see as they fall through the water.

4. Which particle size settled in the shortest average time? The longest?
The largest (from the top sieve) settled in the shortest time; the smallest (from the pan) required the longest time.

5. State the relationship between particle size and settling time.
Settling time increases as particle size decreases.

6. Which particle size settled at the highest average speed? The slowest?

The largest (from the top sieve) had the highest average speed; the smallest (from the pan) had the lowest average speed.

7. State the relationship between particle size and settling speed.

Larger particles settle at higher speeds.

8. Does this experiment support your hypothesis from procedure step 1?

Students should not be penalized if the results do not support their hypothesis.

9. From the results of Part A, explain why coarse particles are likely to be deposited near shore while finer particles are deposited away from shore.

Coarse particles settle out faster and cannot be carried far before being deposited. Fine particles settle slower and can be carried farther from shore before settling out.

10. A sedimentary rock layer that extends over a large underwater area has coarse particles on its eastern side and fine particles on its western side. In which direction was the land area from which the particles in this sedimentary rock came? Explain.

The land must have been to the east. Coarse particles are deposited near the land area, fine particles farther out.

11. In Part B, on what did you base your hypothesis?

Accept any reasonable answer.

12. In your experiment, what factors had to be controlled? What factors could be varied?

Factors to be controlled include particle size, particle shape, and distance the particles fall. Only one factor should be variable—particle density.

Students should complete questions 13 and 14 only if they performed their experiments from Part B.

13. Using data you collected while performing your experiment, explain the relationship between particle density and settling rate. Did your results support your hypothesis?

Student's data should confirm that denser particles settle faster. Student's hypotheses may or may not have been supported.

14. What sources of error were present in your experiment?

Answers may include difficulty in obtaining accurate times, variable shapes of particles, variable sizes of particles, etc.

ENVIRONMENTAL **CONNECTIONS**

The rivers of America are a valuable resource. Are they being used wisely? Or are many rivers being exploited, polluted, changed from healthy ecosytems to streams of pollution?

- Collaborate with your classmates to draw a map of the river that drains the area in which you live. Include on your map any dams that have been built on the river.
- Make a list of ways in which your river is used. For example, your river may be used for recreation or transportation, or as a source of water for drinking, manufacturing, or irrigation.
- Ask older residents of your area what changes they have observed in the river during their lifetimes. How have the uses that people have made of the river affected its ecology and natural beauty?
- Brainstorm with your classmates what should be done to ensure a healthy future for your river. Make a list of things you could do.

NAME ____________________

CLASS ____________ DATE ____________

MAP ACTIVITY

Water Gaps

Just to the north of Harrisburg, Pennsylvania, the Susquehanna River has cut its way through a number of mountain ridges that lie directly in its path. The narrow part of the valley passing through the ridge is called a **water gap.** The Susquehanna River is shallowest in its water gaps.

Map Skills and Objectives

- To **relate** the action of moving water and weathering to information found on maps

Materials

- Topographic map Harrisburg, PA, Appendix B, page 652 of your text
- hand lens or magnifying glass

Procedure

1. Locate the Susquehanna River on the Harrisburg map in your text. Measure and record the width of the river (in kilometers) at its gap through Second Mountain and Blue Mountain.

The width of the river is approximately 0.6 km at Second Mountain and 1.0 km at Blue Mountain.

2. Measure and record the width of the river (in kilometers) at Marysville (midway between the two gaps) and at the city boundary that crosses McCormick Island, south of Blue Mountain gap. How do these widths compare to the widths at the gaps?

The width of the river is approximately 1.2 km at Marysville and 1.5 km at McCormick Island. At the gaps, the river is narrower.

Analysis and Conclusions

1. Compare the height and steepness of the valley walls in the gaps to their height and steepness at Marysville and McCormick Island.

The valley walls in the gaps are much higher and steeper.

2. Rocks in the Harrisburg area are composed primarily of sandstone, conglomerate, and shale. Which of these rock types most likely makes up the mountain ridges and which makes up the valleys? Explain your answer. (Refer to Chapter 8 if you need help.)

The conglomerate and sandstone most likely make up the ridges, and the shale makes up the valleys. In terms of erosion, conglomerate and sandstone are longer-lasting rocks than shale.

3. Which of the rock types in question 2 does the Susquehanna River most likely cross at the water gaps? How can you tell?

The more resistant conglomerate and sandstone most likely occur at the water gaps since the river is shallowest and narrowest there.

4. How does running water break up and remove bedrock to form water gaps?

Running water breaks up bedrock by abrasion and then carries the eroded material away in solution, in suspension, or as bed load.

5. Why does the river flow faster through the gaps than it does between them?

The river is narrower and shallower in the gaps, so it must travel faster in order for the same amount of water to flow through the gaps.

6. The general shape and orientation of many of the islands in the Susquehanna River suggest that they are sandbars formed as the river subsided after flooding. What part could Blue Mountain gap have played in the formation of McCormick Island? (Hint: Note that the river flows southward.)

As the river flowed beyond the narrow rock walls of the gap, the river widened and its speed decreased, causing sediment to be deposited. The sediment formed McCormick Island and the other islands.

7. Explain why an area just upstream from a water gap is in particular danger during flooding.

In a water gap, rock walls prevent the river from overflowing its banks onto the flood plain. Therefore, the gap acts like a bottleneck, and the water floods the area upstream.

NAME ______________________

CLASS ______________ DATE ______________

LAB INVESTIGATION

Analysis of Glacial Till

Glaciers deposit two kinds of materials—till and outwash. **Till** consists of material that was carried by the glacier and deposited as the ice melted. A till deposit contains particles of all sizes in an unlayered mass. **Outwash** is material deposited by streams flowing from the ice. The moving water sorts the materials so that, in an outwash sample from any given area, one particle size is more common than any of the other sizes. Outwash deposits usually occur in distinct layers.

Lab Skills and Objectives

- To **identify** the particle sizes found in glacial material

Materials

- safety goggles
- unknown glacial sediment (either till or outwash)
- sieve set consisting of four screen sizes (#6, #20, #40, and #100 or similar), pan, and cover
- balance
- 400-mL beaker
- graph paper

If glacial deposits are not available in your area, make a quantity of artificial, unsorted till by mixing sand and gravel together. Make outwash in the same way, but make sure that one grain size category is more abundant than any other so the material appears sorted.

Procedure

If only one sieve set is available, do the data collection as a class project. Then have students complete the remainder of the laboratory on their own.

1. **Put on your safety goggles.**

2. Determine the mass of the empty beaker and record the value in Figure 11.1.

3. Determine the masses of each of the empty sieves and the pan. Record each of these masses in Figure 11.1.

4. Use the beaker to obtain a sample of the glacial sediment. Limit your sample to about two thirds of the beaker's volume.

5. Determine the total mass of the beaker with the glacial sediment and record this mass in Figure 11.1. To find the mass of the sediment alone, subtract the mass of the empty beaker from the mass of the beaker plus sediment. Record this value in Figure 11.1. Note that this mass is the total mass of the original sediment sample, so the percent of the total equals 100.

6. Stack the sieves and the pan in the correct order of their screen sizes, so that the smallest mesh is on the bottom (above the pan) and the largest mesh is on the top.

7. Pour all of the glacial sediment from the beaker onto the top screen. Place the sieve cover on the top. Shake the set of sieves to sift the sample through the screens.

8. When the shaking is completed, carefully separate each sieve from the one below it.

9. Determine the mass of each sieve or pan together with the sediment it contains. Record each value in Figure 11.1.

10. Subtract the mass of each empty sieve or pan from the mass of the container plus the sediment obtained in procedure step 9. The total mass of sediment from all the sieves and the pan should equal the total mass of the original sediment sample obtained in procedure step 5. If the difference in the two values is more than 1 g, discard all parts of this sample and return to procedure step 4.

If the mesh number is not on each sieve, use the following information:
No. 4: 4.76 mm
No. 5: 4.00 mm
No. 6: 3.36 mm
No. 8: 2.38 mm
No. 10: 2.00 mm
No. 16: 1.19 mm
No. 18: 1.00 mm
No. 20: 0.84 mm
No. 25: 0.71 mm
No. 30: 0.59 mm
No. 35: 0.50 mm
No. 40: 0.42 mm
No. 50: 0.297 mm
No. 60: 0.250 mm
No. 80: 0.177 mm
No. 100: 0.149 mm
No. 120: 0.125 mm
No. 140: 0.105 mm
No. 170: 0.088 mm
No. 200: 0.074 mm
No. 230: 0.062 mm
No. 270: 0.053 mm
No. 325: 0.044 mm

11. To find the percent of the total mass, divide the mass of sediment retained on each screen or pan by the total mass of the original sediment sample. Multiply each of these answers by 100 to change to a percentage. Record this information in Figure 11.1.

12. Plot the percentage values as a bar graph on Figure 11.2 to show the relative percentages retained on each screen.

13. Find out from your teacher the screen size of each sieve. Record each of the screen sizes on the lines provided in Figure 11.1.

Object	Mass of Empty Container (g)*	Mass of Container plus Sediment (g)	Mass of Sediment (g)	Percent of Total Mass of Sediment (g)
beaker	143.3**	582.2	(Total Mass of Sediment) 438.9	100
top, or largest, screen	180.8	222.9	42.1	9.6
second screen from top	165.9	282.9	117.0	26.7
third screen from top	159.4	383.2	223.8	51.0
bottom, or smallest, screen	149.3	200.1	50.8	11.6
pan	123.0	128.1	5.1	1.2

Figure 11.1

* Record all values to the nearest tenth of a unit. ** Sample data

Mesh Sizes

Top, or largest, screen = 3.36 mm
Second screen from top = 0.84 mm
Third screen from top = 0.42 mm
Bottom, or smallest, screen = 0.149 mm

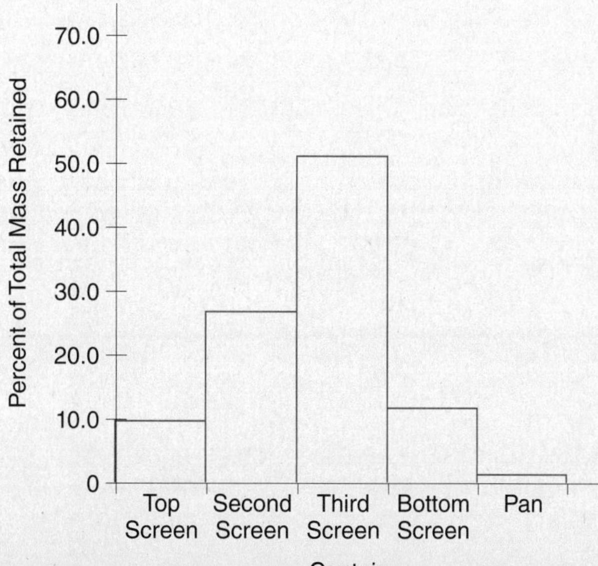

Figure 11.2

11 NAME ______ CLASS ______ DATE ______

Analysis and Conclusions

1. Which screen retained the largest percentage of sediment?

Answers will depend upon the sample used.

2. Do you think that the glacial sediment you analyzed came from outwash or till? Explain your answer.

Outwash is indicated by the fact that one screen retains significantly more sediment than any of the others. A till sample will have very poor sorting—each sieve is likely to retain about the same amount as each of the other sieves.

3. Figure 11.3 shows the sizes and names of the major sedimentary particles. Locate each of the screen sizes on the figure. At each, draw a vertical line across the strip below the figure. Write the name of each screen in the area between your vertical lines. For example, if the third screen size is 0.5 mm, the vertical line separating medium sand from coarse sand would be extended across the strip and "third screen" would be written in the space to the right of the line.

The answers given reflect only the use of mesh numbers 6, 20, 40 and 100.

0.01		0.0625	0.125	0.25	0.5	1.0	2.0	4.0	8.0
Fine Silt	Medium Silt	Coarse Silt	Very Fine Sand	Fine Sand	Medium Sand	Coarse Sand	Very Coarse Sand	Granules	Small Pebbles

Pan	Bottom Screen	Third Screen	Second Screen	Top Screen

Figure 11.3

On which screen were particles 0.6 mm in diameter retained?

0.6 mm particles were retained on the third screen.

4. On which screen was very coarse sand retained?

The second screen from the top retained all of the very coarse sand.

5. List the particle sizes that were retained on the bottom screen.

The bottom screen retained fine and medium sand.

6. Where did the silt-size particles end up?

Silt-size particles were in the pan at the bottom.

7. Only rarely does the total mass on the screens exactly equal the total mass of the original sample. Why? Where does the missing mass go?

The dust that went off into the room when a sieve was opened accounts for some of the missing mass. Other particles are lost in moving the sieves on and off the balance.

ENVIRONMENTAL CONNECTIONS

Each summer massive icebergs break from the continental glaciers of Greenland and Antartica and slowly drift south or north with ocean currents. One iceberg that calved from the Antartica ice sheet in 1987 was estimated to be large enough to supply all the water needs of Los Angeles for 675 years. Some engineers see these vast supplies of fresh water as a resource that should be used. They suggest that icebergs could be towed to water-starved areas of the world. Do you think this proposal is practical? What problems would need to be solved in order to make use of icebergs in this way?

CHAPTER 12

NAME ______

CLASS ______ DATE ______

LAB INVESTIGATION

Effects of Blowing Winds

Wind can be an important agent of erosion in dry areas. Although wind has difficulty in picking up larger particles, smaller particles may be kept in suspension in the air for long periods of time before settling into deposits. Dunes are one kind of wind deposit. The **windward** side of a dune is the side toward the wind and the **leeward** side is away from the wind.

Lab Skills and Objectives

- To **observe** and **compare** the effects of moving air on different particle sizes
- To **observe** some features of wind deposits

Materials

- safety goggles
- dust mask
- hair dryer with cool heat setting
- large cardboard box (about 30 cm wide, 60 cm long, 10 cm high) with one end cut away
- samples of clay (or silt), sand, and gravel
- 400-mL beaker
- twigs with a number of branches
- candle
- matches
- rocks or rubber stoppers of various sizes
- protractor
- cardboard strip (15 cm × 5 cm)
- thin string
- paper clip
- tape

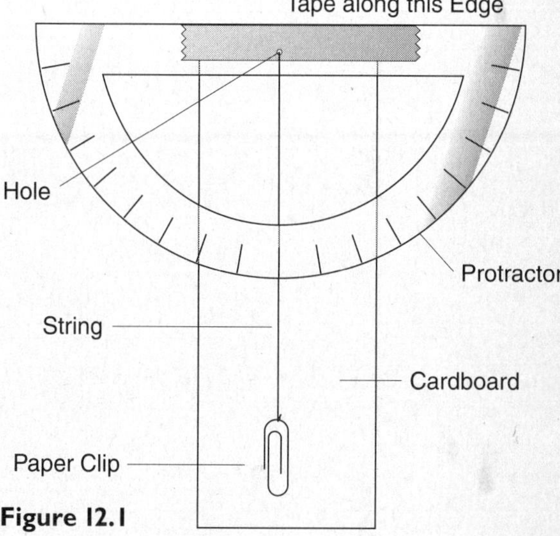

Figure 12.1

Procedure

The needle of a drawing compass or the end of an opened paper clip can be used to make the hole in the cardboard.

CAUTION: Have students handle sharp objects with care.

Use the dryers only on circuits with ground-fault interrupters.

1. With tape, attach the straight side of the protractor to the top of the cardboard strip, as shown in Figure 12.1. Punch a hole in the cardboard to correspond to the hole in the protractor. Thread one end of the string through the hole and tie it. Attach a paper clip to the other end of the string. The paper clip must hang between the bottom of the cardboard and the bottom of the protractor. Set the protractor aside.

2. **Put on your safety goggles and dust mask.**

3. Use the beaker to obtain a sample of sand. Distribute the sand over the bottom of the box to form a layer 1 cm thick.

4. **Make sure your hands are dry at all times while handling the hair dryer.** Plug in and turn on the hair dryer, using only the lowest heat setting. Carefully move the hair dryer horizontally toward the sand (Figure 12.2). Try holding the dryer at different distances from the box. Observe the effect on the sand. Turn off the dryer.

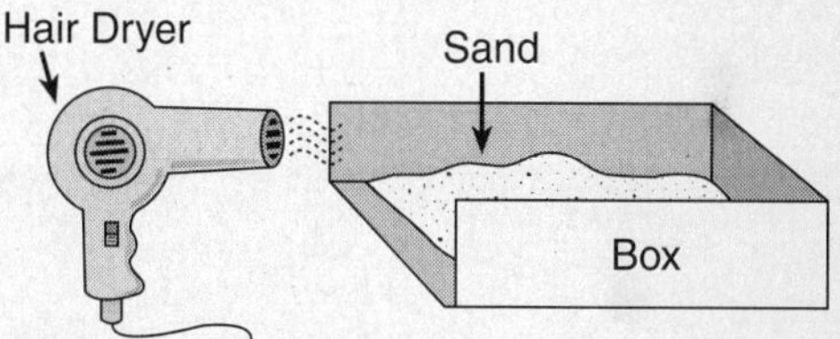

Figure 12.2
Position of hair dryer and box

5. Redistribute the sand evenly over the bottom of the box. Place two or three rocks (or rubber stoppers) in the sand. Repeat procedure step 4 until a sand dune forms. Turn off the dryer and carefully remove the rocks or stoppers from the box.

6. Using the protractor constructed in procedure step 1, carefully measure the angle of the sand on the windward and leeward sides of the dune (Figure 12.3). Subtract the reading on the protractor indicated by the hanging string from 90 degrees. Record all values on the table in Figure 12.4.

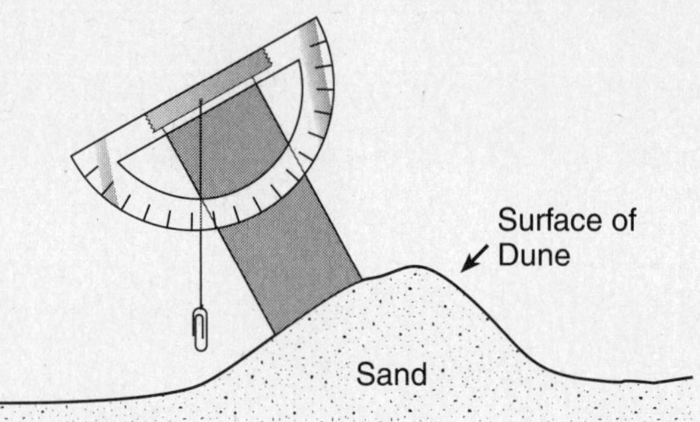

Figure 12.3

Figure 12.4

Data Table		
Side	**Angle on Protractor**	**Difference between Angle and 90 degrees**
Windward Side	80°	10°
Leeward Side	65°	35°

7. Smooth out the sand in the box. Place a twig in the sand. Repeat procedure step 4.

8. Remove the twig from the box. Smooth out the sand again. Invert the beaker and press it into the sand. Direct the dryer at the beaker. Observe how the sand moves around the beaker. Turn off the dryer.

9. Place the candle in the sand directly behind the beaker and light it. **CAUTION: Keep hair and clothing away from the flame.** Hold the dryer at a distance of about 30 cm in front of the beaker. Direct the dryer at the beaker and observe the results. While keeping the dryer at a fixed distance in front of the beaker, back the candle away from the beaker about 3 cm at a time and observe the results. Turn off the dryer.

10. Extinguish the candle and remove it and the beaker from the box. While continuing to operate the dryer, have a partner add more sand very slowly to the box by pouring it from a height of 30 cm. Be sure this is done near the end of the box closest to the hair dryer to avoid blowing the sand out of the box.

11. Remove all but 100 mL of the sand from the box and return it to its container. With the 100 mL of sand in the beaker, dampen the sand slightly with water so that it barely sticks together. Pour the sediment into the center of the box. Dry your hands and direct the dryer at the pile of damp sand and observe what happens. **Keep the dryer away from the water.** Turn off the dryer.

12. Repeat procedure steps 4 and 11 using gravel.

13. Add about 200 mL of dry sand to the damp gravel, mixing well. Notice what happens to the mixture when the dryer is directed at it.

14. Repeat procedure steps 4 and 11 using clay. The clay is light. Do not blow the clay in the direction of other students.

Analysis and Conclusions

1. Compare and contrast the ease with which each sediment size was moved by the wind. What was the result when sand and gravel were mixed together?

Sand moved most easily. Gravel was unaffected at any distance. Clay did not move until the dryer was very close (compared to the distance for the sand) but once in the air remained suspended longer. When sand and gravel were mixed together, the sand was removed but the gravel remained behind.

2. What changes did you observe in the movement of the sand and clay when they were wet?

Neither moved when wet.

3. Where did sand dunes form relative to any obstacle you placed in the sand?

The dunes formed in front of the obstacles.

4. Which side of the dune was steeper? On which side was erosion dominant? On which side was deposition dominant?

The leeward side was steeper. Particles were eroded from the gently sloping windward side and deposited on the more steeply sloping leeward side.

5. The twigs simulated plants on the surface of the sediments. How did they affect the movement of the sediments?

The plants held the sediments in place preventing erosion of the surface. Some blowing particles were stopped by the plants.

6. Describe the effect of the candle's position behind the beaker on its flame.

The candle was not blown out when it was placed directly behind the beaker. The candle was blown out when it was moved far enough behind the beaker.

7. How did the sand move relative to the beaker? What is the relationship between the place where the sand was deposited behind the beaker and the place where the candle was blown out?

There was no sand deposited directly behind the beaker. The sand was deposited at a distance behind the beaker that is approximately the same as the distance at which the candle was blown out.

8. Compare the movement of the sand around the beaker to its movement around the dunes that formed.

The sand moved up the windward slope of the dune and rolled down the leeward slope, while the sand was carried around and some distance behind the beaker.

9. Why are dunes in dry areas unlikely to contain much gravel or clay?

Gravel is too large to be picked up and clay is likely to remain in suspension.

10. In some parts of the United States, snow fences are placed beside highways to prevent blowing snow from drifting across the highway. Would the snow fence be placed on the windward or leeward side of the highway? How would it work?

The snow fence would be placed on the windward side of the highway. The fence slows the wind down so that it drops its load of snow particles at the fence rather than on the highway.

CHAPTER

13A

NAME ______________________

CLASS ____________ DATE ____________

LAB INVESTIGATION

Patterns of Magnetic Polarity Reversals

While no one is quite sure why reversals in Earth's magnetic field occur, the evidence for reversals is permanently recorded in Earth's crust. In fact, oceanic crust has been likened to a tape recorder moving on a giant seafloor conveyor belt. As magma along seafloor spreading centers cools and solidifies, magnetic minerals align themselves with Earth's magnetic field. The magnetic minerals store a permanent record of the direction of Earth's magnetic field at the time. These recordings are not only helpful in understanding a part of Earth's geologic history but they also provide the data necessary to make comparisons of spreading rates in different ocean basins. Figure 13.1 shows the magnetic reversals that have occurred in three different ocean basins over the last 80 million years. In this investigation, you will use the patterns of magnetic polarity reversals to compare rates of seafloor spreading.

Lab Skills and Objectives

- To **measure** the rate of seafloor spreading using patterns of magnetic reversals
- To **compare** the rates of seafloor spreading in several different oceans

Materials

- colored pencils or markers (minimum of three different colors needed)
- straightedge
- scrap paper

Procedure

1. Along the time scale at the top of Figure 13.1, locate 25, 50, and 75 million years. With a straightedge, draw a line from those three dates straight down to the pattern for the South Atlantic. Then, using the slanted lines already drawn as guides, draw straight but similarly slanted lines to match the South Atlantic pattern to those for the North Pacific and Pacific Antarctic.

2. Using any color, shade in the portion of each pattern between 0 and 25 million years. With a different color, shade in the portion between 25 and 50 million years on each pattern. Repeat with a different color for the portion between 50 and 75 million years.

3. Lay the edge of a sheet of scrap paper on the South Atlantic reversal pattern beside the interval you have just colored for 0 to 25 million years. Mark off the distance on the edge of the scrap paper. Transfer the marked distance to the appropriate bar in Figure 13.2 for the South Atlantic. Repeat for each of the intervals on each of the other patterns.

4. Draw a straight line across the top of each bar at the distance you have marked. Using the same colors you used on the magnetic reversal pattern, shade in each column to the height of your line.

Analysis and Conclusions

1. Is Earth's current polarity normal or reversed? What does normal polarity mean?

Earth's current polarity is normal, that is Earth's magnetic north pole is located near the geographic north pole. During a reversal, the magnetic north pole is located near the geographic south pole.

Earth's magnetic north pole is offset from the geographic north pole. The angle between geographic north and magnetic north is called *magnetic declination*. Magnetic declination varies from location to location on Earth's surface.

 NAME ______ CLASS ______ DATE ______

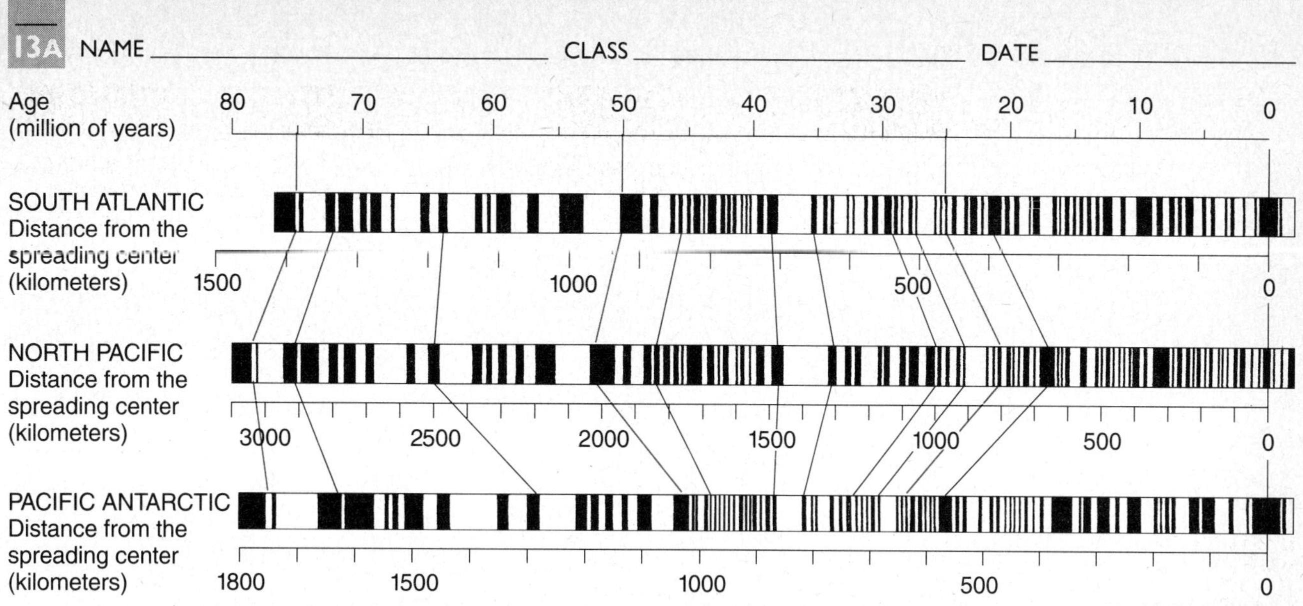

Figure 13.1
Pattern of magnetic polarity reversals at three seafloor spreading centers. Normal intervals are black. The slanted lines between the patterns are used to align equivalent magnetic intervals. While spacing is different in each pattern, they all show the same sequence of magnetism.

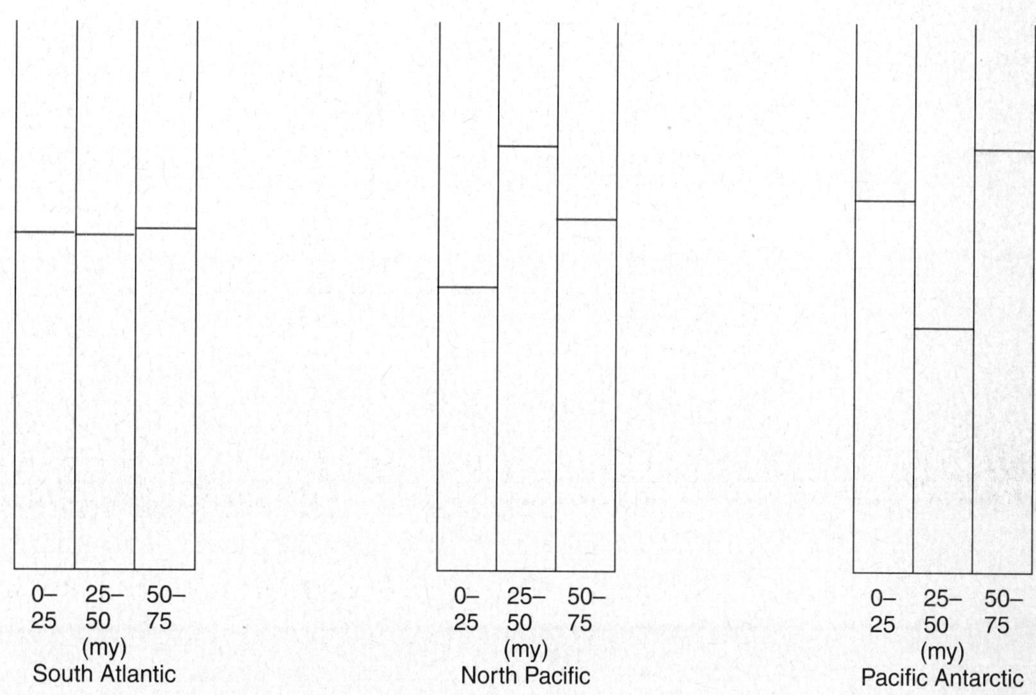

Figure 13.2
Bar graphs for comparing the spreading rates at three spreading centers during the time intervals from 0 to 25, 25 to 50, and 50 to 75 million years (my) ago.

2. How does your bar graph In Figure 13.2 for the South Atlantic show that the spreading rate has been relatively uniform there over the last 75 million years?

All three bars are approximately the same height.

3. For the North Pacific, in which time interval was the spreading rate

(a) fastest? 25–50 million years

(b) slowest? 0–25 million years

4. For the Pacific Antarctic, in which time interval was the spreading rate

(a) fastest? 50–75 million years

(b) slowest? 25–50 million years

5. In Figure 13.1, use the distance scale for each of the three ocean basins to determine, to the nearest 100 kilometers, the total distance from the spreading center to the seafloor that is 75 million years old (the oldest dates you have colored) for the

(a) South Atlantic. 1400 km

(b) North Pacific. 3000 km

(c) Pacific Antarctic. 1700 or 1800 km

6. According to your results in question 5, for which ocean basin has the overall spreading rate been the slowest? the fastest?

The spreading rate has been slowest for the South Atlantic. The North Pacific has had the most rapid spreading rate.

7. Using your values from question 5, calculate the spreading rate, in centimeters per year, for (a) the slowest ocean and (b) the most rapid ocean. **Show your work.** (1 km = 10^5 cm, 1 million = 10^6)

(a) $$\text{rate} = \frac{1400\text{ km}}{75\text{ my}} = \frac{1400 \times 10^5\text{ cm}}{75 \times 10^6\text{ yr}} = 1.87\text{ cm/yr}$$

(b) $$\text{rate} = \frac{3000\text{ km}}{75\text{ my}} = \frac{3000 \times 10^5\text{ cm}}{75 \times 10^6\text{ yr}} = 4.00\text{ cm/yr}$$

8. At a location in the Atlantic Ocean where the spreading rate is 1.5 cm/yr, the distance across the ocean is 6600 kilometers. How many million years has the Atlantic Ocean taken to open to that distance at that location? (Remember that the spreading center is the middle of the ocean and not at the edge.) **Show your work.**

Since the total width is 6600 kilometers, either leading edge is 3300 kilometers from the spreading center.

$$\frac{3300 \times 10^5\text{ cm}}{1.5\text{ cm/yr}} = 2200 \times 10^5\text{ yr} = 220\text{ million years}$$

NAME ______________________

CLASS ______________ DATE ______________

MAP ACTIVITY

Plate Boundaries

The place where two plates meet is called a **plate boundary.** Plate boundaries are described by the motions of the two plates. In this activity, you will study the boundaries of the plates that form Earth's surface.

Map Skills and Objectives

- To **recognize** the boundaries of Earth's plates and their direction of motion

Materials

- Physical World Map, Continents and Ocean Floor, Appendix B, pages 656–657 of your text
- Figure 13.1 on page 233 of your text

Procedure

1. Plates that carry continents are called continental plates, while plates that do not carry continents are called ocean plates. Which plates shown on the Physical World map are continental plates? (Refer to textbook Figure 13.1 to identify plate names.)

Eurasian, Indian, North American, South American, African, and Arabian plates. (The Antarctic Plate is also continental, but it is not shown clearly.)

2. Look at the continental plates and the ocean plates on the Physical World map. Are the continental plates made up of only continental crust? Are the ocean plates made up of only ocean crust? Explain your answer.

Continental plates contain ocean crust as well as continental crust; ocean plates contain only ocean crust, except for small landmasses (islands).

Analysis and Conclusions

1. Based on the plate boundaries shown on the map, what is the name of the largest tectonic plate? Is it an ocean plate or a continental plate?

Pacific Plate; ocean plate

2. Name the converging boundaries of the plate in question 1.

Tonga, Mariana, Japan, Kuril, and Aleutian trenches

3. Name at least two diverging plate boundaries shown on the Physical World map.

mid-Atlantic Ridge, East Pacific Rise, Southwest Indian Ocean Ridge, Southeast Indian Ocean Rise, Mid-Indian Ocean Rise

4. Compare the shape of the diverging and the converging plate boundaries.

In general, the converging boundaries occur as curved lines, whereas the diverging boundaries occur as uneven, zigzagged lines.

5. The continent of South America is moving in a westerly direction. In what direction is the ocean plate directly west of South America moving? Explain your answer.

Since South America and the ocean plate are separated by a converging boundary (the Peru-Chile Trench), the ocean plate must be moving east.

NAME ____________________

CLASS ____________ DATE ____________

LAB INVESTIGATION

Volcanic Rocks and Their Formation

Rhyolite, andesite, and basalt are three types of volcanic igneous rocks. The composition of each rock can tell you something about the volcanic conditions under which it was formed. In this lab, you will use graphs to discover the differences among the three samples and then relate each rock to the kind of plate boundary at which it may have formed.

Lab Skills and Objectives

- To **construct** pie graphs for four unknown volcanic rocks
- To **compare** and **contrast** pie graphs for rhyolite, andesite, and basalt with graphs of unknown rock specimens
- To **identify** four unknown volcanic rocks and **classify** them according to the conditions of their formation

Materials

- specimens of rhyolite, andesite, and basalt identified by number
- colored pencils
- calculator
- protractor
- Physical World Map: Continents and Ocean Floor, Appendix B, pages 656–657 of your text

Procedure

Unlabeled specimens of rhyolite, andesite, and basalt should be procured and prepared ahead. Identify them with numbers.

1. On Figure 14.1, use any colored pencil to lightly shade the section labeled *Silica* in each of the pie graphs. Shade the *Silica* box in the key below the graphs. Using a different color, shade the aluminum oxide sections of each pie graph and the key. Using different colors, continue to shade the remaining graph sections and boxes.

Figure 14.1
Pie graphs representing composition of rhyolite, andesite, and basalt.

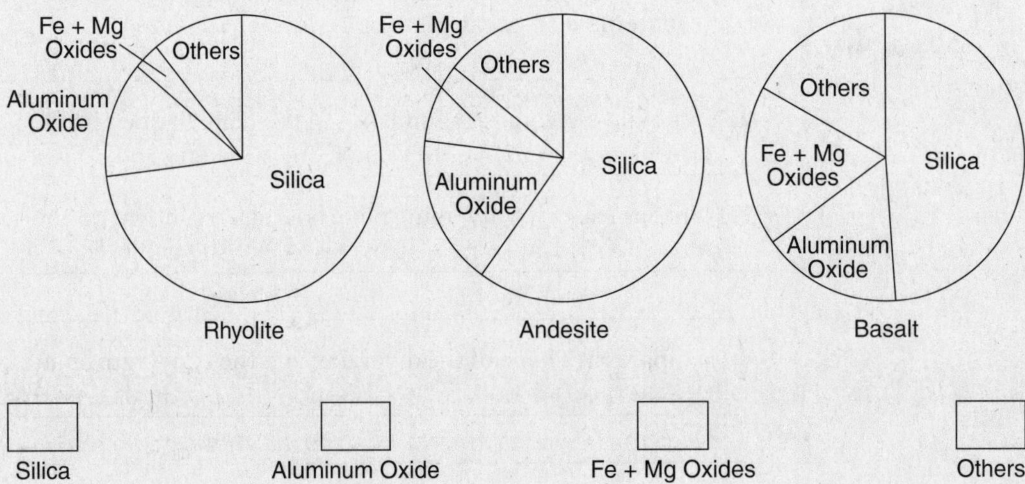

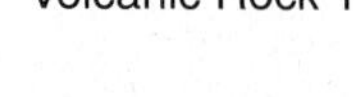

Volcanic Rock 1

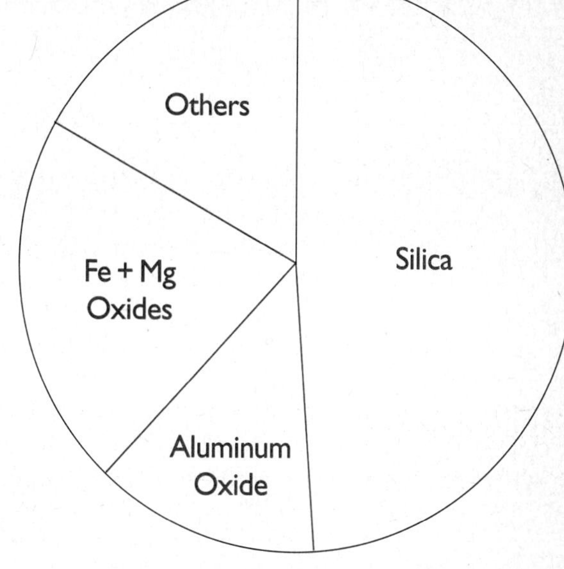

Volcanic Rock 3

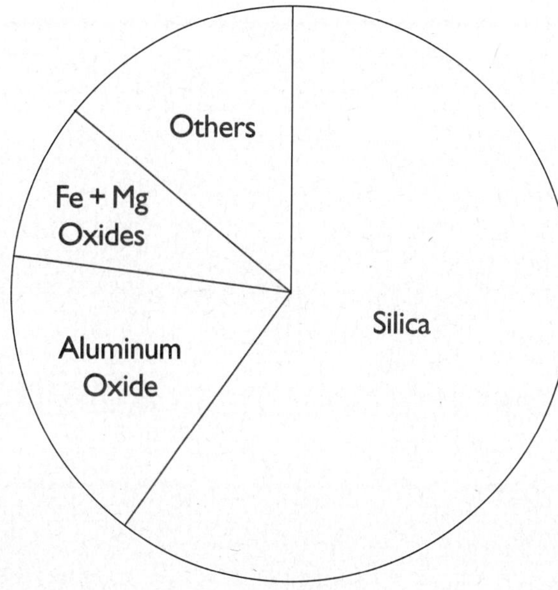

Volcanic Rock 2

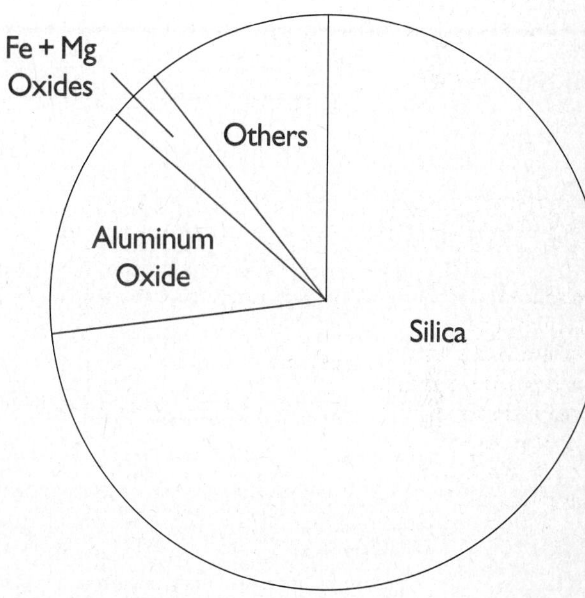

Volcanic Rock 4

Figure 14.2

Composition	Volcanic Rock 1		Volcanic Rock 2		Volcanic Rock 3		Volcanic Rock 4	
	Percent	Degrees	Percent	Degrees	Percent	Degrees	Percent	Degrees
Silica	49	176	60	216	49	176	73	263
Aluminum oxide	16	58	17	61	13	47	13	47
Fe and Mg oxides	18	65	9	32	21	76	3	11
Other	17	61	14	50	17	61	11	40
Total	100	360*	100	360	100	360	100	360

*Totals of 359 and 361 are also correct.

Figure 14.3 Compositions of igneous rocks

Students may be concerned that the degree totals in Figure 14.3 do not add up to exactly 360° in each case. The cause of this discrepancy is the rounded values used for the percentages in the first column. Values within ±1 of 360 degrees are considered to be 360 degrees. Values with greater differences should be checked.

2. Figure 14.3 shows the compositions of four volcanic rock samples. Note that the amount of each substance contained in the rock is shown as a percentage of the total. To begin constructing your pie graphs, you will first calculate the number of degrees of a complete circle that corresponds to each percentage. (A complete circle is 360°.) For example, 49 percent of Volcanic Rock 1 is silica. Thus 49 percent of the pie graph for Volcanic Rock 1 is silica. 49% of 360° = 0.49×360 = 176 degrees. In this way, determine the number of degrees for each of the other percentages. Record your percentages in the spaces provided in Figure 14.3.

3. Using a protractor and your degree data from Figure 14.3, construct a pie graph for Volcanic Rock 1. Use the appropriate circle in Figure 14.2. Start with the silica data and plot it in a clockwise direction from the vertical line. Label each section on the graph as you plot it . Use the same color for each mineral that you used in Figure 14.1 Shade the segments of your pie graph.

4. Repeat procedure steps 2 and 3 for each of the other volcanic rocks.

Analysis and Conclusions

1. Felsic rocks tend to be higher in silica but lower in iron and magnesium oxides. Which rock in Figure 14.1 (rhyolite, andesite, or basalt) is most felsic? Explain your answer.

Rhyolite is most felsic because it has the greatest percentage of silica but the least amount of iron and magnesium oxides.

2. Mafic rocks are lower in silica but higher in iron and magnesium oxides. Which rock in Figure 14.1 is most mafic? Explain your answer.

Basalt is most mafic because it has the smallest amount of silica and the greatest amount of iron and magnesium oxides.

3. Felsic rocks tend to be light in color, while mafic rocks tend to be dark. Which rock (rhyolite, andesite, or basalt) should be lightest in color?

Rhyolite should be lightest in color.

Which rock should be darkest?

Basalt should be darkest in color.

4. On the basis of color, texture, and appearance, identify your three rock samples as rhyolite, andesite, or basalt.

Students can identify rhyolite as light-colored and basalt as dark-colored. Encourage students to use all the information they learned from Chapter 5 to make their identifications.

5. Identify the four volcanic rocks represented by each of your pie graphs as rhyolite, andesite, or basalt.

Volcanic Rocks 1 and 3 are basalts, Volcanic Rock 2 is andesite, and Volcanic Rock 4 is rhyolite.

6. Of your four pie graphs, which two are mafic? How do you know?

Volcanic Rocks 1 and 3 are mafic because they have the lowest content of silica and the highest content of iron and magnesium oxides.

7. Explosive eruptions produce lavas with felsic compositions. Which two rocks are most likely to result from an explosive eruption?

Rocks 2 and 4

8. Smooth flowing lavas are higher in magnesium and iron. Which two of the volcanic rocks are most likely to have formed from smooth-flowing lavas?

Volcanic Rocks 1 and 3

9. Volcanic Rocks 1 and 3 are found in Iceland and along the East Pacific Rise. Locate Iceland and the East Pacific Rise on the Continents and Ocean Floor map on pages 656—657 of your text. What kind of plate boundary is likely to produce Volcanic Rocks 1 and 3?

diverging boundary

10. Volcanic Rocks 2 and 4 are formed in eruptions like that of Mount St. Helens in Washington. Mount St. Helens is located along the boundary of the Juan de Fuca Plate and the North American Plate. Using the Continents and Ocean Floor map, determine what kind of plate boundary is likely to produce Volcanic Rocks 2 and 4.

subduction boundary

11. The lava that erupts or flows from volcanos is magma that has risen to the surface of Earth. Consider your answers to questions 9 and 10. What are the sources of the magmas? Why are felsic rocks produced in one instance and mafic rocks produced in the other?

At divergent boundaries, magma from the asthenosphere rises to the surface. Magma from the asthenosphere is high in iron and magnesium and forms basaltic rocks. Along subduction boundaries, the plate that is subducted melts under pressure to form magma. This magma is high in silica and results in andesitic and rhyolitic rocks.

NAME ______________________

CLASS ______________ DATE ______________

CHAPTER 15

LAB INVESTIGATION

Locating an Earthquake Epicenter

The epicenter is the point on Earth's surface directly above an earthquake. Seismic stations detect earthquakes by the tracings made on seismographs. Tracings made at three separate seismic stations are needed to locate an earthquake epicenter.

Lab Skills and Objectives

- To **identify** the location of an earthquake epicenter using a time-travel graph and three seismograph tracings

Materials

- paper
- drawing compass
- time-travel graph on page 275 of your text

Procedure

1. Turn to the time-travel graph on page 275 of your text. Locate the *P*-wave curve and the *S*-wave curve on the graph. To practice using the graph, answer Analysis and Conclusions questions 1–5.

2. Study the three seismograph tracings (Figure 15.1). Notice the time scale below each tracing. Each mark on the time scale represents one minute.

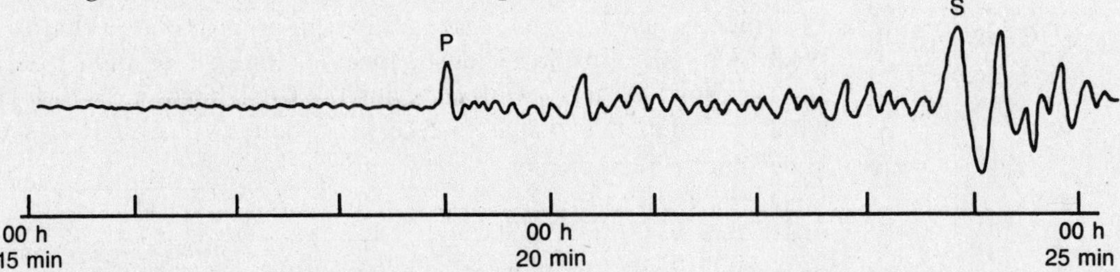

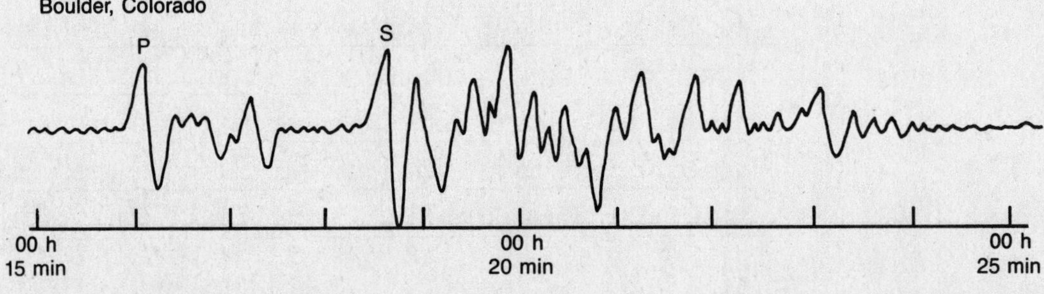

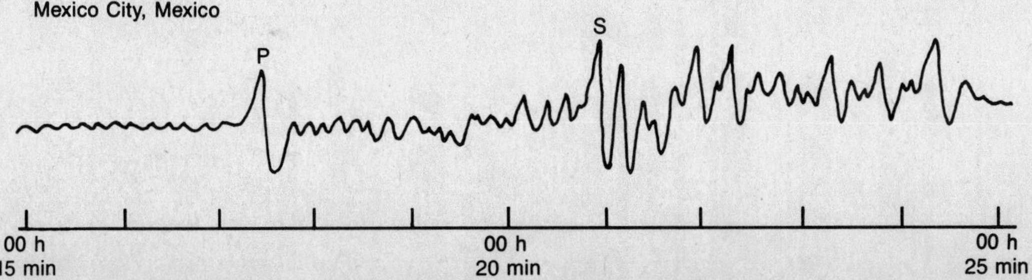

Figure 15.1

3. Start with the first tracing, labeled Balboa Heights. Locate the *P*, which indicates the arrival time of the *P* wave at the seismic station, and the *S*, which indicates the arrival time of the *S* wave. Draw a line straight down from the peak of the *P* wave to the time scale and another line from the peak of the *S* wave to the time scale.

Remind students that 50 s is not half a minute.

4. Determine the difference between the arrival times of the *P* and *S* waves. For Balboa Heights, the time difference is about 4 min 50 s.

5. Turn to the time-travel graph on page 275 of your textbook. Lay the edge of a piece of paper along the vertical axis of the graph. Place a mark on the edge of the paper at 0 on the vertical axis and another mark corresponding to 4 min 50 s. Keeping the edge of the paper straight up and down, slide the paper across the graph to the place where the *P* and *S* curves are the same distance apart as the two points you marked. The point where the paper meets the distance scale at the bottom of the graph indicates the distance to the epicenter. Determine the distance to the epicenter from Balboa Heights. The distance for a time difference of 4 min 50 s is about 3200 km.

6. Now locate Balboa Heights on the map (Figure 15.2). Balboa Heights is marked BH. Place the point of your drawing compass at 0 on the map scale.
CAUTION: The point of the compass is very sharp. Adjust the compass so that the pencil point is at 3200 km on the map scale. Without altering the compass, place the point at the center of the mark for Balboa Heights. Draw a circle with a radius of 3200 km around Balboa Heights. Answer Analysis and Conclusions question 6.

7. Return to the seismograph tracings. Repeat procedure steps 3–6 for Golden and Mexico City. Golden is indicated on the map by BC and Mexico City is indicated by MC. Answer Analysis and Conclusions questions 7–14 as you do each step.

Analysis and Conclusions

1. According to the time-travel graph on page 275 of your textbook, how long does it take a *P* wave to travel 4000 km?

It takes a *P* wave 7 min to travel 4000 km.

2. How long does it take an *S* wave to travel 4000 km?

It takes an *S* wave about 12.5 min, or 12 min 30 s, to travel 4000 km.

3. What is the difference in arrival times for a *P* wave and *S* wave that have traveled 4000 km?

The difference is 12.5 min minus 7 min, or 5.5 min (5 min 30 s).

4. What is the distance to the epicenter if the difference in the arrival times of the *P* wave and *S* wave is 5.5 min?

This the same earthquake as in question 3; the distance is 4000 km.

5. As the distance to the epicenter increases, how does the amount by which the *S* wave lags behind the *P* wave change?

As the distance to the epicenter increases, the *S* wave lags farther behind the *P* wave.

6. Where is the earthquake epicenter located relative to the circle you drew for Balboa Heights?

The epicenter is somewhere on the circumference of the circle.

7. At Golden, Colorado, what is the difference in arrival times of the *P* wave and *S* wave?

The difference is 2.5 min (2 min 30 s).

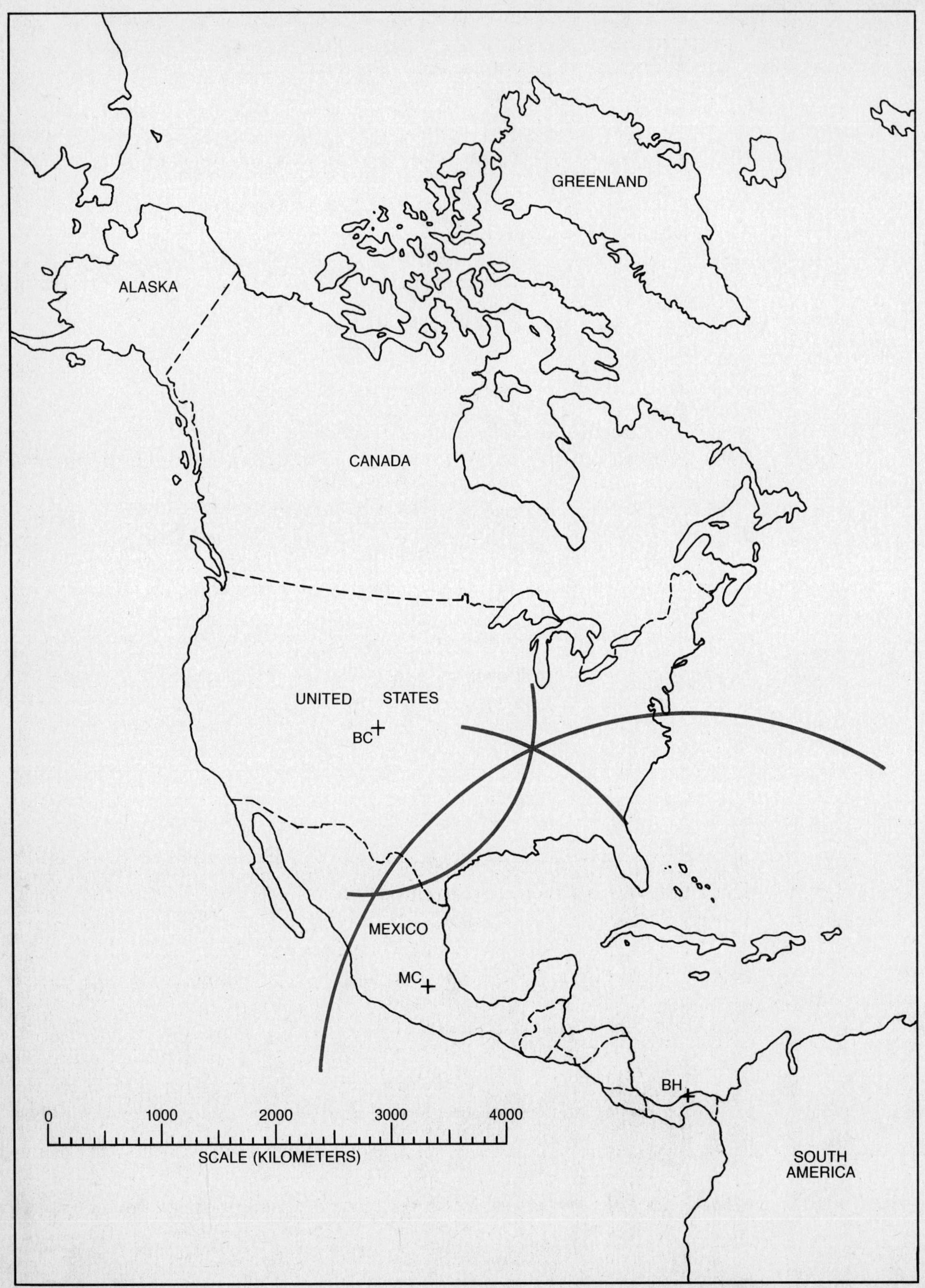
GREENLAND
ALASKA
CANADA
UNITED STATES
BC
MEXICO
MC
BH
SOUTH AMERICA
0
1000
2000
3000
4000
SCALE (KILOMETERS)

Figure 15.2

8. According to the time-travel graph, what is the distance from Golden to the earthquake epicenter?

The epicenter is about 1400 km from Golden.

9. After drawing the circle for Golden, you now have two circles on your map. Relative to these two circles, where is the earthquake epicenter?

The epicenter is at one of the points where the two circles cross each other.

10. At Mexico City, what is the difference in arrival times of the *P* wave and *S* wave?

The difference is 3.5 min (3 min 30 s).

11. According to the travel-time graph, what is the distance from Mexico City to the earthquake epicenter?

The epicenter is about 2200 km from Mexico City.

12. After drawing the circle for Mexico City, you now have three circles on your map. Relative to the three circles, where is the earthquake epicenter?

The epicenter is located where the three circles intersect.

13. What major earthquake in the past occurred in the same area as the epicenter you have just located? (Your textbook will help you answer this question.)

The epicenter is at approximately the same location as the New Madrid earthquakes of 1811–1812 (see Chapter 15, Topic 16).

14. Would it be possible for an earthquake at this same location to be felt where you live? Why or why not?

Answers will vary depending on the location. A major earthquake at New Madrid might be felt all over the North American Plate. A California earthquake of equal magnitude would be felt over a much smaller area.

ENVIRONMENTAL **CONNECTIONS**

What is the probability of an earthquake in the area in which you live? Some areas have experienced earthquakes often throughout history. Others areas have had relatively few. A map of earthquake activity in the United States shows that no area can be considered free of the possibility of an earthquake.

Suppose that you have all the resources needed to build a dwelling that will protect you in the event of an earthquake. To plan for the construction of your home, write the answers to these questions.

- What factors should you take into account in deciding on a location for your home?
- What kind of dwelling would withstand an earthquake best?
- Are there ways of constructing the building that could make it more stable?
- What considerations should you give to how your home is furnished?
- What supplies do you think you should put aside for emergencies?
- What information should you have available in case an earthquake causes electric, gas, or water lines to break?

NAME ____________________

CLASS ____________ DATE ____________

Faulting and Folding

Faulting occurs when rocks on one side of a break in the crust move relative to the rocks on the other side. Movement can be up, down, sideways, or in any other direction. Folding occurs when pressure bends rock layers. Both faulting and folding occur during mountain building.

Lab Skills and Objectives

- To **form models** of different fault and fold structures
- To **evaluate** differences in tectonic features in order to form models

Materials

- shoebox
- waxed paper
- scissors
- 2 boards, each 30 cm × 30 cm × 5 cm
- sand
- tape
- newspaper
- modeling clay, 2 colors
- pencil
- plastic knife

Each student will need two portions of clay (different colors), each about the size of a stick of margarine.

Procedure

Part A Faulting

1. **CAUTION: Handle scissors with care.** Use the scissors to cut out the bottom of the shoebox. Line the insides of the box with waxed paper, using tape to secure the paper to the box.

2. Place the two boards on a sheet of newspaper and place the shoebox on top of the boards. Fill the shoebox with wet sand. Pack the sand down. Your completed setup should look like Figure 16.1.

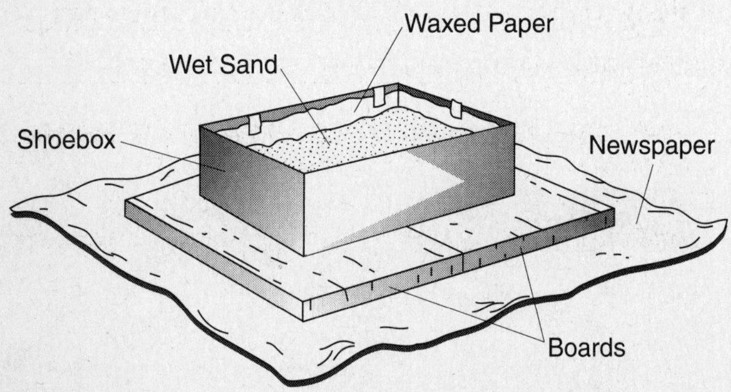

Figure 16.1

3. Have a partner stand at one end of the shoebox, holding onto the shoebox and one of the boards. Stand at the other end of the shoebox and pull the board at that end all of the way out from under the shoebox. Carefully lift off the shoebox and observe the structure of the sand. Answer Analysis and Conclusions questions 1 and 2.

4. Use the newspaper to pick up and remove all of the sand.

5. Set up the shoebox, sand, board, and newspapers as you did before. Now, while your partner pulls on one of the boards, you pull on the other board until the two boards are about 15 cm apart. Do not pull either board all the way out from under the shoebox. Carefully remove the shoebox and observe the structure of the sand. Answer Analysis and Conclusions questions 3–5.

Part B Folding

6. Place a sheet of waxed paper on your desk. Use the modeling clay only on top of waxed paper.

7. Obtain modeling clay in two different colors. Break each sample of modeling clay into four equal pieces. You now should have eight pieces of modeling clay.

8. Form a piece of the first color into a sheet about 5 cm wide and 10 cm long. Use a round pencil as a roller to help you flatten your sheet.

9. In the same way, make another clay sheet of the same color and then a sheet of the second color. You should now have three 5 cm x 10 cm sheets of modeling clay, two of one color and one of the second color.

10. Stack the three sheets of clay into a sandwich, with the second color in the middle.

11. Return to your unused pieces of clay. Form two equal-sized spheres from one piece of the second color. Lay one of the spheres on top of the waxed paper on your desk and press one end of the clay sandwich down on top of it. Then turn the sandwich over. Press the other end of the clay sandwich down on top of the second sphere. Use your hand to press the whole structure as flat as possible.

12. Use the knife to cut through the clay structure the long way. Try to slice slowly and smoothly, without sawing back and forth. Observe the structure of the clay layers. Answer Analysis and Conclusions questions 6 and 7.

Part C

13. Choose any two of the following tectonic features to model: plutonic dome mountain, tectonic dome mountain, fault-block mountain, or overturned rock layers.

Answers will vary.

14. In the space below, write out the materials and procedures you would use to create each of your models.

Materials and procedures will vary. Tectonic dome mountains can be modeled with a clay sandwich of one color pressed onto a clay sphere of a second color used to represent an intrusion. A plutonic dome mountain can be modeled in the same way except the clay sphere is the same color as the bottom layer of the clay sandwich. A fault block-mountain can be modeled with multiple clay layers first cut to represent normal faulting, then uplifted by an underlying clay layer so that layers are visible along a steep slope. Overturned rock layers can be formed by creating folded layers as in Part B, but to a greater extreme.

15. Using your materials and procedures from question 14, form models of the tectonic features your have chosen. Answer Analysis and Conclusions questions 8–10.

Analysis and Conclusions

1. Use the space below to sketch a side view of the structure of the sand from Procedure step 3. Label your sketch.

Figure TAE 16.1

2. Compare your sketch with the illustrations in Chapter 16 of your text. Which illustration most closely resembles your sketch? What is the name of this structure?

Student drawings should resemble the top part of Figure 16.3 in the text. The structure is a normal fault.

3. Use the space below to sketch a side view of the structure of the sand from Procedure step 5. Label your sketch.

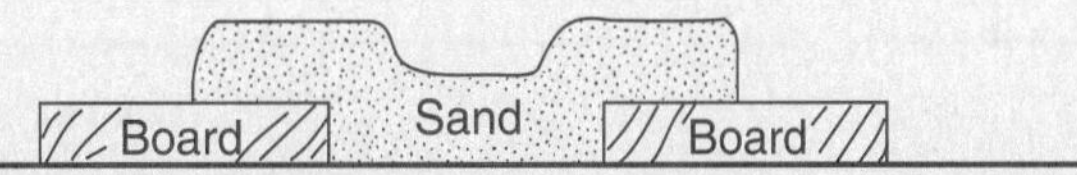

Figure TAE 16.2

4. How many faults occurred in the second structure? What kinds of faults are they?

Two faults formed in the second structure; both are normal faults.

5. What kind of feature is often found associated with the second structure? Give an example. (Use your text to help you answer this question.)

Lakes form in the piece of crust that drops down between the two fault planes; Lake Baikal in Asia is an example.

6. In the space below, sketch a side view of the layers in your clay structure from Procedure step 12.

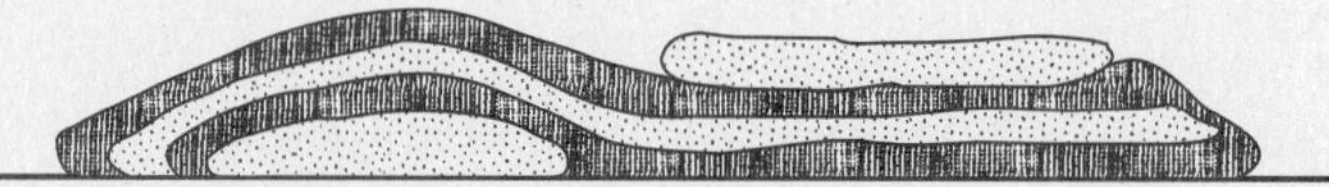

Figure TAE 16.3

7. Compare your sketch with the illustrations in Chapter 16 of your text. Which illustration most closely resembles your sketch? Identify and describe the two major parts of the structure.

Student drawings should resemble Figure 16.5 of the text. The clay layers should form an anticline and a syncline.

8. In the space below, sketch a side view of the layers in each of your structures from procedure step 16. Label which tectonic feature your models represent.

Student's sketches may vary depending on methods used to create models.

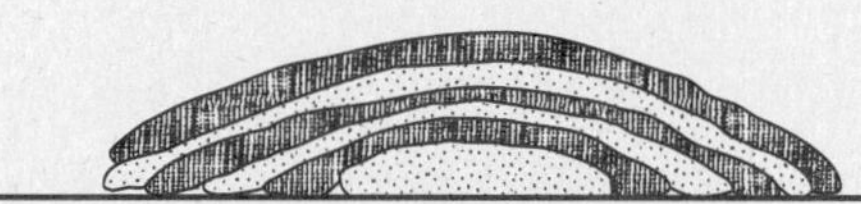

Tectonic Dome Mountain

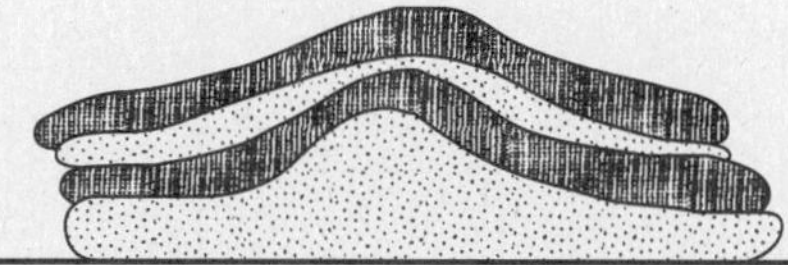

Plutonic Dome Mountain

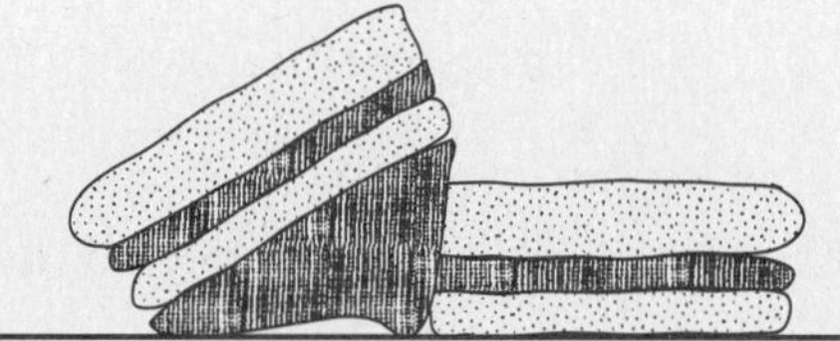

Fault-Block Mountain

Overturned Rock Layers

Figure TAE 16.4

9. As you made your models, did you add (or remove) any materials or procedure steps from your original plan? If so, explain why those changes were necessary.

Answers will vary.

10. Compare your models with models of the same tectonic feature made by your classmates. How are they the same? How do they differ?

Answers will vary.

NAME ______________________________

CLASS ______________ DATE ______________

Faults and Tilted Layers

The Geologic Map: Flaming Gorge, UT, on page 653 of your text, represents a portion of a USGS map showing the geology along the upper Green River in northeastern Utah. Meandering through the area, the Green River has carved deep, steep-sided canyons that expose a number of rock layers. On the map, each rock layer is represented by a different color. The map includes a surface map and a geologic cross section along line A-A′. A geologic cross section is a topographic profile that shows the configuration of rocks below the surface.

Any single rock layer, or **bed,** whether horizontal, folded, faulted, or tilted, has a strike and a dip. The strike is the orientation (compass direction) of the bed where it is exposed at the surface. The dip is similar to the slope. It is the angle that the bed is tilted in comparison with the horizontal. The map symbols for strike and dip and for movement along a fault are shown in Figure 16.1.

Fault Symbol

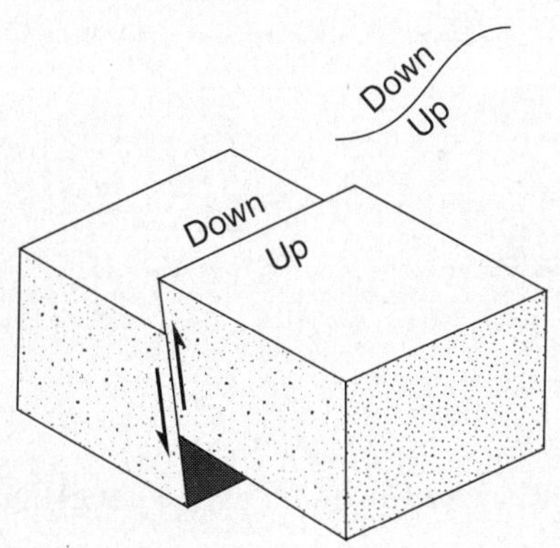

Strike and Dip Symbol

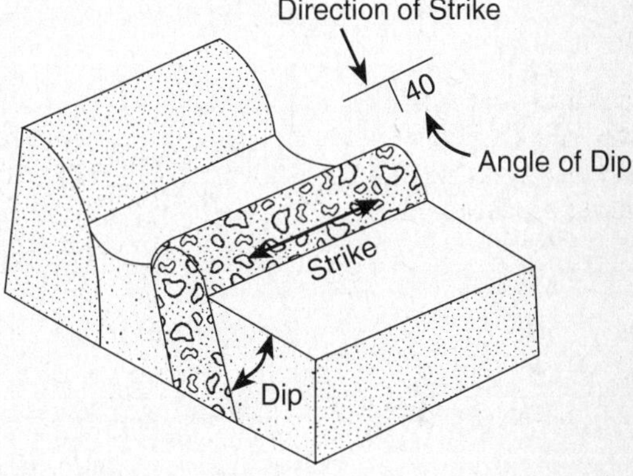

Figure 16.1

Map Skills and Objectives

- To **interpret** the geology of an area from the symbols used on a geologic surface map and cross section

Materials

- protractor
- Geologic Map: Flaming Gorge, UT, Appendix B, page 653 of your text
- Figure 16.5, page 295 of your text
- Figure 32.16, page 611 of your text

Procedure

1. Use a protractor to determine the dip of the fold labeled in Figure 16.5 on page 295 of your text. Answer Analysis and Conclusions question 1.

2. Study the surface map and cross section on page 653 of your text. Be sure you understand all the symbols used. Answer Analysis and Conclusions questions 2–8.

16B NAME ______ CLASS ______ DATE ______

Analysis and Conclusions

1. What is the dip you measured in Procedure step 1? What would be the dip of a level bed? What would be the dip of a vertical bed (standing on end)?

approximately 30°; 0°; 90°

2. Locate line A-A′ on the map and cross section. Describe the topography along that line. What are the highest and lowest elevations?

Starting at point A, the topography includes a hill, a valley, a low hill, a deep canyon, a higher hill, and a valley. The highest elevation is approximately 7250 feet, and the lowest is approximately 5800 feet.

3. Look at the surface map. Are the rock layers in the area level or tilted? How can you tell?

They are tilted. The symbols on the map indicate that the beds dip at an angle greater than 0°.

4. (a) Locate the fault on the map and the cross section. Describe the direction of movement of each block along this fault. (Note that north is to the left on the map.)

The southeast block moved up and over the northwest block, which moved under the southeast block.

(b) What kind of fault is this? What is a common cause of this kind of fault?

It is a reverse fault. Reverse faults result from stresses that push toward each other.

5. What are the strikes of the beds along line A-A′? How do they compare to the overall strike of the fault?

approximately northeast-southwest; They are approximately the same.

6. As indicated on the surface map, how do the dips of the beds along line A-A′ change as, starting from point A′, you move toward, over, and away from the fault? How do they change as you move in the same direction on the cross section?

The dip is greater near the fault, then it decreases sharply, and then gradually increases again. The pattern is the same on the cross section.

Refer to the table in Figure 32.16 on page 611 of your text to answer questions 7 and 8.

7. To what rock family or families do the rocks in the Green River area belong?

sedimentary and metamorphic

8. Which is the more easily eroded rock unit in this area: Morgan or Weber? How can you tell?

The Weber Sandstone is more easily eroded. In the cross section, the Green River cut a deep canyon in the Weber Sandstone. The limestone surface rock of the Morgan Formation protected the sandstone beneath it.

NAME ______________________________

CLASS ______________ DATE ______________

LAB INVESTIGATION

Sea Water and Fresh Water

The tool used to test the charge on an automobile storage battery is a kind of hydrometer. A similar instrument is used to check the concentration of radiator antifreeze in an automobile's radiator.

Common salt, or sodium chloride, is the most common dissolved mineral material in sea water. Tap water (water drawn from a faucet) is fresh water; it contains dissolved mineral material, but in much smaller quantities than sea water. Seawater is basically fresh water that contains more dissolved minerals. Artificial sea water, a mixture of fresh tap water and common salt, can be used as a model of sea water for this laboratory.

A **hydrometer** is an instrument used to determine the density of liquids. The depth at which the hydrometer floats in the liquid depends on the density of the liquid. You will make a simple hydrometer and use it to compare the densities of salt water and fresh water.

Lab Skills and Objectives

- To **compare** the densities of salt water and fresh water
- To **predict** the behavior of salt water and fresh water in nature

Materials

- safety goggles
- balance
- 2 400-mL beakers
- graduated cylinder
- modeling clay
- plastic drinking straws
- spray vegetable oil
- metric ruler
- marking pen
- salt
- stirring rod
- scissors
- paper towels

Procedure

1. Put on your safety goggles. To make artificial sea water, determine the mass of a beaker to the nearest tenth of a gram. Record the result in the table in Figure 17.1.

Making Artificial Sea Water	
Item	**Mass (g)**
beaker	136.7
salt	7.0
beaker + salt	143.7
tap water	193.0
beaker + salt + tap water	336.7

Figure 17.1

2. You need 7 g of salt to make 200 mL of artificial sea water. Add 7 g to your value for the mass of the beaker. Set the sliders of the balance so they equal the sum of the two numbers. Pour just enough salt into the beaker for the pointer on the balance to be centered again. *Be exact*—this is only a small quantity of salt.

3. You need 193 g of tap water to make 200 mL of sea water. Add 193 g to your value for the mass of the beaker and salt. Set the balance on this new sum. Carefully pour just enough tap water into the beaker on the balance to bring the balance pointer back to center.

4. Remove the beaker from the balance. Stir the solution until all of the salt is dissolved. Set the beaker to one side.

5. Refill the second beaker with about 200 mL of tap water. Observe the water in both beakers and answer Analysis and Conclusions questions 1 and 2.

6. **CAUTION: Scissors are sharp. Handle them with care.** To make a hydrometer, obtain a plastic drinking straw, marking pen, metric ruler, scissors, and a piece of modeling clay. Starting at one end of the straw, mark off as many 6-cm lengths as you can over the length of the straw. Cut the straw at each of your marks.

7. Shape the piece of modeling clay into a rough cube about 2 cm on each side.

One can of spray vegetable oil can be used for the entire class if the can is placed in one convenient location. Other kinds of sprays, such as silicon lubricant, should not be used because they may be toxic.

8. Take one of your pieces of straw to the location of the can of spray vegetable oil. Place one open end of your straw right on the nozzle of the can so that the spray goes directly into the end of the straw. Press the nozzle just long enough to coat the inside of the straw with vegetable oil—this will only be a second or less. Now spray an equal amount of oil on your index finger and rub it over the outside of the straw on the same end.

9. Return to your lab station. Press the sprayed end of the straw into the cube of clay. Push the straw completely through the clay. You should have about 1.5 cm of clay inside the straw once you have done this. Remove any clay that extends below the end of the straw. This is your hydrometer.

10. Place the hydrometer, clay end down, in the beaker of tap water. The hydrometer should stand straight up in the water (Figure 17.3). If it tips over, repeat procedure steps 7–9 using another section of straw until you construct a hydrometer that does stand up. Do not try to remove the clay from one straw before making another hydrometer. Just set the used straw and clay aside.

Hydrometer Measurements	
	Distance from Base of Straw to Water Level (cm)
tap water	2.9
salt water	2.6

Figure 17.2

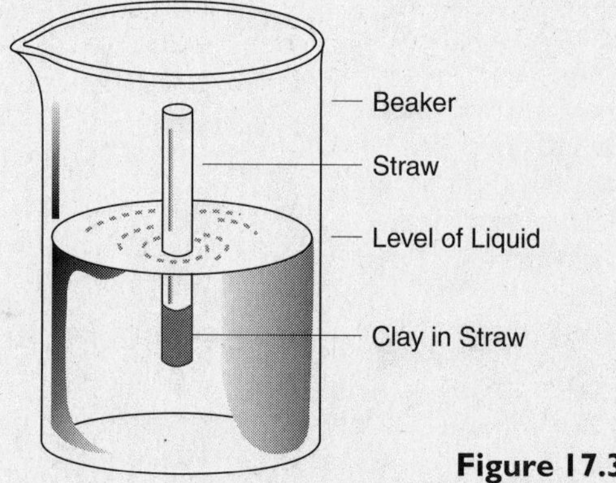

Figure 17.3
The hydrometer must be vertical in the liquid.

11. With the marking pen, put a mark on the straw where the water level meets the side of the hydrometer. Be patient in making the mark, as the hydrometer moves very easily. Remove the hydrometer from the water and roll it gently on a paper towel to dry. Do not rub off the mark as you dry the hydrometer.

12. Now place the hydrometer in the salt water. Mark the water level on the side of the hydrometer, as you did earlier.

13. With the metric ruler, measure to the nearest tenth of a centimeter the distance from the bottom of the straw to each of the marks. Record your measurements in Figure 17.2. Answer Analysis and Conclusions questions 3 and 4.

14. Now you will measure the mass and volume of the samples so that you can directly calculate the densities of the samples. Obtain a graduated cylinder. Use the balance to determine the mass, to the nearest tenth of a gram, of the cylinder. Record the mass at the top of each column in Figure 17.4.

Calculating Water Densities from Direct Measurements		
Values	**Tap Water**	**Salt Water**
mass of empty cylinder (g)	131.2	131.2
mass of cylinder + 100 mL liquid (g)	231.1	233.3
mass of liquid (g)	99.9	102.1
volume of liquid (mL)	100.0	100.0
density of liquid (g/mL)	0.999	1.021

Figure 17.4

Save the salt water made for this lab for the Chapter 19 lab on density currents. If possible, store it under refrigeration so it will be ready to use.

15. Fill the cylinder to the 100-mL level with tap water. Find the new mass of the cylinder and record it in Figure 17.4. Pour the water from the cylinder and allow the cylinder to drip-dry for a moment.

16. Repeat procedure step 15 with salt water. When you are through, pour the salt water back into the beaker. Then pour the beaker of salt water into a container designated by your teacher. Rinse out all glassware and return each piece to its proper location. Clean up your work area.

17. Answer Analysis and Conclusions questions 5–10.

Analysis and Conclusions

1. How does the appearance of the liquid in the beaker of fresh water compare with that of the liquid in the beaker of salt water?

The salt water tends to be cloudy. This is especially true if iodized salt was used, since such salt contains tiny amounts of several insoluble substances. Tap water also contains tiny amounts of impurities.

2. Look at Figure 17.4 on page 312 in your textbook. Explain why a salt-to-water ratio of 7 g to 193 g correctly represents the salinity of sea water.

The ratio of salt to water in Figure 17.4 is 35 g of salt to 965 g of water. If both values are divided by 5, the result is a ratio of 7:193.

3. A hydrometer floats higher in higher-density liquids. Which liquid is more dense, salt water or fresh water?

The hydrometer floats higher in salt water. The salt water is more dense.

4. The density of the salt water can be determined from the measurements you made on the hydrometer (Figure 17.2). To find the density of the salt water, divide the distance from the bottom of the hydrometer to the fresh water level by the distance from the bottom to the salt water level and multiply by 1 g/mL, or

$$\text{Density} = \frac{\text{distance in tap water}}{\text{distance in salt water}} \times 1 \text{ g/mL}$$

Show all your work. Round off your answer to the nearest tenth. Label your answer with the correct units.

$$\text{Density} = \frac{2.9 \text{ cm}}{2.6 \text{ cm}} \times 1 \text{ g/mL} = 1.2 \text{ g/mL}$$

5. Complete the data table in Figure 17.4 by calculating the density for the tap water and the salt water using the formula D = m/V. Show all work. This time, round off your answer to the nearest thousandth. Label your answer.

(a) Density of tap water

$$D = \frac{m}{V} = \frac{99.9 \text{ g}}{100.0 \text{ mL}} = 0.999 \text{ g/mL}$$

(b) Density of salt water

$$D = \frac{m}{V} = \frac{102.1 \text{ g}}{100.0 \text{ mL}} = 1.021 \text{ g/mL}$$

If students are concerned that the density of tap water is not the same as distilled water, provide distilled water to test. The level on the hydrometer will be slightly different.

6. The density of the tap water should be very close to the density of distilled water, which is 1.000 g/mL. Determine the percentage by which your value for the density of the tap water differs from 1.000 g/mL. Use the formula for percent difference and show all work.

$$\text{Percent difference} = \frac{\text{difference between two values}}{\text{accepted value}} \times 100$$

$$\text{Percent difference} = \frac{1.000 - 0.999}{1.000} \times 100 = 0.1 \text{ percent}$$

7. Do the values you determined for the densities of tap water and salt water support or refute your answer to question 3? Explain.

The value for the density of salt water is greater, and supports the answer for question 3.

8. The average density of sea water is 1.028 g/mL. Determine the percent by which your value for the density of sea water determined with the hydrometer (question 4) differs from the average value. Do the same for your value for the density of salt water determined by measurements of volume and mass (question 5). Show all work.

(a) Density by hydrometer

$$\text{Percent difference} = \frac{1.2 - 1.028}{1.028} \times 100 = 16.7 \text{ percent}$$

(b) Density by measurements

$$\text{Percent difference} = \frac{1.028 - 1.021}{1.028} \times 100 = 0.7 \text{ percent}$$

9. The freshwater Susquehanna River flows into Chesapeake Bay in the Atlantic Ocean. Would the water from the Susquehanna River be found on the surface of Chesapeake Bay or at the bottom? Explain your answer.

Susquehanna River water should be found at the surface of Chesapeake Bay because the fresh water in the river is less dense than the salt water in the ocean and therefore cannot sink through it.

Encourage students to keep their hydrometers to try on solutions at home, such as liquid detergent, shampoo, vinegar, and cooking oil.

10. The time it takes for an object to sink in a liquid depends in part on the density of the liquid. How would the time for a sand-sized particle to settle through 100 m of calm fresh water compare with the time for it to settle through 100 m of calm salt water?

The particle should settle through the fresh water in less time because the fresh water is less dense. (Imagine the sand settling through a thick liquid, such as shampoo, as a comparison.)

NAME ______________________________

CLASS ________________ DATE ________________

Seafloor Analysis

In this laboratory you will use data gathered by an oceanographic research vessel to learn about the seafloor. The map in Figure 18.1 shows the location of a portion of the North Atlantic Ocean floor extending from 35° to 40° N latitude and from 65° to 70° W longitude. The research vessel stopped at 20 locations within this area. At each location the depth of the seafloor was measured. In addition, samples of sediment were obtained from the seafloor. The samples were analyzed for several chemical compounds, one of which is aluminum oxide (Al_2O_3). The seafloor region from which each sample was taken was also recorded.

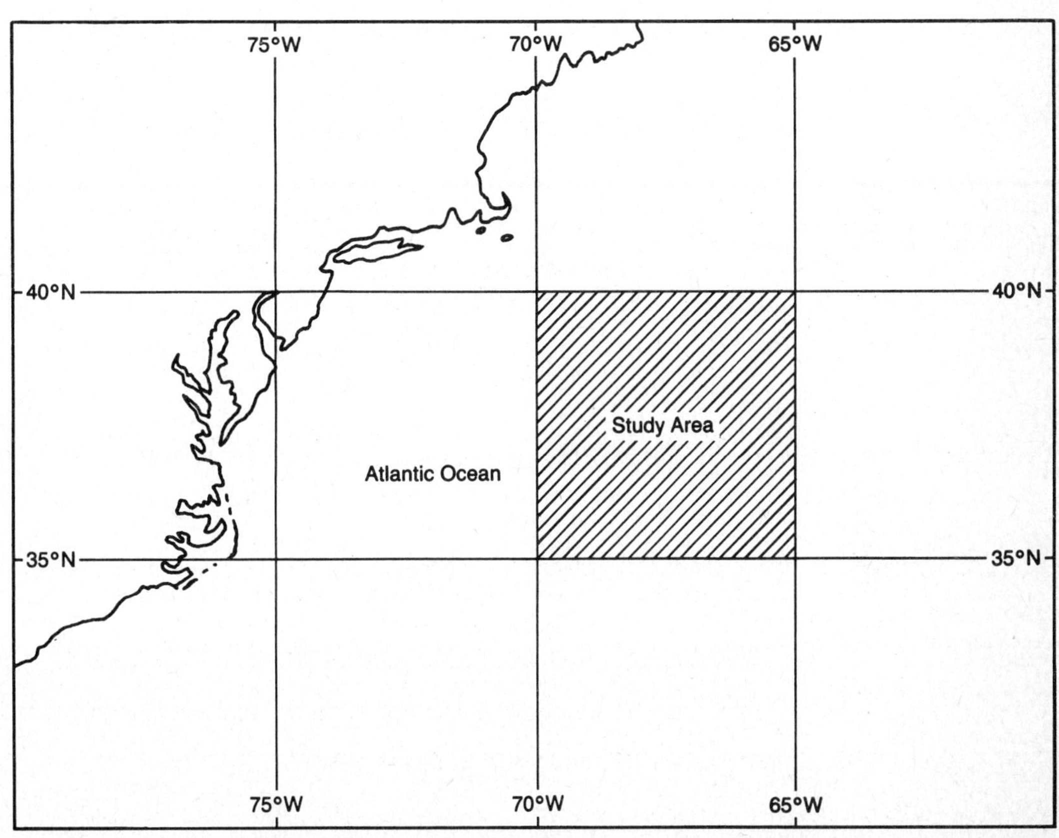

Figure 18.1

The data were collected in the area between 35° to 40° N latitude and from 65° to 70° W longitude.

Lab Skills and Objectives

- To analyze a set of data from a portion of the Atlantic Ocean floor

Materials

- graph paper
- 3 sheets of tracing paper
- paper clips
- pencil
- ruler or straightedge

Remind students that a degree is divided into 60 min. Each line of the graph grid represents 10 min of latitude or longitude.

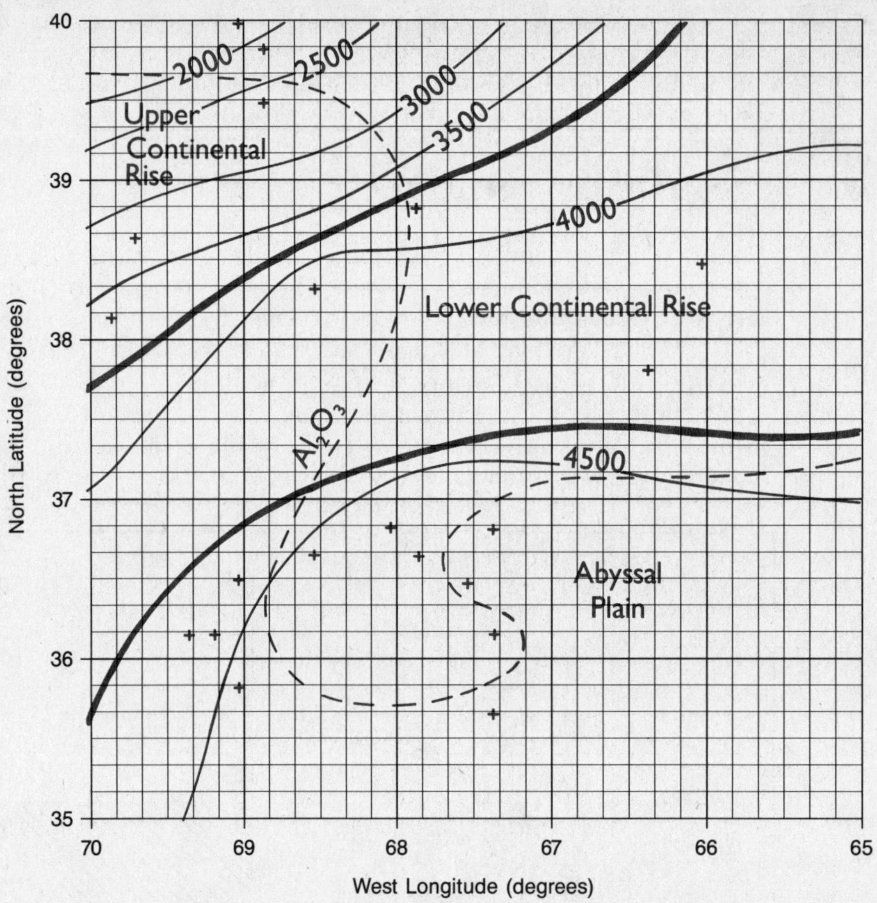

Figure 18.2

Procedure

1. Label graph axes on a piece of graph paper, as shown in Figure 18.2. You will plot the seafloor data on this grid.

2. The data table (Figure 18.3) provides seafloor data for 20 locations. Each location is identified by its latitude and longitude. Plot the 20 locations on your graph grid. Place a plus sign (+) at each location and write the location number to the lower left of the plus sign.

3. Use paper clips to fasten a piece of tracing paper over your location map. With a straightedge, copy the outer boundary of the location map onto the tracing paper. Then trace each location plus sign, but without copying the location number. Instead, write the depth of the seafloor to the upper right of each plus sign. Remove the tracing paper form the location map and label it "Depth."

4. Now draw contour lines on your depth map to show the shape of the seafloor. Use a contour interval of 500 m. (Hint: Start with the 4500-m contour line. It should start on the lower edge of the map and end on the right side.)

5. Use paper clips to attach a second piece of tracing paper to your location map. As before, trace the boundaries and plus signs onto your tracing paper. This time, however, refer to the last column in Figure 18.3, the one labeled "Seafloor Region." Write the seafloor region to the upper right of the plus sign for each location. Use the abbreviation AP for abyssal plain, LCR for lower continental rise, and UCR for upper continental rise. Remove the tracing paper from the location map and label it "Regions."

6. Now draw two lines, similar to contour lines on your Regions map to separate the three seafloor regions. To do this, lay the Regions map on top of the Depths map and draw a line to separate the abyssal plain from the lower continental rise. The line should be north of the 4500-m depth line and approximately parallel to it. Draw another line to separate the lower continental rise from the upper continental rise. This line should be between the 3500-m depth line and the 4000-m depth line. Write the name of each region in the appropriate area of your Regions map.

7. Use paper clips to attach the third piece of tracing paper to your location map. As before, trace the map boundaries and plus signs onto the tracing paper. This time, write the percent aluminum oxide for each location and label it "Al_2O_3."

8. On your Al_2O_3 map, draw a small circle around each plus sign that has a value of ten or higher. Now draw a single line on your map to separate all circled plus signs from the uncircled ones. The line will start at the upper left side of the map and end on the right side.

Data Table

Location Number 1	Latitude (North)	Longitude (West)	Depth (m)	Al_2O_3 (percent)	Seafloor Region
1	36°31′	67°31′	4845	13.0	abyssal plain
2	38°08′	69°51′	3675	11.0	upper continental rise
3	35°43′	67°20′	4940	11.0	abyssal plain
4	36°06′	67°19′	4810	2.2	abyssal plain
5	36°08′	69°08′	4480	10.0	abyssal plain
6	35°47′	68°56′	4665	10.0	lower continental rise
7	36°45′	67°23′	4845	13.0	abyssal plain
8	36°47′	68°04′	4845	7.0	abyssal plain
9	36°44′	67°52′	4790	2.0	abyssal plain
10	36°13′	69°24′	4370	12.0	abyssal plain
11	36°29′	69°00′	4390	13.0	abyssal plain
12	38°42′	67°52′	3970	9.0	lower continental rise
13	38°20′	68°25′	4005	13.0	lower continental rise
14	39°32′	68°47′	2650	12.0	upper continental rise
15	39°45′	68°53′	2270	2.0	upper continental rise
16	39°56′	68°58′	1790	8.0	upper continental rise
17	36°43′	68°32′	4700	9.0	abyssal plain
18	38°43′	69°40′	3090	13.0	upper continental rise
19	38°30′	66°01′	4480	9.0	lower continental rise
20	37°49′	66°22′	4410	9.0	lower continental rise

Figure 18.3

Analysis and Conclusions

1. In what two general areas of your map are the abyssal plain and the upper continental rise located?

The abyssal plain is in the southern part of the map. The upper continental rise is in the northwest part of the map.

2. What seafloor region is located at 36° N , 66° W?

The seafloor region at 36° N , 66° W is the abyssal plain.

3. What seafloor region would you expect to find at 33° N , 67° W?

This point is just to the south of the abyssal plain on the map area, so it would be expected to be the abyssal plain.

4. In which seafloor regions would the depths of 3300 m and of 5000 m most likely occur?

A depth of 3300 m would be expected to occur in the upper continental rise; 5000 m would occur on the abyssal plain.

5. According to your Al_2O_3 map, would you expect the amount of aluminum oxide on the seafloor sediments at 36° N, 67° W to be more or less than 10 percent?

This location is on the side with lower values, so it would be expected to have a value less than 10 percent.

6. On your Al_2O_3 map, locate the areas where the sediments contain 13 percent Al_2O_3. Do these values occur within a single seafloor region? Do you think that ocean depth affects the aluminum content of the sediments? What is the evidence for your answer?

Values of 13 percent for Al_2O_3 occur in all three seafloor regions. Therefore, depth does not affect the concentration of Al_2O_3 in seafloor sediments.

7. Is the area where the 20 locations were studied part of an active continental margin or part of a passive continental margin? Give at least two pieces of evidence to support your answer.

The area is part of a passive continental margin. Figure 18.1 shows that the area is part of the Atlantic Ocean, and the east coast of the United States is a passive continental margin. Also, this area has a continental rise, and active continental margins do not have a continental rise.

8. Which is the more likely source of the aluminum oxide—the continents or the shells of ocean animals? Explain.

It is more likely to come from the land. Aluminium is the third most abundant element in the continental crust. Most shells are made of calcite.

CHAPTER 19

NAME ______________________

CLASS ____________ DATE ____________

Density Currents

Density currents occur when water that is denser than the water around it sinks. An example is the sinking of Antarctic Bottom Water around the continent of Antarctica. After sinking, this water slowly moves northward over the floors of the ocean basins. Similar sinking occurs in the Arctic region. In this laboratory, you will observe a density current on a small scale.

Lab Skills and Objectives

- To **observe** and **measure** a density current
- To **design an experiment** to determine what happens when warm river water flows into cold ocean water

Materials

- plastic shoebox
- cardboard
- 4 plastic-backed red or blue liquid-filled Celsius thermometers with the plastic backing cut off behind the bulbs*
- marking pencil
- 400-mL beaker
- paper cup
- tape
- scissors
- cold salt water
- warm tap water
- metric ruler
- straight pin
- watch or timer
- graph paper

The proportions to use in making the salt water are 35 g of salt to 965 g of water. Refrigerate the salt water or place it in an ice bath. Do not add ice to it. Place a thermometer in the saltwater solution.

* Cut the plastic backing from behind the bulb so that water can contact the entire surface of the bulb. Use inexpensive classroom thermometers (up to 50°C).

Use caution in cutting the plastic.

Procedure

Once the "thermometer bridges" are constructed, they can be reused by students in other classes.

Have students work in groups of four—one to pour the salt water, one to time the data collection, one to read the thermometers, and one to record the temperatures.

Part A Constructing a "Thermometer Bridge"

1. **CAUTION: Scissors are sharp. Handle them with care.** The purpose of the "thermometer bridge" is to hold the thermometers at the proper depth in the water. Use a scissors to cut a rectangular piece out of the cardboard so that the cardboard forms a bridge that straddles the middle of the plastic shoebox, as shown in Figure 19.1.

2. Use the marking pencil to label the thermometers A, B, C, and D.

3. Tape thermometer A at the center of the cardboard bridge. Position the thermometer so that the bulb is just above the bottom of the shoebox. The tape should be on the plastic backing of the thermometer and across the arch of the bridge, as shown in Figure 19.1.

4. In the same way, tape thermometer B to the left of thermometer A. Position thermometer B so that its bulb is 2 cm higher than the bulb of thermometer A.

5. Tape thermometer C to the right of thermometer A. Its bulb should be 4 cm higher than the bulb of thermometer A.

6. Tape thermometer D to the left of thermometer B. Its bulb should be 6 cm higher than the bulb of thermometer A.

7. Place the thermometer bridge across the shoebox. Tape it to the outside of the box so that it will not tip over when water is placed in the box.

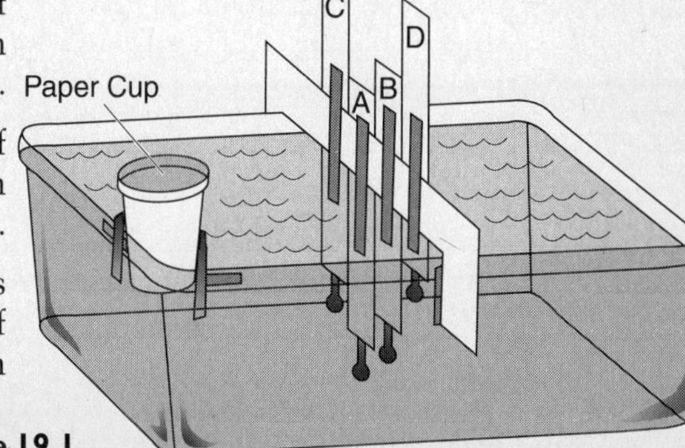

Figure 19.1

Part B Making a Density Current

8. **CAUTION: Take care in using sharp objects.** Use a straight pin to punch no more than three holes in the bottom of a paper cup. Tape the cup securely in one corner of the shoebox, as shown in Figure 19.1. The bottom of the cup should be 3 cm below the top of the box. Use a beaker to fill the shoebox with warm water until the water level is about 1 cm from the top of the box.

9. Wait until the readings on all the thermometers have stopped changing. Then take a reading on each of the thermometers. Read the thermometers to the nearest whole degree. Record these readings on the data table (Figure 19.2) in the space for time 0.

10. *Read procedure steps 10–12 before you proceed.* Fill your beaker from the classroom container of salt water. Read the temperature of the salt water from the thermometer in the container and record this temperature in the space provided below Figure 19.2.

11. Now carefully pour the cold salt water into the paper cup inside the shoebox. As you pour, hold the paper cup with one hand to be sure it doesn't slip. As the level of the water in the paper cup falls, continue pouring salt water until your beaker is empty.

12. Exactly 1 minute after you began pouring salt water into the paper cup, read each of the thermometers. Record the readings in the data table. Continue to read the thermometers at 1-min intervals for 10 min. Record each reading in the table.

13. Set up the graph paper as shown in Figure 19.3. Next to each plus sign (+) on the graph paper, write the temperature for that level and time.

14. Draw lines on your graph to show the pattern of temperature change. Follow the rules for drawing isolines. Each line should represent a whole degree—for example, 31, 32, 33. Most of the lines will start at the bottom of your graph and end at either the top or the right-hand side. Answer Analysis and Conclusions questions 1–4 before continuing.

15. Using what you have learned from this investigation, write a hypothesis that could explain what happens when the warm fresh waters of a river pours into the cold ocean.
Students may hypothesize that the warm waters would flow on the surface of the cold ocean.

	Temperature (°C)			
Time (min)	**D**	**B**	**A**	**C**
0				
1				
2				
3				
4				
5				
6				
7				
8				
9				
10				

Figure 19.2 Temperature of the cold salt water __________ °C

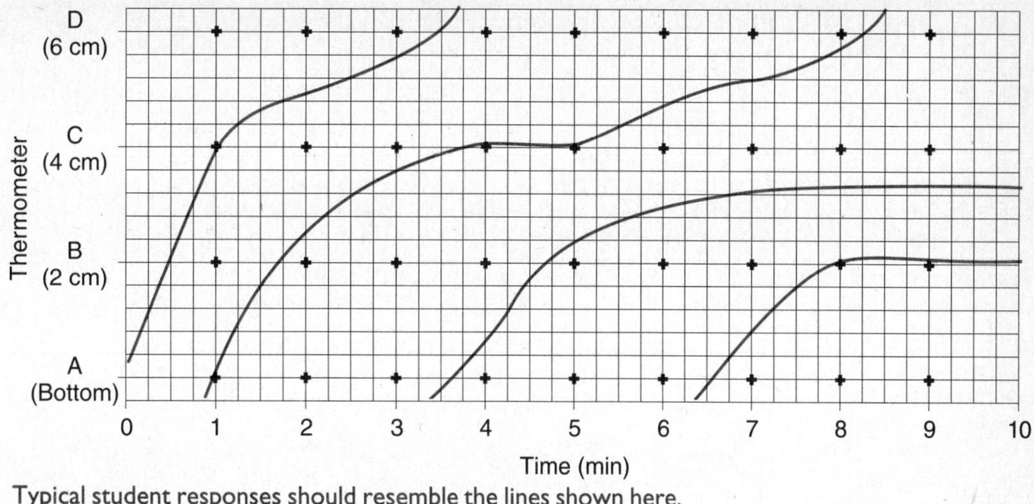

Figure 19.3

Typical student responses should resemble the lines shown here.

Analysis and Conclusions

1. What two factors explain why the salt water is denser than the tap water in the shoebox?

The salt water is denser because it is colder and saltier than the tap water.

2. Describe the way in which the cold salt water moved after it passed through the holes in the paper cup. Why did it move in this way?

The cold salt water flowed to the bottom of the shoebox and then across the bottom. It was denser than the tap water and, therefore, could not rise through it.

3. Did the water at the bottom of the shoebox ever become as cold as the salt water that was poured into the paper cup? Why or why not?

no; The salt water was warmed somewhat by the warm tap water in the shoebox and possibly by the hand of the person holding the beaker.

4. Which best represents Antarctic Bottom Water—the warm tap water or the cold salt water? Which best represents the water of an ocean basin?

The cold salt water represents Antarctic Bottom Water; the warm tap water represents ocean basin water.

5. How might the procedure for this experiment be changed so that the density currents could be observed visually?

Food color or ink could be added to the salt water.

6. Write the steps in a laboratory experiment to determine if the hypothesis you wrote in procedure step 15 is correct.

Students could outline steps similar to the procedure steps in Part B. Based on their answers to question 5, students may design an experiment using food coloring to study the currents visually rather than by temperature.

NAME ______________________

CLASS ____________ DATE ____________

CHAPTER 20

INQUIRY LAB

The Refracting Telescope

Parallel rays from an object converge at the focal plane. Rays coming from a very distant object are considered parallel.

A refracting telescope consists of an objective lens and an eyepiece lens at opposite ends of a long tube. The objective lens gathers light and forms an image of a distant object. This image is usually very small, so an eyepiece lens is used to magnify the image. In one kind of refracting telescope the lenses are both convex. A **convex** lens is thicker at the center than at the edges. The **focal plane** of a lens is the place at which the lens forms a clear image of a distant object. The **focal length** of a convex lens is the distance from the center of the lens to its focal plane. In this lab you will investigate the locations of the eyepiece and objective lens in a simple refracting telescope.

Lab Skills and Objectives

- To **measure** the focal length of the lenses in a refracting telescope
- To **observe and describe** the parts of a simple refracting telescope
- To **design an experiment** to determine the optimum eyepiece location in a simple refracting telescope

Materials

Be sure that each student has lenses with different focal lengths. The lenses do not need to have the focal lengths listed in the materials, but the results will be better the closer they are to those lengths.

- meterstick
- 2 lens holders
- 1 screen holder
- 2 convex lenses: focal length of 5 to 10 cm and focal length of 20 to 40 cm
- 2 3 × 5-in. index cards: one uncut, the other with a 3-cm square screen of wax paper
- 1 ring stand and burette clamp (or optical bench)

The index cards with the wax paper screens must be prepared ahead. Cut a 3-cm square out of each card. Cover the hole with wax paper and tape the wax paper onto the card (do not let the tape show in the opening).

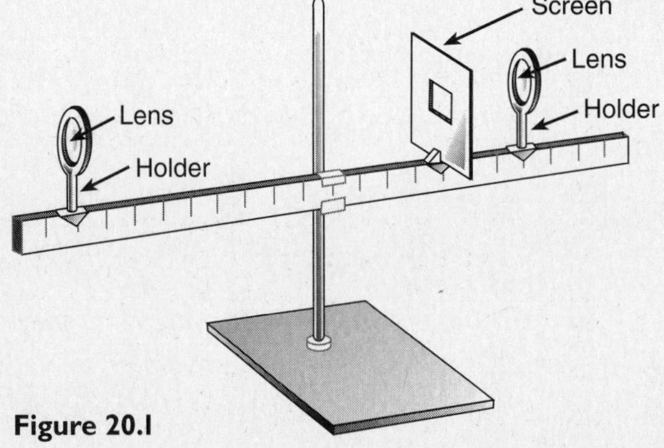

Figure 20.1

Procedure

Part A

1. Use the burette clamp to attach the meterstick to the ring stand, as in Figure 20.1.

2. Place the uncut index card in the screen holder at the 50-cm mark on the meterstick.

3. First, find the focal length of each lens. Place one of the lenses in a lens holder at exactly 20 cm on the meterstick. Point the lens toward a window. Move the screen holder toward the lens until an object outdoors, at least 100 m from the lens, forms a sharp image on the card. Record the location of the screen holder in Figure 20.2. Repeat for the second lens.

4. Find the distance of each lens from the card by subtracting 20 cm from the location of the screen holder. The result is the focal length of each lens. Record the focal lengths in Figure 20.2. Answer Analysis and Conclusions question 1.

Finding Focal Lengths			
Item	Location on Meterstick (cm)		Focal Length of Lens (cm)
	Lens	Screen Holder	
first lens	20	29.9	9.9
second lens	20	34.9	14.9
sum of both focal lengths (cm)			24.8

Figure 20.2

Lens Distances in Telescope		
Item	Location on Meterstick (cm)	Distance from Screen (cm)
lens with shorter focal length	20	9.9
wax paper screen	29.9	X
lens with longer focal length	44.8	14.9

Figure 20.3

5. Find the sum of both the focal lengths. Record this value in Figure 20.2.

6. To set up a refracting telescope, place the shorter focal length lens at 20 cm on the meterstick. Add 20 cm to the sum of the focal lengths of the two lenses. Place the second lens at that location on the meterstick. Record this location in Figure 20.3.

7. Replace the uncut index card with the card with the wax paper screen. Place the screen holder between the two lenses, with the longer focal length lens nearer the window.

8. Look at the wax paper screen through the shorter focal length lens. Move the card holder until the image of a distant object on the screen is clear. Record the location of the screen holder in Figure 20.3. Find the distance of each lens from the screen and record it in Figure 20.3. Answer Analysis and Conclusions question 2.

9. Observe the image on the wax paper screen, first with your eyes alone and then through the shorter focal length lens. Answer Analysis and Conclusions question 3.

Make sure students realize that the wax paper screen is used in this experiment *only* to locate the image formed by the objective lens. For normal viewing, there is no screen in a refracting telescope.

10. Without moving the lenses, remove the screen holder and look through the shorter focal length lens at the window.

11. Turn the ring stand around so that the shorter focal length lens is nearer to the window. Look through your telescope at the distant object with the lenses in reverse order. Answer Analysis and Conclusions questions 4–8.

Part B

12. In Part A, you investigated the locations of the eyepiece and objective lens in a simple refracting telescope by using a wax paper screen. In Part B, you will investigate the *optimum* location for the eyepiece. How will the magnification and clarity (focus) of the image change as the distance between the eyepiece and the screen is changed? Before starting your inquiry, write a hypothesis.

Accept any reasonable answer.

Procedures and materials may vary among students. Accept any safe, reasonable procedures that can be performed with the equipment and time available.

13. On a separate sheet of paper, write the procedure you will use to investigate your hypothesis. Be sure to include a data table and any additional materials you may want to use. Have your teacher check your procedure before moving on.

14. Use your procedure to determine the optimum location of the eyepiece in a simple refracting telescope. Answer Analysis and Conclusions questions 9–12.

Analysis and Conclusions

1. Identify two ways in which the image seen through the two lenses is different from the actual scene viewed without the lenses.

The image is upside down; the image is backward, or reversed.

2. How does the focal length of each lens compare with its distance from the screen holder in the telescope?

For each lens, the distance should be very similar if not the same.

Students may ask why the eyepiece is able to magnify the image in the telescope setup, even though it forms a small image when it projects on a screen. When a lens is used as an eyepiece, the viewer is seeing a *virtual* image that is larger than the object being viewed. When a lens is used as an objective, the projected image is a *real* image. In a telescope setup, the viewer looks through the eyepiece at the real image formed by the objective lens. For a more complete discussion of lenses and their images, consult a high school or college physics text.

3. How is the image on the wax paper screen different when viewed by your eyes alone than when viewed through the shorter focal length lens?

The image is larger through the lens than with the eyes alone.

4. Look first through the lens with the longer focal length. What happens to the image?

The image is smaller than before.

5. Which of the two lenses that you used serves better as the objective lens?

The longer focal length lens serves better as the objective lens.

6. Which lens serves better as an eyepiece?

The shorter focal length serves better as the eyepiece.

7. In a camera, a lens focuses light onto a piece of film. If a telescope is to be used as a camera, where should the film be placed?

The film should be placed where the wax paper screen was located, or at the focal length of the longer focal length lens. (The eyepiece lens has no role in the camera.)

8. How would you change your simple refracting telescope to gather more light and form a brighter image?

Use an objective lens with a larger diameter.

9. What happened to the focus and magnification of the image as the eyepiece was moved closer to the screen? further from the screen?

The image was reduced, but remained focused as the eyepiece moved closer to the screen. The image was enlarged but became unfocused as the eyepiece moved further from the screen.

10. What did you determine to be the optimum location for the eyepiece for a simple refracting telescope.

The optimum location is one focal length from the screen.

11. Do your results support your hypothesis?

Student's hypotheses may or may not have been supported.

12. What sources of error were present in this experiment?

measurement error, instability of set-up, focal length found using object too close to lens

ENVIRONMENTAL **CONNECTIONS**

Because radiation from the sun is damaging to eyes, optical telescopes are not useful for studying the sun. At Kitt Peak National Observatory a special solar telescope projects an image of the sun into a room deep underground. Astronomers study the image while wearing special glasses to protect their eyes. Produce your own image of the sun using an index card and a larger piece of cardboard. Make a small circular hole (about the diameter of a pencil tip) in the index card. Stand with your back to the sun and position the index card and the cardboard so that sunlight comes through the hole and focuses on the cardboard. Adjust the position of the cardboard until you get a sharp image. This is a good way to watch an eclipse of the sun.

NAME ______________________

CLASS ______________ DATE ______________

CHAPTER 21

LAB INVESTIGATION

Properties of Stars

The Hertzsprung-Russell diagram, or H-R diagram, is a graph in which a star's temperature is plotted against its absolute magnitude. From such a diagram, other information about a star's properties and life cycle can be determined. A simplified H-R diagram appears in your textbook (Figure 21.6, page 382). In this laboratory, you will construct an H-R diagram using data on the 20 stars that are nearest to our sun (Figure 21.1) and the 20 stars that appear brightest in our sky (Figure 21.2). Then you will use the finished diagram to describe the properties and life cycles of stars.

In the tables in Figures 21.1 and 21.2, the unit used for distance is the parsec. A **parsec** is equal to 3.26 light-years (LY). The Kelvin (K), or absolute temperature scale, is used in the tables and in the diagram (Figure 21.3).

Lab Skills and Objectives

- To **graph** a simplified Hertzsprung-Russell diagram
- To **identify** the characteristics of a star from data in the diagram
- To **classify** a star by its position in the diagram
- To **compare** the life cycle stages of stars based on their positions in the diagram

Materials

- data for nearest and brightest stars (Laboratory 21 Figures 21.1, 21.2)
- graph (Laboratory 21 Figure 21.3)
- sample Hertzsprung-Russell diagram (textbook Figure 21.6, page 382)
- pencil

A Hertzsprung-Russell diagram is plotted on logarithmic graph paper, which is probably unfamiliar to students. "Log paper" is useful because with it, data that cover an enormous range of values can be presented on one graph without sacrificing accuracy. You may need to assure students that the graph paper is acceptable and correct, even though the lines and values are not evenly spaced.

Procedure

1. Study the lists in Figures 21.1 and 21.2 and answer Analysis and Conclusions questions 1 and 2.

In procedure steps 2 and 3, you will graph the stars onto the diagram. The following tips will be helpful to remember when graphing stars:

a. Temperature is on the horizontal axis; absolute magnitude is on the vertical axis.

b. Notice that the graph lines used to plot temperature are unevenly spaced, and that the number of Kelvins between each line is not constant. Carefully check a star's temperature and the value of a particular graph line before plotting each star.

c. Absolute magnitude decreases as the value becomes more positive. Thus, an absolute magnitude of +4.4 plots below the +4.0 line, not above.

2. Using a plus sign (+), graph each of the nearest stars (listed in Figure 21.1) on the diagram (Figure 21.3).

3. Using a circled dot (⊙), graph each of the brightest stars as seen from Earth (listed in Figure 21.2) on the diagram. Show stars that appear on both tables using a circled plus sign (⊕).

4. Answer Analysis and Conclusions questions 3–10.

The 20 Nearest Stars			
Name	Distance (parsecs)	Temperature (K)	Absolute Magnitude
Alpha Centauri	1.31	5800	+4.4
Barnard's Star	1.83	2800	+13.2
Wolf 359	2.35	2700	+16.8
Lalande 21185	2.49	3200	+10.5
Sirius	2.67	10 400	+1.4
Luyten 726-8	2.67	2700	+15.4
Ross 154	2.94	2800	+13.3
Ross 248	3.16	2700	+14.7
Epsilon Eridani	3.30	4500	+ 6.1
Ross 128	3.37	2800	+13.5
Luyten 789-6	3.37	2700	+14.9
61 Cygni	3.40	2800	+7.5
Procyon	3.47	6800	+2.7
Epsilon Indi	3.51	4200	+7.0
Sigma 2398	3.60	3000	+11.1
BD +43°44	3.60	3200	+10.3
Tau Ceti	3.64	5200	+5.7
CD –36°15693	3.66	3100	+9.6
BD +5°1668	3.76	3000	+11.9
CD –39°14192	3.92	3500	+8.7

Figure 21.1

The 20 Brightest Stars as Seen from Earth			
Name	Distance (parsecs)	Temperature (K)	Absolute Magnitude
Sirius	2.7	10 400	+1.4
Canopus	30.0	7400	–3.1
Alpha Centauri	1.3	5800	+4.4
Arcturus	11.0	4500	–0.3
Vega	8.0	10 700	+0.5
Capella	14.0	5900	–0.7
Rigel	250.0	11 800	–6.8
Procyon	3.5	6800	+2.7
Betelgeuse	150.0	3200	–5.5
Achernar	20.0	14 000	–1.0
Beta Centauri	90.0	21 000	–4.1
Altair	5.1	8000	+2.2
Alpha Crucis	120.0	21 000	–4.0
Aldebaran	16.0	4200	–0.2
Spica	80.0	21 000	–3.6
Antares	120.0	3400	–4.5
Pollux	12.0	4900	+0.8
Fomalhaut	7.0	9500	+2.0
Deneb	430.0	9900	–6.9
Beta Crucis	150.0	22 000	–4.6

Figure 21.2

Analysis and Conclusions

1. Compare the two star lists, Figures 21.1 and 21.2. How many stars appear on both the Nearest Stars list and the Brightest Stars as Seen from Earth list? Name them.

Three stars are found on both lists. They are Sirius, Procyon, and Alpha Centauri.

2. What does your answer to question 1 indicate about the nearest stars? Are the nearest stars also the brightest stars as seen from Earth?

no; Only three of the stars nearest to Earth are also among the brightest stars as seen from Earth.

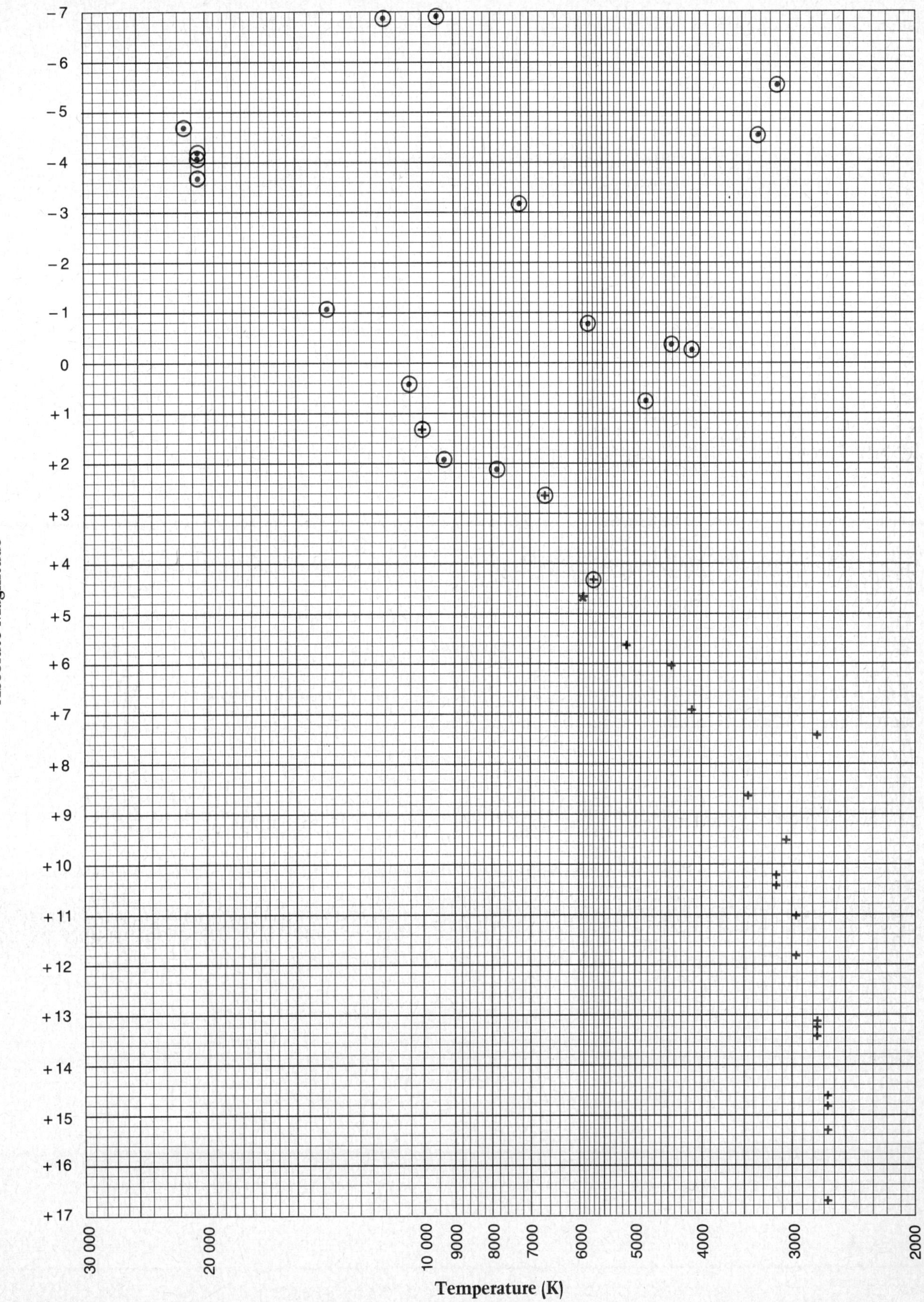

Absolute Magnitude
−7
−6
−5
−4
−3
−2
−1
0
+1
+2
+3
+4
+5
+6
+7
+8
+9
+10
+11
+12
+13
+14
+15
+16
+17
30 000
20 000
10 000
9000
8000
7000
6000
5000
4000
3000
2000
Temperature (K)

Figure 21.3

3. A star located in the lower right portion of Figure 21.3 is cool and dim. What are the characteristics of a star in the upper left of the diagram? In the upper right?

A star in the upper left is hot and bright, while one in the upper right is cool but bright.

4. Refer to Figure 21.6 on Page 382 of your textbook. To which group do most of the stars on your diagram belong?

Most of the stars on the diagram are on the main sequence.

5. According to your diagram and Figure 21.6, are any of the 20 nearest or 20 brightest stars white dwarf stars? What is the evidence for your answer?

no; The temperature and absolute magnitude of white dwarf stars place them in the lower left area of the diagram. None of the stars in the two lists is plotted in that area of the diagram.

6. Our sun has a temperature of 6000 K and an absolute magnitude of +4.7. Use an asterisk (*) to show the location of the sun on your diagram. To what group does the sun belong?

The sun is a main sequence star.

7. Compare the absolute magnitude and temperature of the sun with those of the other stars in its group.

Compared to the other stars, the absolute magnitude and temperature of the sun are average.

8. Betelgeuse is 150 parsecs away and has a surface temperature of only 3200 K. Yet Betelgeuse is one of the brightest stars as seen from Earth. What does this indicate about the size of Betelgeuse? Is your answer supported by the location of Betelgeuse on the diagram?

Because Betelgeuse is so far away and so cool, it must be enormous for it to appear as a bright star to observers on Earth. According to the diagram, Betelgeuse is a supergiant, which supports the answer.

9. On your diagram, there is another star that is plotted near Betelgeuse. What is the name of the star? What kind of star is it?

The star is Antares; it is also a supergiant.

10. Compare our sun with the red supergiant Antares. Which star is further along in its life cycle? How do you know?

Antares is further along in its life cycle than the sun. Antares is a red supergiant, which forms after a main sequence star has used up a certain portion of its lighter elements.

CHAPTER 22

NAME ______________________

CLASS ____________ DATE ____________

Retrograde Motion of Mars

The **celestial sphere** is the imaginary dome of the sky on which the sun, stars, and other objects appear to be located. A sky map shows part of the celestial sphere. Like objects on the sphere of Earth's surface, locations of objects on the celestial sphere are described using imaginary lines and points. The *celestial equator* is a circle in the sky directly above Earth's equator. The *celestial poles* are the points in the sky directly above Earth's North and South poles. **Declination** is celestial latitude. Values for declination range from 0° to +90° for locations between the celestial equator and North Pole, and from 0° to –90° for locations between the celestial equator and South Pole. **Right ascension** is celestial longitude. It is marked off in units called hours and minutes. The starting point for right ascension is the point at which the sun crosses the celestial equator on the spring equinox; right ascension is measured eastward from this point. The right ascension and declination of an object in the sky do not change unless the object changes its position on the celestial sphere. The sun, moon, and planets do change their positions on the celestial sphere. The apparent path of the sun across the celestial sphere is called the *ecliptic.* The circle of the ecliptic corresponds to the plane in which most planetary orbits lie (Figure 22.1). In this laboratory, you will plot the path of the planet Mars across the celestial sphere during a period of retrograde motion.

Lab Skills and Objectives

- To **graph** part of the celestial sphere
- To **interpret** data on the motion of Mars across the celestial sphere
- To **predict** the motions of other planets

Materials

- graph paper
- pencil

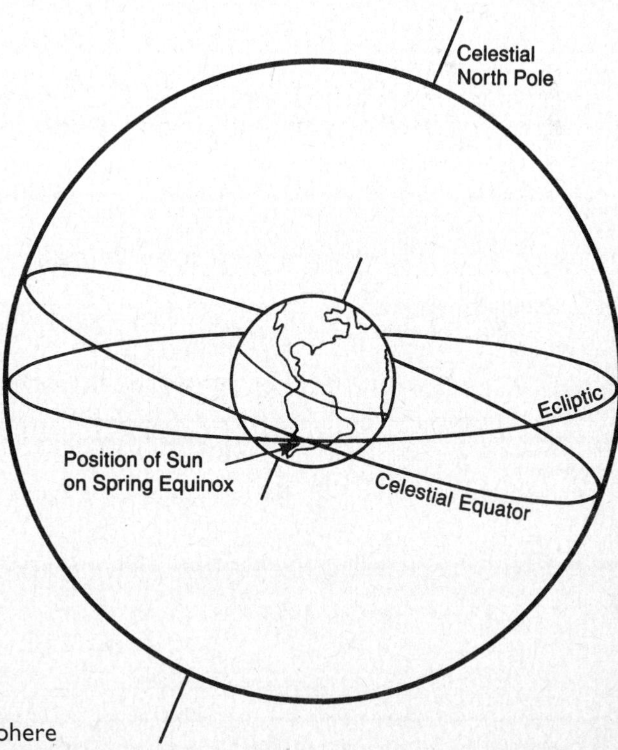

Figure 22.1 Locations on the celestial sphere

 NAME ______________ CLASS ______________ DATE ______________

Procedure

1. Study the introductory material and answer questions 1–3 in Analysis and Conclusions.

2. On the graph paper, set up the graph as shown in Figure 22.3. Using the data in Figure 22.2, plot the locations of the ecliptic on the graph paper. Connect the points with a dashed line and label the line "Ecliptic." On your graph, the ecliptic curves slightly.

3. Using the data in Figure 22.4, plot the locations of the 15 brightest background stars in the portion of the sky through which Mars is moving. Plot the first-magnitude stars (magnitude +1.0 to +1.9) with circled plus sign (⊕). Use a circled dot (⊙) to plot second-magnitude stars (magnitude +2.0 to +2.9). Use a plain plus sign (+) to plot third-magnitude stars (magnitude +3.0 to +3.9). You will find it helpful to fill in the "Symbol on Graph" column in Figure 22.4 before you begin.

Locations of Selected Points on Ecliptic

Right Ascension (hours)	Declination (degrees)
9	+16.6
10	+11.8
11	+6.1
12	0
13	–6.1
14	–11.8
15	–16.6

Figure 22.2

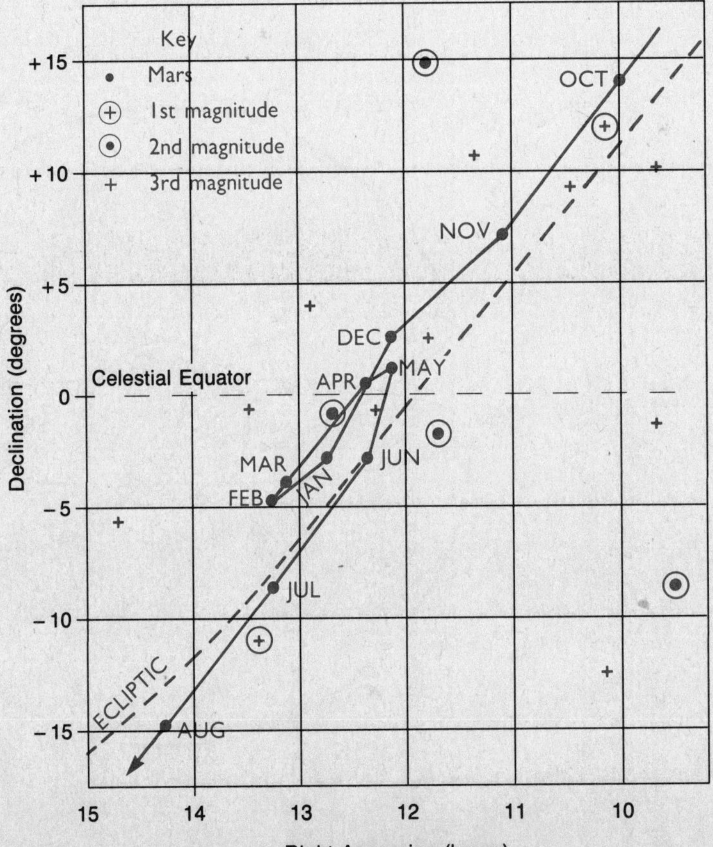

Figure 22.3

4. Plot the positions of Mars on the graph, using the data in Figure 22.5. Use a solid circle (●) to show each position. Label each circle with the month in which Mars had that position.

5. When you have plotted and labeled all the positions of Mars, draw a solid line connecting the positions, starting with October and continuing in order of occurrence. Your line traces the path of Mars across the celestial sphere during this period.

6. In the upper left corner of your graph, make a key of the symbols you used.

7. Answer questions 4–9 in Analysis and Conclusions.

Mars does not retrograde during the same months each year.

Locations and Magnitudes of Stars

Right Ascension (hours)	Declination (degrees)	Apparent Magnitude	Symbol on Graph
9.6	+10.1	3.5	+
10.1	+12.2	1.4	⊕
10.5	+9.6	3.8	+
11.4	+10.8	3.9	+
11.8	+14.9	2.1	⊙
12.3	–0.4	3.9	+
12.7	–1.2	2.8	⊙
12.9	+3.7	3.4	+
13.4	–10.9	1.0	⊕
13.5	–0.3	3.4	+
14.7	–5.4	3.9	+
9.4	–8.4	2.0	⊙
9.6	–0.9	3.9	+
10.1	–12.1	3.6	+

Figure 22.4

Positions of Mars

Right Ascension (hours)	Declination (degrees)	Month of the year
10.0	+13.8	October
11.1	+7.7	November
12.1	+2.0	December
12.8	–2.6	January
13.3	–4.6	February
13.1	–3.7	March
12.4	+0.4	April
12.1	+0.9	May
12.4	–2.7	June
13.3	–8.4	July
14.3	–14.8	August

Figure 22.5

Analysis and Conclusions

1. Polaris, the North Star, is located directly over Earth's North Pole. What is the declination of Polaris on the celestial sphere?

Polaris is at the celestial North Pole; its declination is +90°.

2. There are 24 hours of right ascension around the celestial sphere. There are 360° in a circle. How many degrees on a circle would be equal to one hour of right ascension? Show your work.

$$\frac{24 \text{ hours}}{360 \text{ degrees}} = \frac{1 \text{ hour}}{? \text{ degrees}}$$

(24 hours x ? degrees) = (360 degrees x 1 hour) = 15 degrees/1 hour

3. The ecliptic is the sun's path through the stars. Every day, the sun rises at a different point on the ecliptic. Sunrise makes one complete trip around the path of the ecliptic in one year (365.25 days). Approximately how many degrees along the ecliptic does the point of sunrise move each day? Show your work.

The sun moves 360 degrees in 365.25 days; 360 degrees/365.25 days equals approximately 1 degree per day.

4. During which months was Mars in retrograde motion?

Mars was in retrograde motion from February through May.

5. Is the retrograde motion of Mars a real or an apparent motion?

Retrograde motion is an apparent motion.

6. Which side of your graph represents the eastern part of the sky? How do you know?

The planets move eastward through the stars. Except for retrograde motion, Mars is moving from upper right to lower left on the graph. Therefore the left side of the graph must be the eastern side.

7. Compare Mars' path through the stars with the sun's path through the stars (the ecliptic). Where are the paths relative to each other?

The two paths are roughly parallel.

8. How would the paths of the other planets through the stars compare with the paths of Mars and of the sun? How do you know?

The paths of the other planets should be parallel to the paths of Mars and the sun. The ecliptic corresponds to the plane of most planetary orbits; the planetary orbits should all lie in or near the ecliptic.

9. Jupiter is farther from Earth than Mars. How would you expect the rate of Jupiter's motion through the stars to be different from the rate of Mars? Explain.

Jupiter moves more slowly through the stars. Since Jupiter is farther from the sun, it has a larger orbit that takes longer to complete.

CHAPTER 23

NAME ______________________

CLASS ______________ DATE ______________

LAB INVESTIGATION

Jupiter and the Galilean Moons

The Galilean moons of Jupiter—Io, Europa, Ganymede, and Callisto—can *almost* be seen from Earth with the unaided eye. Only a slight magnification (opera glasses, small telescope) is needed to observe the four moons as they orbit Jupiter. The data table in Figure 23.1 summarizes the changing positions of the moons relative to Jupiter over a period of 14 days. In the event column of the table, the letters A, D, R, E, I, B, and D are listed. These letters refer to the position of a given moon relative to Jupiter. In this investigation, you will plot the positions of the four Galilean moons relative to Jupiter on the graph grid provided. On the graph, the relative dimensions of each orbit are marked with arrows at the top. Time, in days, is indicated on the left side. Each day is divided into four-hour intervals. The changes over the first two days for Io are already plotted on the graph for you to use as a guide.

Lab Skills and Objectives

- To **construct a graph** of the changing positions of the Galilean moons relative to Jupiter
- To **analyze** the graph to determine patterns in the moons' motions
- To **compare and contrast** the orbits and positions of the moons

Materials

- colored pencils (minimum of five different colors needed)
- pencil and eraser
- scrap paper

Figure 23.1
The changing positions of each of the Galilean moons relative to Jupiter over a period of several days

I – moon begins to pass in front of Jupiter on right side
E – moon ends passage across Jupiter
A – moon is at farthest point left of Jupiter
D – moon disappears behind Jupiter on left side
R – moon reappears at right edge of Jupiter
B – moon is at farthest point right of Jupiter

Galilean Moon Data

	Io		Europa		Ganymede		Callisto	
Day	Time (hr)	Event	Time (hr)	Event	Time (hr)	Event	Time (hr)	Event
1	0 2 12 22	I E A D	15	A	21	I	20	D
2	0 10 19 21	R B I E	10 14	D R	0	E	0	R
3	7 16 18	A D R	10	B	18	A		
4	4 13 15	B I E	6 9	I E				
5	1 11 13 22	A D R B	4 23	A D	11 14	D R		
6	8 10 20	I E A	3 23	R B			2	B
7	5 7 17	D R B	19 22	I E	7	B		
8	2 4 14 23	I E A D	17	A				
9	1 11 20 23	R B I E	12 16	D R	1 6	I E		
10	8 18 20	A D R	12	B	21	A	4 7	I E
11	6 15 17	B I E	8 11	I E				
12	3 12 14	A D R	6	A	14 18	D R		
13	0 10 12 22	B I E A	1 5	D R				
14	7 9 20	D R B	2 21	B I	11	B	13	A

Procedure

1. In Figure 23.2, locate the two parallel but unlabeled lines down the middle of the grid. The space between the two lines represents the diameter of Jupiter. With a colored pencil, shade in the area between the two lines. Color the key to match your color for Jupiter.

2. Now turn to the data for Io in Figure 23.1. On Day 1, Io passes in front of Jupiter beginning (I) at Hour 0 and ending (E) at Hour 2. Io continues in its orbit until, as seen from Earth, it is at its greatest distance to the left of the planet (A) at Hour 12. Io disappears (D) behind the left side of the planet at Hour 22 and reappears (R) on the right at Hour 0 on Day 2. Io reaches the right limit of its orbit (B) at Hour 10 on Day 2 before returning to again move from right to left in front of Jupiter (I and E) from Hours 19 to 21. These points have been plotted on the graph in Figure 23.2. Note that the line is broken when Io is located behind Jupiter. The plotted points are connected with a smooth curve.

Students may need help understanding how to read the data table. Go through procedure step 2 as a group exercise. Have students plot the first two days of Io data, even though the curve has already been draw.

3. Continue the plot of Io using the data from the table. Use a colored pencil to connect the points with a smooth curve. Remember to break the line when Io is located behind Jupiter. Color in the key for Io. Complete the curves for Europa, Ganymede, and Callisto.

Analysis and Conclusions

1. (a) Which moon has the shortest distance to complete one orbit? Io

(b) Which moon has the longest distance to complete one orbit? Callisto

(c) Which moon orbits Jupiter in the least amount of time? Io

(d) Which moon orbits Jupiter in the greatest amount of time? Callisto

2. On the data table, Ganymede began to pass in front of Jupiter on Day 1 at Hour 21.

(a) On what day and hour did Ganymede again begin to pass in front of Jupiter?

Day 9 at Hour 1

(b) Determine, to the nearest tenth of a day, the period of revolution of Ganymede. **Show your work.**

Hours remaining in Day 1 = 3

Hours in Days 2–8 = (24×7) = 168

Hours in Day 9 = 1

Total Hours = 172

$$\frac{172 \text{ Hours}}{24 \text{ Hours/Day}} = 7.2 \text{ Days}$$

3. Remember that Jupiter and its moons, like the other planets and moons, are illuminated by the sun and thus cast shadows. Use your graph in Figure 23.2 to determine the best time to see the shadow of Callisto projected onto Jupiter's surface.

Day 10

Because Jupiter's shadow has not been accounted for with this data, the actual time of disappearance or reappearance will vary as the moons move through the shadow.

4. (a) When viewed from a position above the north pole of Jupiter, do the Galilean moons appear to move in a clockwise or a counterclockwise direction?

The moons appear to move clockwise around Jupiter.

(b) When viewed from a similar position above our North Pole, in what direction does our moon move around Earth? (See Figure 24.12 on page 444 of your text.)

Earth's moon moves counterclockwise.

(c) An image through binoculars is in a normal position, while an image through a telescope is upside down and backward. Does your graph represent a view of the Galilean moons through binoculars or through a telescope? Explain how you know.

The graph must represent a view through a telescope. Jupiter's moons, like Earth's moon, revolve counterclockwise. Since the motion appears backward, the image must be reversed.

5. Graphs like the one in Figure 23.2 are used primarily to aid in identifying the moons while viewing. Suppose these data represent the positions of Jupiter's moons in the next 14 days. The best viewing hours of Jupiter are from Hour 20 to Hour 24 each evening. If you wanted to observe all four moons spaced as far apart from Jupiter and one another as possible, which day would you choose? Name the moons from left to right.

Day 6: Io, Europa, Ganymede, Callisto. Day 13: Callisto, Io , Europa, Ganymede

The graph drawn here is a part of a graph that appears each month in many astronomy magazines. If such magazines are available, you could show students an example.

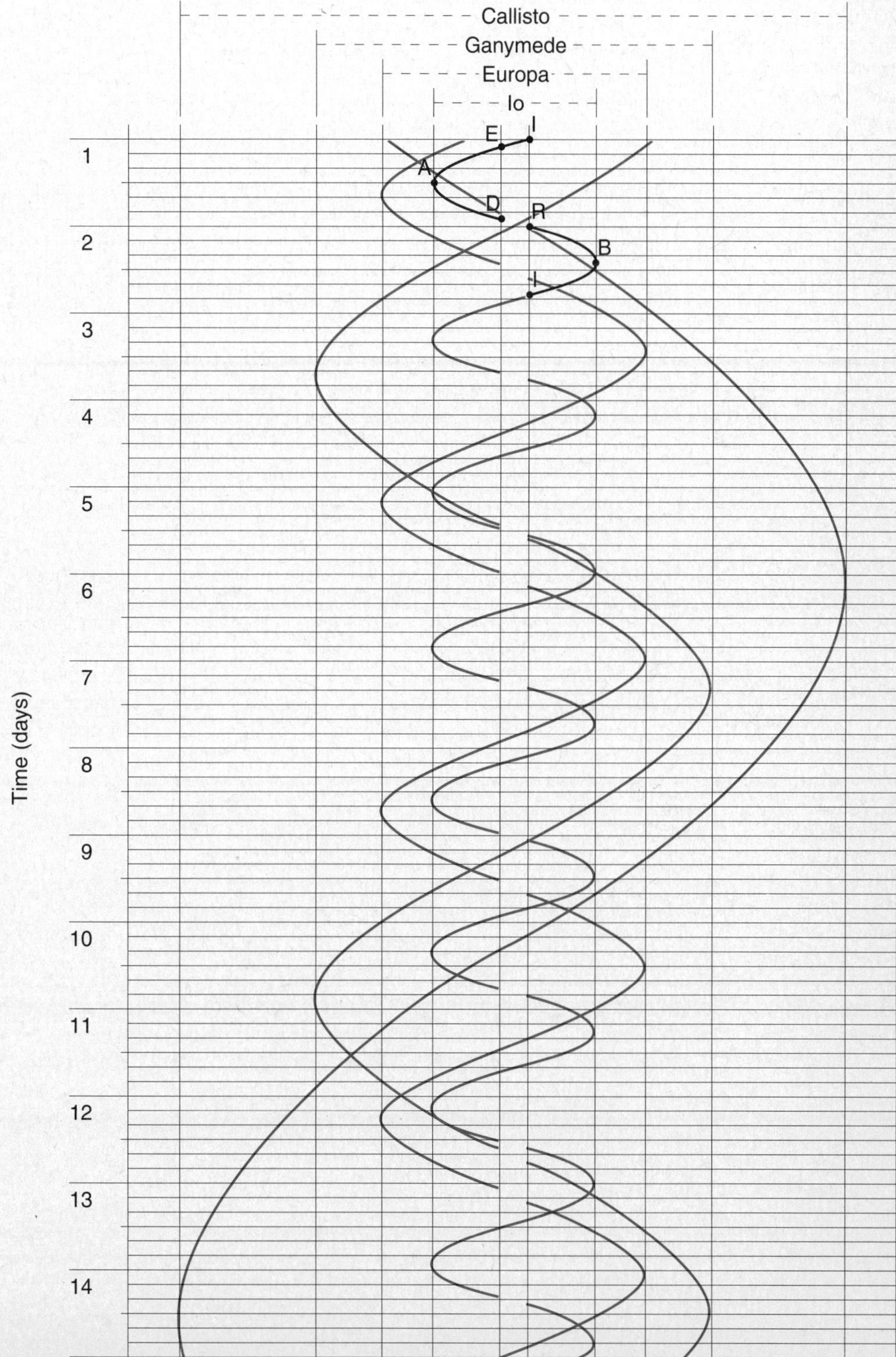

Color Key

Jupiter ☐
Io ☐
Europa ☐
Ganymede ☐
Callisto ☐

Figure 23.2

CHAPTER

24

NAME ______________________________

CLASS ______________ DATE ______________

Diameter of the Moon and the Ecliptic Limit

Early astronomers were able to determine the size of the moon using simple geometry. They knew the size of Earth from Eratosthenes' measurement (Chapter 2). These astronomers also knew that both Earth and the moon cast a cone-shaped shadow out into space. As the moon passed through Earth's shadow during a lunar eclipse, they noted that Earth's shadow was about 2.4 times the diameter of the Moon. In Part A, you will use the same methods the early astronomers used to determine the size of the moon.

The early astronomers also found that the moon's path through the sky can be as much as 5 degrees above or below the sun's path (the ecliptic). This meant that the moon's shadow would often end in space above or below Earth, rather than falling on Earth to cause a solar eclipse. For the same reason, the moon can pass above or below Earth's shadow, rather than passing through the shadow to cause a lunar eclipse. Eclipses can occur only when the moon is at or near the ecliptic. The part of the moon's orbit when this occurs is called the **ecliptic limit.** Although the moon crosses the ecliptic twice each month, eclipses do not occur that often. For an eclipse to occur, the moon must be in a new moon or full moon phase when it is in the ecliptic limit. In Part B, you will determine the average length, in kilometers, of an ecliptic limit.

Lab Skills and Objectives

- To **measure** the moon's diameter using the method of early astronomers
- To **identify** the portion of a lunar orbit where an eclipse could occur

Materials

- 2 sheets plain paper
- pencil
- metric ruler
- drawing compass
- protractor

The ecliptic limit for lunar eclipses and solar eclipses is slightly different, but for this laboratory, the two will be considered the same. Consult a college astronomy text for a more detailed discussion of determining eclipse frequency.

Procedure

Part A

1. To determine the size of the moon, you will draw a model of Earth and the moon. In this model, imagine yourself as an observer out in space looking at Earth and the moon. To draw the model, turn a sheet of paper so the long side is toward you. Draw a thin line that divides the paper in half lengthwise. This thin line serves as a guideline for procedure steps 1, 2, and 3. Use the compass to draw a circle 4 cm in diameter centered on the guideline and close to one edge of the paper. (Remember that a diameter of 4 cm means a radius of 2 cm.) The circle represents Earth.

2. Using the edge of the ruler, draw a line from the top of the circle to the point where the guideline meets the far edge of the paper. Then draw a similar line from the bottom of the circle to the same point. Your drawing should now look something like an ice-cream cone with a scoop of ice cream in the end (Figure 24.1). The cone shape represents Earth's shadow out into space.

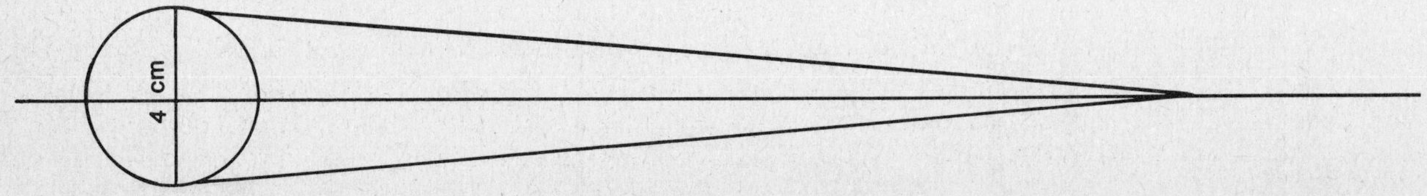

Figure 24.1

3. With the protractor, measure the entire angle at the point of the cone-shaped shadow. Measure carefully and estimate the size of the angle to the nearest tenth of a degree. Call your measurement angle A and record its value in the table in Figure 24.5.

4. Angle A is the angular width of Earth's shadow on your model. At the moon's distance from Earth, Earth's shadow is about 2.4 times as wide as the moon. Multiply angle A by 2.4 and record this value as angle B in Figure 24.5.

5. Angle B will be used to determine the width in kilometers of Earth's shadow. Divide angle B by two and record the value in Figure 24.5. Place your protractor at the point where your guideline crosses the circle of Earth. Measure half of angle B above the guideline and make a small mark. Then measure half of angle B below the guideline and make another small mark. Draw lines from the point where the guideline crosses Earth out to each of the small marks. This should form a second cone (Figure 24.2).

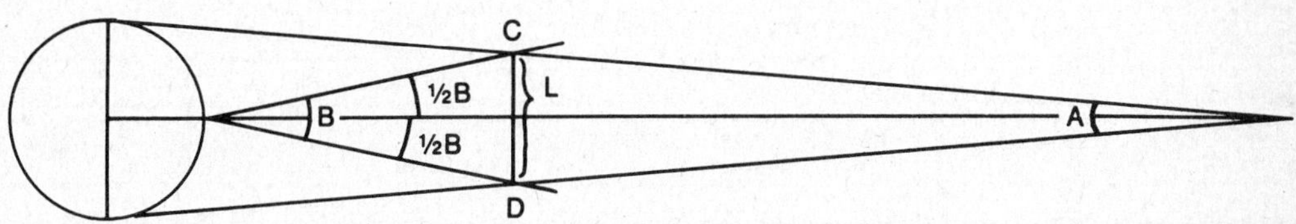

Figure 24.2

6. Label the points where the two lines of the second cone cross the lines of the first cone point C and point D. Draw a straight vertical line between the two points. Label the line L. L represents the average width of Earth's shadow at the distance of the moon's orbit. Measure the length of line L in centimeters and record the value in Figure 24.5.

7. Line L is 2.4 times the diameter of the moon. Divide L by 2.4. Call this value L′ and record its length in Figure 24.5. L′ is the diameter of the moon on the scale of your model.

8. In order to determine the fractional size of the moon by comparing it to the size of Earth, the size of Earth needs to be considered as the value 1. Since your original circle, Earth, was 4.0 cm in diameter, the cone-shaped shadow you drew is 4 times too large for this purpose. Divide L′ by 4.0 and record the answer. L′ divided by 4 is the fractional size of the moon's diameter compared to Earth's diameter. Use the value L′ divided by 4 to answer Analysis and Conclusions questions 1 and 2.

Part B

If time is short, Part B may be saved for the next lab period, or it may be excluded.

9. Now you will construct another model to determine the length of an ecliptic limit. In this model, imagine yourself as the sun facing earth and the moon. (To simplify the drawing, everything in the model will be shown in the plane of the paper.) Take a new sheet of paper and hold it with the long side toward you. Mark a point 2.5 cm from the left (short) edge, and 10 cm from the top (long) edge. Label this point X. Use point X as the center of another 4-cm circle to represent Earth.

10. At the right side of the paper, measure and mark three points from the top edge of the paper. The three points should be at distances of 8, 10, and 12 cm from the top edge. Draw a line with the straightedge from the top edge of the circle to the top mark. Then draw a line from the center of the circle to the second mark. Finally, draw a third line from the bottom of the circle to the bottom mark. These three lines should be parallel (Figure 24.3). The center line represents Earth's orbit. The top and bottom lines represent the upper and lower edges of Earth's shadow in space. Although the shadow is actually cone-shaped, the cone is so long that for the small part shown in this model, the taper of the cone would not show.

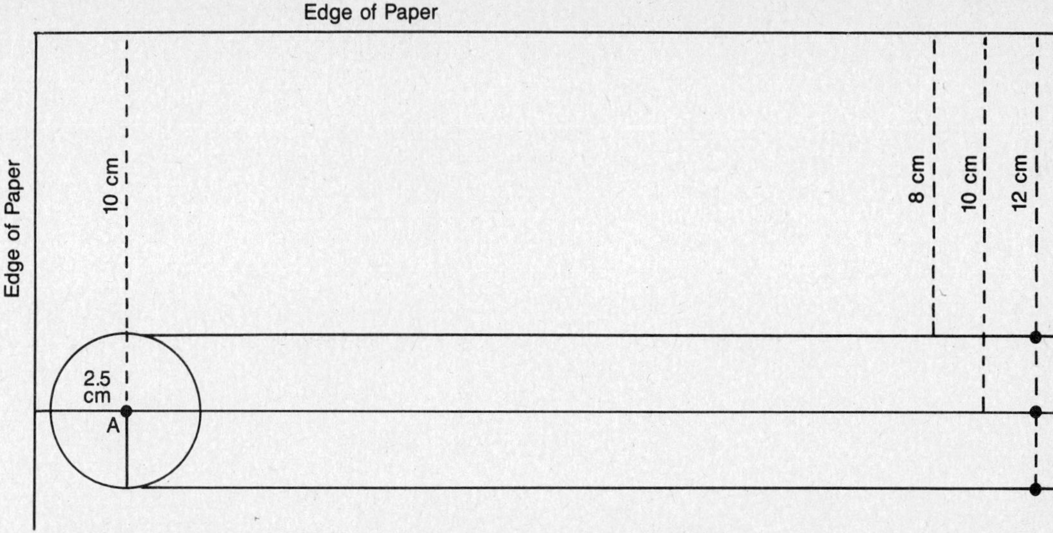

Figure 24.3

11. The moon can be above or below Earth's path around the sun by a maximum of 5 degrees. From the center of the circle, measure an angle of 5 degrees above the center line and make a small mark. Measure very carefully as a small error now will cause a large error later.

12. Carefully draw a line through the center of the circle and the mark to the edge of the paper. This line should cross the top parallel line just before the end of the paper (Figure 24.4). This line represents part of the moon's orbit that is tilted 5 degrees above the plane of Earth's orbit.

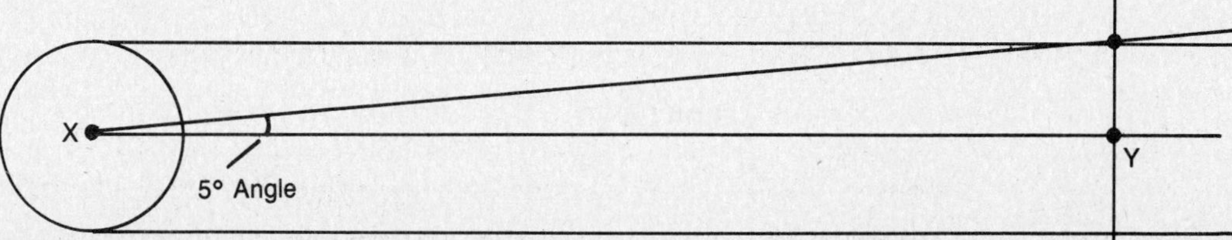

Figure 24.4

13. Draw a perpendicular line from the point where the 5-degree line crosses the top line down through the three parallel lines. Label the point where this line crosses the center line point Y.

14. Measure the distance from point X along the center line to point Y. Record this value in Figure 24.5. The line represents one-half the distance of the ecliptic limit. The other half of the ecliptic limit would extend off the paper to the left, to the point where the moon's orbit, tilted down 5 degrees, crosses the lower limit of Earth's shadow. Determine the total length of the ecliptic limit on your model by multiplying the length of line XY by 2. Record this value as XY′ in Figure 24.5. Answer Analysis and Conclusions question 3.

Part A diameter of original circle (cm)	4.0
angle A, to the nearest tenth of a degree	about 10
angle B (angle A times 2.4)	about 24
angle B divided by 2	about 12
length of line L (cm)	2.6 to 2.7
length of L′ (L divided by 2.4)	about 1.1
L′ divided by 4	0.23 to 0.30
Part B length of line XY (cm)	23 to 24
XY′ (length of line XY times 2)	46 to 48

Figure 24.5

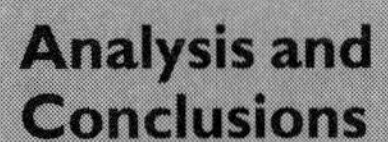

1. Using an Earth diameter of 12 800 km and your fractional diameter of the moon, determine the value for the moon's diameter based on your model. Set up the problem and show your work.

The calculation is the fractional size times 12 800, for example, 0.24 × 12 800 km = 3072 km. Students' results should be between 3070 km and 3840 km.

2. The moon's actual diameter is 3476 km. Determine the percent difference between your value for the moon's diameter and the moon's actual diameter. Show all work.

$$\text{Percent difference} = \frac{\text{difference between calculated and actual value}}{\text{actual value}} \times 100$$

Student answers will vary. If a student's value was 3467 km, the percent difference would be

$$\text{Percent difference} = \frac{3476 \text{ km} - 3467 \text{ km}}{3476 \text{ km}} \times 100 = 0.3 \text{ percent}$$

3. Since Earth's diameter is 12 800 km, your model has a scale of 1 cm = 3200 km (12 800 km/4 cm). Determine the number of kilometers represented by the line XY′.

The calculation is the length of the line XY′ in cm times the number of km represented by each cm, for example, 46 cm x 3200 km = 147 200 km. Student results should be between 147 000 km and 154 000 km.

Your answer is the length in kilometers of the ecliptic limit.

NAME ____________________

CLASS ____________ DATE ____________

LAB INVESTIGATION

Time and the Sun

The altitude of any object in the sky is its vertical angle above the horizon. The altitude of Polaris, the North Star, can be used to determine the latitude of an observer on Earth. In Part A, you will find your latitude by measuring the altitude of Polaris in the night sky.

The altitude of the sun varies with the time of day, reaching its highest altitude at solar noon. However, the sun is seldom at its highest altitude at exactly noon on the clock. The altitude of the sun shows apparent solar time, while clock time is set to show average solar time. Solar time is either ahead of or behind clock time, depending on the season of the year. When the sun reaches its highest altitude before noon on the clock, apparent solar time is ahead of clock time. When the sun reaches its highest altitude after noon on the clock, apparent solar time is behind clock time.

The **analemma** is a graph that shows both the altitude of the sun and the difference between solar time and clock time for any day of the year. The table in Figure 25.4 shows the latitude at which the sun is directly overhead at solar noon on each of the dates given. These latitudes vary between 23.5° N and 23.5° S of the equator. The clock time at which the sun is directly overhead is also listed. In Part B, you will use these data and your own latitude to determine the noon altitudes of the sun at your location throughout the year. You will then use the altitudes of the sun and the time of solar noon to graph an analemma for your latitude.

Lab Skills and Objectives

- To **measure** latitude by measuring the altitude of Polaris
- To **graph** an analemma
- To **compare** the altitude of the sun on different dates using the analemma
- To **identify** the seasons during which solar time is ahead of and behind clock time

Materials

- protractor
- thread—about 15 cm
- paper clip
- Seasonal Star Maps, Appendix B, pages 660–661 of your text
- graph paper

Note that students must do Part A as a homework assignment before the laboratory period. If desired, you may omit Part A and provide students with the local latitude determined from a map.

Procedure

Part A

1. First you will make a device to measure the altitude of Polaris. Tie the paper clip to one end of the piece of thread. Tie the other end of the thread through the small hole in the protractor. (If there is no small hole in the protractor, tie the string around the center mark on the straight side.)

2. On a clear night with visible stars, locate Polaris in the sky. Refer to Seasonal Star Maps as needed.

3. Hold the protractor with the straight side pointing up (Figure 25.1). Sight along the straight edge of the protractor at Polaris. Read the angle on the protractor at the point where the string crosses. Record this value in Figure 25.2.

4. The angle you measured in procedure step 3 is the altitude of Polaris plus 90°. Subtract 90° to determine the altitude of Polaris. Record this value in Figure 25.2. The altitude of Polaris is equal to the latitude of your location. Record your latitude in Figure 25.2.

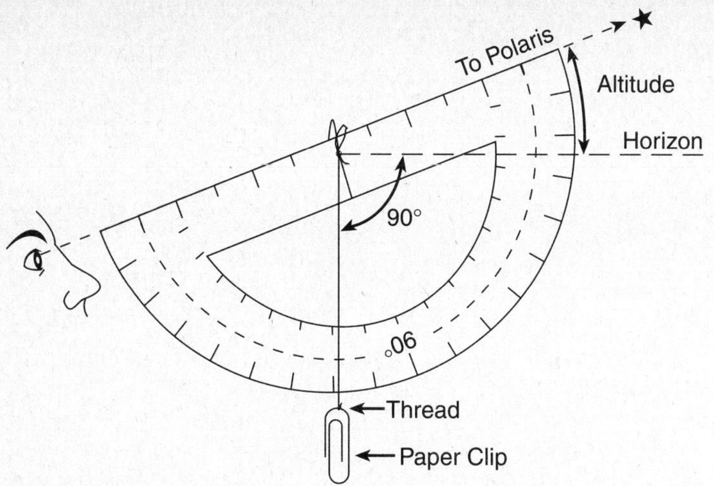

Figure 25.1
Using a protractor to find the altitude of Polaris

Finding Latitude Using Polaris	
Angle on Protractor	132°*
Altitude of Polaris: 90°–angle on protractor	42°
Your Latitude	42°N

* Sample data for 42°N

Figure 25.2

Part B

5. Your latitude, which you measured in Part A, will be used to complete the table in Figure 25.4. The second column of Figure 25.4 shows the latitude on Earth where the sun is directly overhead (altitude 90°) at solar noon on each date. To complete the third column of the table, you need to determine how far away you are, in degrees of latitude, from each location. For locations south of the equator, this means adding that latitude to your latitude. For locations north of the equator, this means subtracting that latitude from your latitude. (Figure 25.3 illustrates why.) Look at January 10 as an example. If you are at 40° N latitude, you are 40° + 22.1°, or 62.1°, from the location where the sun is overhead. Using your latitude, complete the third column in Figure 25.4.

6. Now you will use your distance from the latitude where the sun is overhead at solar noon to find your local sun altitude at solar noon. Your distance from the latitude where the sun is overhead is the same as the local distance of the sun from an altitude of 90°. The altitude of the sun on each date at your latitude is 90° minus your distance from the latitude where the sun is overhead. Using January 10 again, if you are at 40° N and are thus 62.1° from that latitude, the altitude of the sun is 90°–62.1° or 27.9°. Using your latitude, complete the fourth column of Figure 25.4.

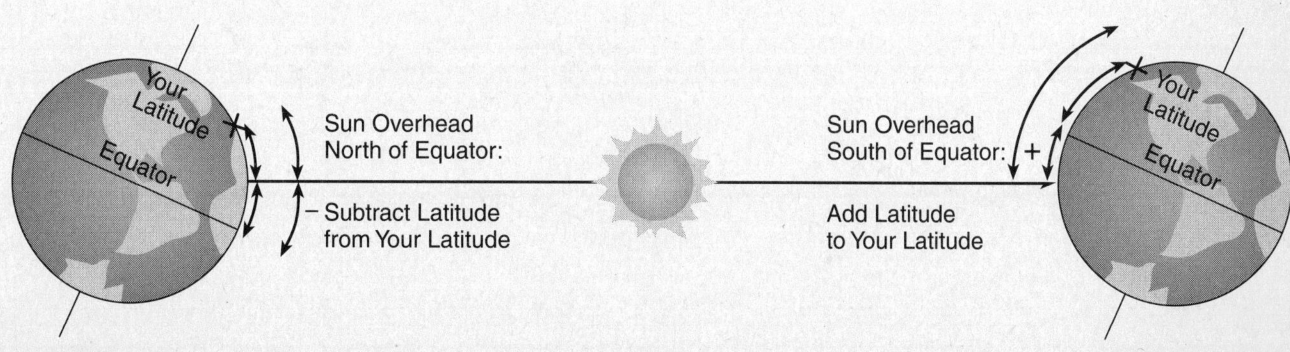

Figure 25.3
Finding your distance from the latitude where the sun is overhead at solar noon

Date	Latitude where Sun Is Overhead at Solar Noon	Your Distance from Latitude in Column 2	Altitude of Sun at Solar Noon at Your Latitude	Clock Time at Solar Noon (h)
Jan 10	22.1°S	64.1°*	25.9°	12:07
Jan 20	20.3°S	62.3°	27.7°	12:11
Jan 30	17.9°S	59.9°	30.1°	12:13
Feb 10	14.6°S	56.6°	33.4°	12:14
Feb 20	11.2°S	53.2°	36.8°	12:14
Mar 5	6.4°S	48.4°	41.6°	12:12
Mar 10	4.4°S	46.4°	43.6°	12:11
Mar 20	0.5°S	42.5°	47.5°	12:08
Mar 30	3.4°N	38.6°	51.4°	12:05
Apr 10	7.6°N	34.4°	55.6°	12:02
Apr 20	11.2°N	30.8°	59.2°	11:59
Apr 30	14.5°N	27.5°	62.5°	11:57
May 10	17.4°N	24.6°	65.4°	11:56
May 20	19.8°N	22.2°	67.8°	11:56
May 30	21.6°N	20.4°	69.6°	11:57
Jun 10	22.9°N	19.1°	70.9°	11:59
Jun 20	23.4°N	18.6°	71.4°	12:01
Jun 30	23.2°N	18.8°	71.2°	12:04
Jul 10	22.3°N	19.6°	70.3°	12:05
Jul 20	20.8°N	21.2°	68.8°	12:06
Jul 30	18.7°N	23.3°	66.7°	12:06
Aug 10	15.8°N	26.2°	63.8°	12:05
Aug 20	12.7°N	29.3°	60.7°	12:04
Aug 30	9.3°N	32.7°	57.3°	12:01
Sep 10	5.3°N	36.7°	53.3°	11:57
Sep 20	1.4°N	40.6°	49.4°	11:54
Sep 30	2.5°S	44.5°	45.5°	11:50
Oct 10	6.3°S	48.3°	41.7°	11:47
Oct 20	10.0°S	52.0°	38.0°	11:45
Oct 30	13.5°S	55.5°	34.5·	11:44
Nov 10	16.9°S	58.9°	31.1°	11:44
Nov 20	19.5°S	61.5°	28.5°	11:46
Nov 30	21.5°S	63.5°	26.5°	11:49
Dec 10	22.8°S	64.8°	25.2°	11:53
Dec 20	23.4°S	65.4°	24.6°	11:57
Dec 30	23.2°S	65.2°	24.8°	12:02

Figure 25.4

*Sample data for 42°N

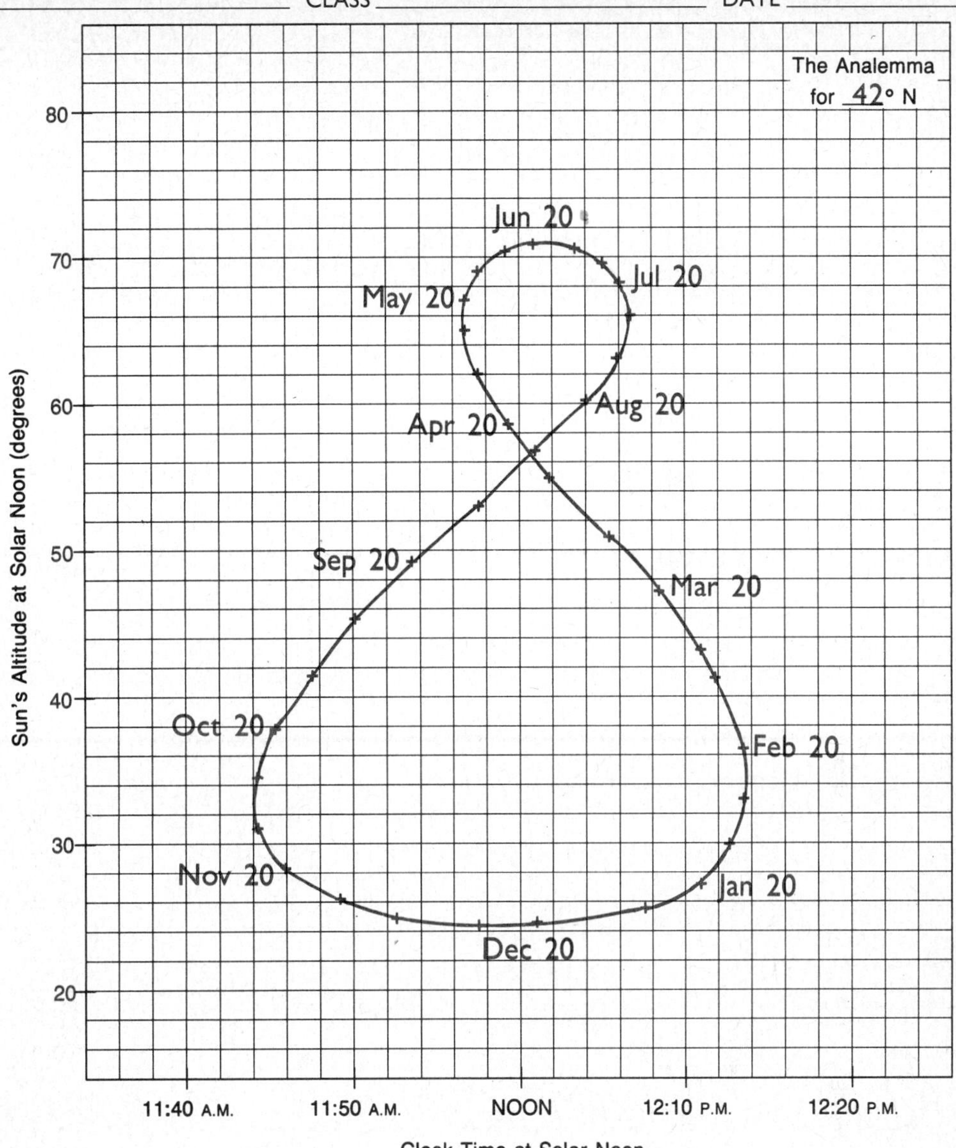

Figure 25.5

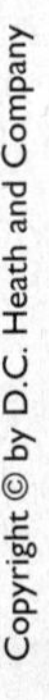

7. You now have complete data to graph an analemma for your latitude. Set up the horizontal and vertical axes of your graph as shown in Figure 25.5. Notice that the vertical axis does not have any values written along it. The values you use depend on your data. To figure out the values you should use, find the highest and lowest values for the sun's altitude in your table (Figure 25.4). Make the lowest value on your graph the closest even multiple of 10 that is below your lowest altitude value. Make the highest value the closest even multiple of 10 that is above your highest altitude value. Label every tenth value in between. Your finished vertical axis will read 10, 20, 30, and so on, or 20, 30, 40, and so on, or 30, 40, 50, and so on, depending on your latitude.

8. For each date, graph the clock time of solar noon (fifth column) against the altitude of the sun at solar noon (fourth column). On the points that represent the 20th of each month, write the date. When you are finished, connect the points in the order of the months of the year.

9. Answer Analysis and Conclusions questions 1–12.

Analysis and Conclusions

1. On your graph, what is the maximum altitude of the sun? On what date does this maximum altitude occur?

Maximum altitude depends upon students' latitude. For the sample data, the answer is 71.4°. The date of maximum altitude is June 20.

2. On the date you gave in question 1, at what latitude was the sun directly overhead at solar noon?

The sun was directly overhead at 23.4° N latitude.

3. What is the name of the imaginary circle around Earth very near the latitude you gave in your answer to question 2? (Refer to Chapter 25 if needed.)

Tropic of Cancer

4. What season begins in the Northern Hemisphere on the approximate date in your answer for question 1?

June 20 is near the date of the summer solstice (first day of summer).

5. On your graph, what is the minimum altitude of the sun? On what date does the minimum altitude occur?

Minimum altitude depends upon students' latitude. For the sample data, the answer is 24.6°. The date of minimum altitude is December 20, in the northern hemisphere.

6. On the date you gave for question 6, at what latitude was the sun directly overhead at solar noon?

The sun was directly overhead at 23.4° S latitude.

7. What is the name of the imaginary circle around Earth close to the latitude you gave in your answer to question 6?

Tropic of Capricorn

8. What season begins in the Northern Hemisphere on the approximate date of your answer for question 5?

December 20 is near the date of the winter solstice (first day of winter).

9. Using the table in Figure 25.4, find the two dates when the sun is overhead closest to the equator at solar noon. Name the seasons that begin close to each of these dates.

The two dates are March 20, near the spring equinox (first day of spring), and September 20, near the autumn equinox (first day of autumn).

10. On your graph, find the dates you listed in your answer to question 9. Where are these dates on the graph?

March 20 and September 20 are halfway between December 20 and June 20.

11. During which two seasons is apparent solar time ahead of clock time? (Review the introduction to this investigation for help.)

Solar time is ahead of clock time in spring and autumn.

12. During which two seasons is apparent solar time behind clock time?

Solar time is behind clock time in summer and winter.

CHAPTER 26

NAME ______

CLASS ______ DATE ______

Absorption and Radiation of Heat Energy

Most people feel cooler in light-colored clothing than in dark clothing when they are out in the hot summer sun. Is there really a difference or is it their imagination? You will find out by comparing the effect of heat absorption and radiation on three different surfaces—one black, one white, and one shiny.

Earth's surface is also affected by the hot summer sun. It consists of two very different components: the land surface and the ocean surface. Even when wavy, the ocean surface is more regular in texture, color, and composition than the land surface. Land has extreme highs (mountains) and lows (valleys) and features of many colors and compositions (vegetation, rocks, buildings). Do land and ocean absorb and radiate heat differently? In the second part of this investigation, you will compare the effect of heat absorption and radiation on the land (represented by soil) and the ocean (represented by water).

Lab Skills and Objectives

Plan this lab for two periods.

- To **record** temperature changes produced by heat absorption and radiation
- To **compare** light and dark materials and dull and shiny materials in terms of the amount of heat they absorb and radiate
- To **compare** the "land" and "ocean" in terms of the heat they absorb and radiate

Materials

- safety goggles
- three empty soup cans, one painted dull white, one painted dull black, and one shiny silver, each with a hole punched in the unopened end for inserting a thermometer
- two small beakers (about 250 mL) or two small, deep, clear glass bowls
- three thermometers with ranges of 0°C to at least 50°C
- desk lamp or clip-on lamp with incandescent light bulb of at least 100 watts
- ring stand
- three ring clamps
- watch with second hand
- topsoil
- water
- two sheets of graph paper

Procedure

Connect lamps to curcuits with ground-fault interrupters.

Part A Light and Dark Materials

1. **Put on your safety goggles. Wear them while performing Part A and Part B.**

2. Set up the apparatus with the black, white, and shiny cans as shown in Figure 26.1. Place the cans with their open ends down and put thermometers through the holes in the closed ends. The thermometers must be at the same angle, slanting in the same direction.

3. Set the incandescent lamp at a height of about 12 cm above the cans. Make sure the cans are at equal distances from the lamp. Before you turn on the lamp, make sure that the three thermometers show room temperature.

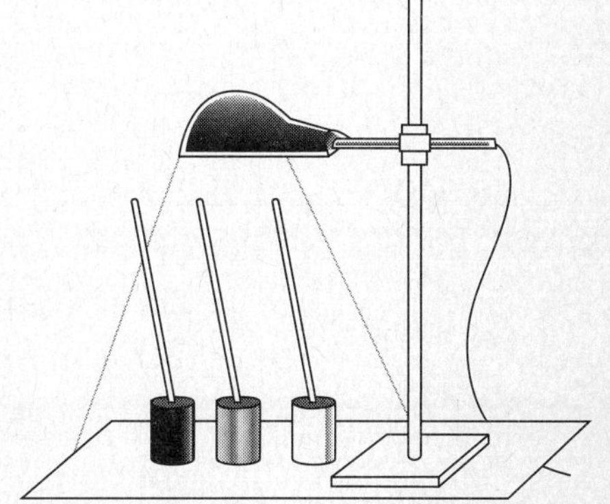

Figure 26.1

4. Use Figure 26.2 to record temperature data. Under 0 min, record the room temperature for all three cans. Then switch on the lamp. Record the temperatures of the cans every 2 min for the next 10 min. At the end of 10 min, turn off the lamp and continue to record the temperatures every 2 min for another 10 min.

	Heating						Cooling				
Time (min)	0	2	4	6	8	10	12	14	16	18	20
Black Can Temperature (°C)											
White Can Temperature (°C)											
Shiny Can Temperature (°C)											

Figure 26.2

5. Draw a graph using the temperature data you recorded. On graph paper, draw a horizontal axis and a vertical axis and label them as shown in Figure 26.3. On your graph, plot the times and temperatures you recorded for the black can and connect the points with a smooth curve. Do the same for the white can and the shiny can. Label each curve. Answer Analysis and Conclusions questions 1–4.

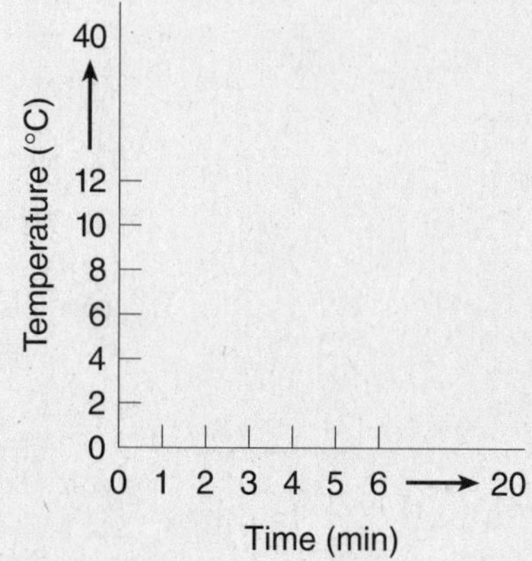

Figure 26.3

Part B Land and Ocean

6. In this section, you will check your answer to Analysis and Conclusions question 4. Fill half of a 250-mL beaker with water at room temperature. Fill half of a second 250-mL beaker with topsoil.

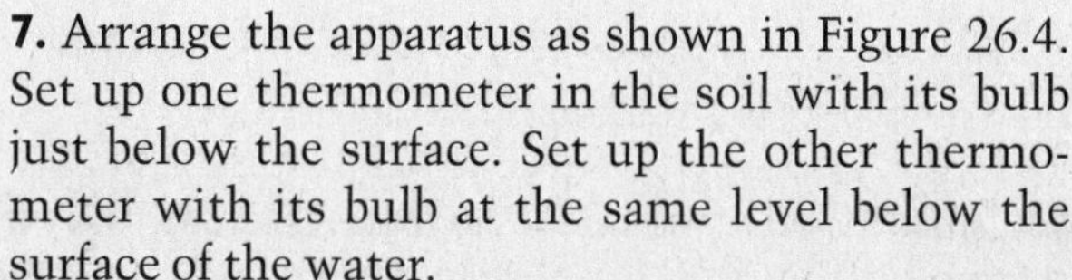

7. Arrange the apparatus as shown in Figure 26.4. Set up one thermometer in the soil with its bulb just below the surface. Set up the other thermometer with its bulb at the same level below the surface of the water.

Connect lamps to circuits with ground-fault interrupters.

8. Set the incandescent lamp at a height of about 30 cm above the water and soil surfaces. Make sure the beakers are at equal distances from the lamp. Before you turn on the lamp, wait until both thermometers show the same temperature.

9. Use Figure 26.5 to record the temperature data. Under 0 min, record the initial temperatures of the soil and water. Then switch on the lamp and record the temperature of both beakers every 2 min for the next 10 min. At the end of 10 min, turn off the light. Continue to record the temperatures every 2 min for another 10 min.

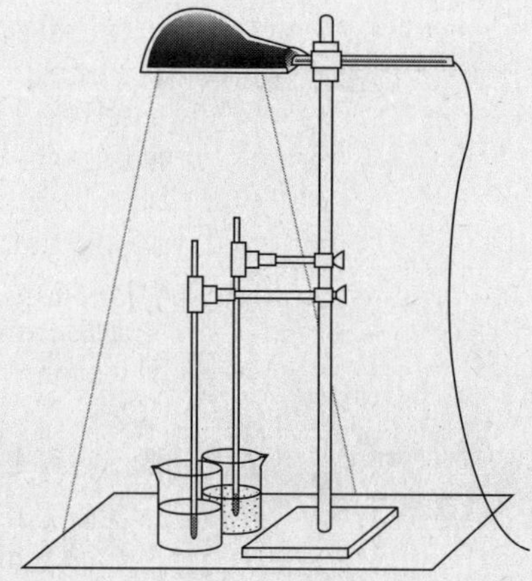

Figure 26.4

10. On a second sheet of graph paper, plot the data the same way you did for Part A. Label both curves. Answer Analysis and Conclusions questions 5–13.

	Heating						Cooling				
Time (min)	0	2	4	6	8	10	12	14	16	18	20
Soil Temperature (°C)											
Water Temperature (°C)											

Figure 26.5

 NAME ______ CLASS ______ DATE ______

Analysis and Conclusions

1. Study the three curves on your graph. Which can warmed up most in the first 10 min? Which can cooled fastest?

the black can; the black can

2. Changes in temperature are caused by heat transfer. The greater the amount of heat absorbed or radiated, the greater the change in temperature. Which can absorbed the most heat? Explain your answer.

The black can absorbed the most heat since its temperature increased the most in the first 10 min.

Which can radiated the most heat? the black can

3. How do surface color and shininess affect absorption and radiation of heat energy?

Dark, dull objects absorb and radiate more heat than light or shiny objects.

4. What type of land surface would warm up and cool off the fastest?

A dark, nonreflective land surface would warm up and cool off fastest.

5. Which material absorbed more heat in the first 10 min? the soil

6. Which material radiated more heat in the second 10 min? the soil

7. On the basis of these conclusions, compare what happens to darker, rougher materials and lighter, smoother materials when the sun shines on them.

Darker, rougher materials absorb more heat than lighter, smoother materials.

8. Compare the graphs from Parts A and B. Which surfaces absorbed and radiated the most heat and how are they similar?

The black can and the soil absorbed and radiated the most heat. They are the darkest colored and roughest (least reflective) of the five surfaces.

9. The hot summer sun shines on the ocean and on a stretch of land several kilometers inland. Which will heat up more during the day? Explain why.

The inland area will heat up more during the day because its surface is darker and rougher. An area 32 km (20 miles) inland can typically be several degrees warmer in summer than the nearest shore.

10. Which area will cool more slowly at night? Explain why.

The ocean will cool more slowly because water is a slower conductor of heat than land and because heat spreads through a greater depth of water than of land.

Pierre is pronounced like pier.

11. Portland, Maine, and Pierre, South Dakota, are located at approximately 44° N latitude. Portland is close to the Atlantic coast, and Pierre is in the middle of the continent. Which city is warmer on the average during the summer? Explain why.

Pierre is warmer because it is inland where more heat is absorbed.

12. In winter, Earth's surface tends to lose heat. Based on your conclusions, which city is colder on the average during winter?

Pierre; It is inland, and the land radiates more heat than the ocean.

13. Why does the other city stay relatively warmer during the winter?

It is near the ocean, which loses less heat and warms the cooler coastal land.

NAME ______________________

CLASS ____________ DATE ____________

The Effects of Acid Rain

A 40-minute period is required the first day, followed by a 40-minute period four days later. If time is limited, any one of the three investigations may be performed individually.

When coal, oil, or gasoline is burned, nitrogen and sulfur oxides are released. These gases combine with moisture in the air to form acid rain. In this lab, you will compare the effects of sulfuric acid on plants, concrete,and steel. Sulfuric acid is one of the acids found in acid rain.

Lab Skills and Objectives

- To **observe** and **measure** the effects of acid rain on plants, concrete, and steel
- To **summarize** and **draw conclusions** from the data obtained

Materials

Warn students that they are studying the harmful effects of sulfuric acid on plants, concrete, and steel. Sulfuric acid can also be harmful to humans.

- lab apron
- plastic gloves
- safety goggles
- 0.1*M* sulfuric acid, 225 mL for each group
- 12 150-mL or 200-mL beakers or plastic cups
- 50-mL graduated cylinder
- 3 cups of potting soil
- alfalfa sprouts
- metric ruler
- medicine dropper
- 4 pieces of concrete
- 8 steel nails
- steel wool
- wax marking pencil
- small scrubbing brush
- tongs

One container of sprouts is sufficient for one class.

You will need 2700 mL of 0.1*M* sulfuric acid for a class of 24 working in pairs. Prepare a 50% excess (4000 mL) so that you will not run out. Purchase 1*M* sulfuric acid.

Wear safety goggles, a lab apron, and plastic gloves when preparing the 0.1*M* sulfuric acid. *For each liter you need to prepare,* measure 900 mL of water into a glass container. While stirring with a stirring rod, slowly add 100 mL of 1*M* sulfuric acid. Students should not have access to the stock 1*M* solution of sulfuric acid.

Procedure

CAUTION: Be sure you are wearing your safety goggles.

Use a rock hammer to prepare pieces of concrete before the start of lab.

1. **Wear your safety goggles, a lab apron, and plastic gloves during procedure steps 1–9.** Organize 12 beakers or cups into three groups of four. Label one group *plants,* a second group *concrete,* and a third group *steel.* Using the wax pencil, label each beaker with your name. Number each group from 1 to 4.

2. Fill *plant* beaker number 1 halfway with potting soil. Gently pull out a plug of alfalfa sprouts about 1–2 cm in diameter from the class container. Measure in cm the length of the sprouts from root tip to leaf top. Record the length in the data table in the column headed *Beaker 1, Before.*

3. Hold the sprouts upright in the center of the beaker. Gently sift some potting soil around the sprouts to plant them. Cover the bottom half of the stems. Press the soil down gently. Repeat procedure steps 2 and 3 for the other three beakers.

4. Water the sprouts with the following liquids:
Beaker 1: 50 mL of tap water
Beaker 2: 10 drops of sulfuric acid mixed in your graduated cylinder with enough water to make 50 mL
Beaker 3: 5 mL (100 drops) of sulfuric acid plus water to make 50 mL
Beaker 4: 50 mL of sulfuric acid

5. Set your sprouts in front of a window. Water all the sprouts with tap water as needed.

6. Fill the beakers labeled *Concrete* with 100 mL of tap water. Dampen four pieces of concrete with tap water and mass them. Record the masses on the data table. Place each piece in the appropriate beaker.

7. Do not add anything to Beaker 1. Add 10 drops of sulfuric acid to Beaker 2, 5 mL (100 drops) of sulfuric acid to Beaker 3, and 50 mL of sulfuric acid to Beaker 4. Allow the beakers to stand undisturbed.

Have students place the soil in a cardboard box. Neutralize the soil with agricultural lime before disposing of it. Lime is corrosive. Follow the safety precautions on the label and wear safety goggles, a lab apron, plastic gloves, and a dust mask when handling lime.

Have students put the liquid contents of their beakers and the rinsings from procedure step 11 into a large, labeled bucket. Do not allow the bucket to remain unattended where students are working. When the investigation is complete, neutralize the acidic water by adding small amounts of agricultural lime while stirring.

8. Fill the beakers labeled *Steel* with 100 mL of tap water. Use steel wool to rub off any plastic coating or corrosion on 8 nails. Mass the nails two at a time and record their masses in the data table. Place each pair of nails in the appropriate beaker.

9. Do not add anything to Beaker 1. Add 10 drops of sulfuric acid to Beaker 2, 5 mL (100 drops) of sulfuric acid to Beaker 3, and 50 mL of sulfuric acid to Beaker 4. Allow the beakers to stand undisturbed.

10. After four days, obtain all your samples.

Put on your safety goggles, a lab apron, and plastic gloves. Use tongs to gently lift the plants from the soil in each beaker, rinse them, and measure their lengths. In the *After* columns of the data table, record the length of the longest plant from each beaker.

11. Use tongs to lift the concrete pieces and the pairs of steel nails from their beakers. Rinse the concrete pieces and use a scrubbing brush to gently rub off any flakes of concrete. Determine the mass of each concrete piece. Use the brush to polish off any corrosion on the nails and determine the mass of each pair of nails. Record the masses on the data table.

Data Table

	Beaker 1 Tap Water		Beaker 2 Tap Water + 10 Drops Acid		Beaker 3 Tap Water + 100 Drops Acid		Beaker 4 Acid	
	Before	After	Before	After	Before	After	Before	After
Plants, length (cm)								
Concrete, mass (g)								
Steel, mass (g)								

Figure 27.1

Analysis and Conclusions

The Analysis and Conclusions questions require students to think through their experimental results, to summarize their results, and to draw conclusions.

1. Write a paragraph summarizing what happened when you watered plants with increasing concentrations of acid. Describe the appearance of the plant roots and leaves. What conclusions did you draw?

Students should describe the plants as being increasingly affected as the acid concentration was increased. Those plants in Beaker 1 will have grown the most. Those in Beaker 4 will have grown the least. Some plants in Beakers 3 and 4 may have died. Roots may be brown, but leaves will not have been affected. Students should conclude that the greater the concentration of acid, the more damage is done to plants.

2. Write a summary of the results you obtained when you exposed concrete and steel to different concentrations of acid. Describe the appearance of the two materials as the amount of acid increased.

Corrosion of steel nails increased with higher concentrations of acid. The masses of the concrete pieces decreased.

3. Explain why your conclusions in question 2 are important, particularly in urban areas where air pollution is high.

Urban areas have high concentrations of pollutants resulting in concentrated acid rain. Structures made of concrete and steel are adversely affected.

NAME ___

CLASS ___ DATE ___

CHAPTER

27B

LAB INVESTIGATION

Cloud Droplets, Light, and Rainbows

Most clouds form in rising air. As air rises, it moves to regions of lower pressure. The air expands and cools, and its relative humidity increases. When the relative humidity becomes 100 percent, water vapor begins to condense on small particles in the air called condensation nuclei. The result is water droplets.

Sunlight is actually seven colors of light combined. Each color has a different wavelength. When light rays pass from the air into a glass prism or into a drop of water, the rays are bent, or refracted. Short-wavelength light (violet) is bent more than longer wavelength light (red). As a result, refraction and reflection of sunlight by many water droplets in the air can separate the colors and produce a rainbow.

Lab Skills and Objectives

- To **observe** the formation of cloud droplets
- To **observe** two different effects of the refraction of light by water
- To **observe** how light is separated into its constituent colors by a prism
- To **demonstrate** how sunlight is refracted by cloud droplets to produce rainbows

Materials

- safety goggles
- shallow glass bowl
- large glass jar with a relatively wide mouth and a cap, such as a 2-L fruit-juice jar
- 250-mL flask with a round bottom and stopper
- glass prism
- small balloon
- pencil with sharp point
- flashlight with a narrow beam
- slide projector
- masking tape
- white cardboard sheet for a screen
- scissors
- wooden matches

Procedure

Part A Formation of Cloud Droplets

1. **Put on your safety glasses. Wear them throughout parts A, B, C and D. CAUTION: Scissors are sharp. Handle them with care.** With the scissors, cut the rolled end off a balloon.

2. Fill the glass jar with water to a level of about 2 cm. Replace the cap. Shake the jar well so the air inside will become as moist as possible.

Enough smoke has collected when you can actually see it inside the jar.

3. Unscrew the cap and light a match. Let the match burn until a steady flame develops. Blow it out and immediately hold it down into the jar so that the smoke will stay inside. Wait a few seconds until you have trapped some smoke in the jar and then remove the match or drop it into the water. Have a classmate hold the jar while you quickly spread the balloon over the mouth of the jar. Work it down over the glass threads as far as you can. Don't tighten it to the point where it becomes flat, since you need a section of the balloon to hold onto.

4. Grasp the neck of the jar with one hand, keeping your thumb and forefinger tight around the threads of the opening. This will steady the jar and keep the balloon on tight. Grab the top of the balloon with your other thumb and forefinger. Pull sharply up on the balloon. You will see a cloud form as the air inside the jar fills with tiny droplets of water. Release the balloon and observe what happens. Pull the balloon up again and observe the effect.

Part B Refraction of Light by Water

5. Now begin your study of light. Fill the shallow glass bowl with water nearly to the top. Hold a freshly sharpened pencil, point down, above the water in the middle of the bowl. Lean down so your head is just above the water level (Figure 27.1). Lower the pencil slowly into the water.

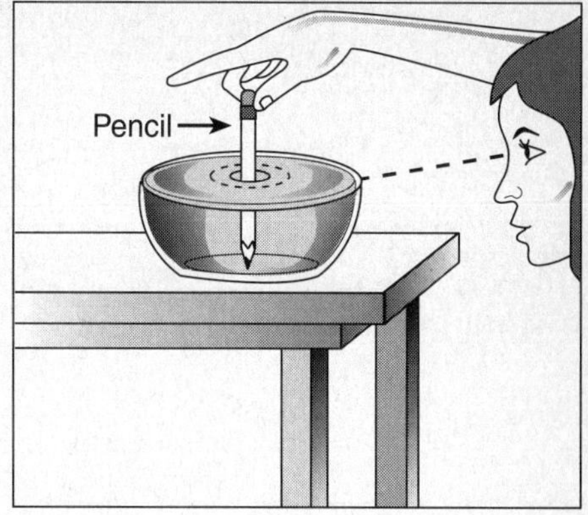

Figure 27.1

6. What appears to happen to the pencil point? In Figure 27.2, draw the end of the pencil as it appears in air and as it appears in water.

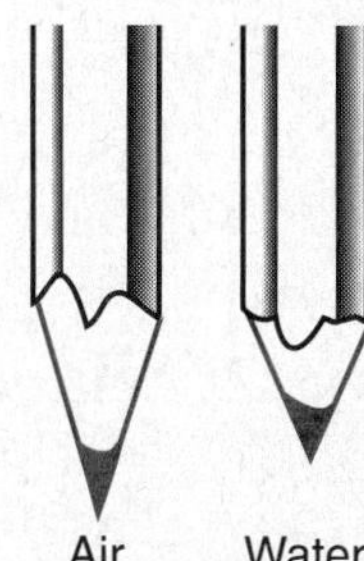

Figure 27.2

Part C Refraction of Light by a Prisms

7. Cover the end of the flashlight with masking tape so that there is a slit only about 1 mm wide for the light to go through.

List the seven colors of the spectrum for students.

8. Stand the prism on end. Secure the cardboard screen about 15 cm behind the prism. Darken the room as much as possible. Hold the flashlight about 15 cm in front of the prism, with the slit positioned vertically. Shine the light through the prism and onto the screen. In order to get the light to reach the screen, you may need to move the light from side to side and change the position of the prism. You should see a narrow band of colors on the screen.

9. In the vertical bands in Figure 27.3, record the colors in the order in which they appear.

Figure 27.3

Part D Cloud Droplets and Rainbows

10. Use the round-bottom flask to represent many raindrops and the projector to represent the sun. Fill the flask with water and stopper it. Set the projector up in such a way that it is tilted downward, as in Figure 27.4.

Connect projector to circuit with ground-fault interrupter.

11. Darken the room as much as possible and turn on the projector. With one person holding the flask and another holding the screen, position the flask and screen as shown in Figure 27.4. Use the path of the light rays in the figure as a guide. Move the flask and screen around until you can see one or two curved spectra.

12. In Figure 27.5, record the colors in the order in which they appear on the screen.

Set the projector at the edge of a table. Tilt the projector by placing a book under the back legs. Hold the flask and screen below the edge of the table. Plug the projector into a grounded outlet.

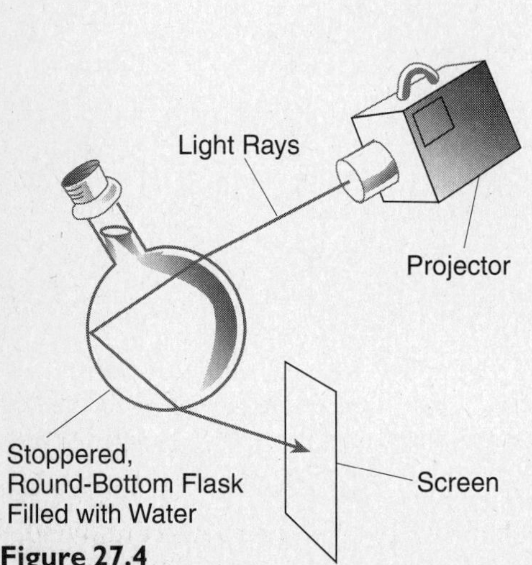

Figure 27.4

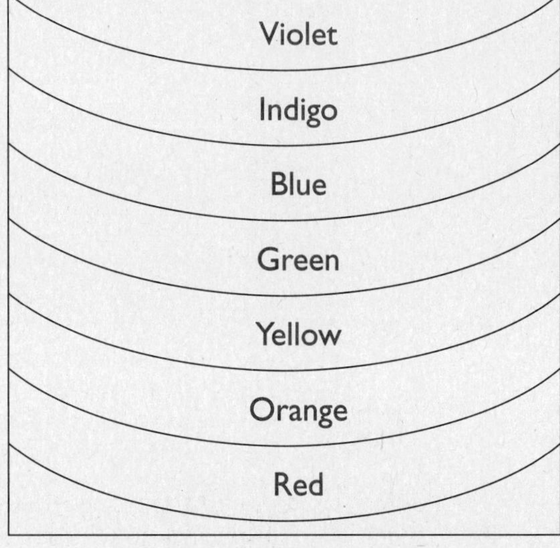

Figure 27.5

Analysis and Conclusions

1. Why did the cloud form when you pulled up on the balloon?

The air inside the jar expanded, the pressure dropped, and the temperature cooled to the dew point.

2. What happened inside the jar when you let go of the balloon?

The air contracted, the temperature rose above the dew point because the pressure rose, and the cloud disappeared.

3. What caused the pencil to look different in water?

The light rays were refracted.

4. Consider the beam of white light as a straight line going from the flashlight through the prism to the screen. Which color on the screen occurs farthest from this straight-line position? In other words, which color is refracted the most?

Violet is refracted the most.

5. Which color is on the inside of the curved spectrum? Which color is on the outside?

Violet is on the inside; red is on the outside.

6. Which color is refracted the most? Which is refracted the least?

Violet is refracted the most; red is refracted the least.

7. Remember that the flask represents many raindrops and the projector represents the sun. The screen represents the position on Earth from which you can see a rainbow. In relation to your position, where must the sun be and where must the raindrops be in order for you to see a rainbow?

The sun must be behind you and the raindrops must be in front of you.

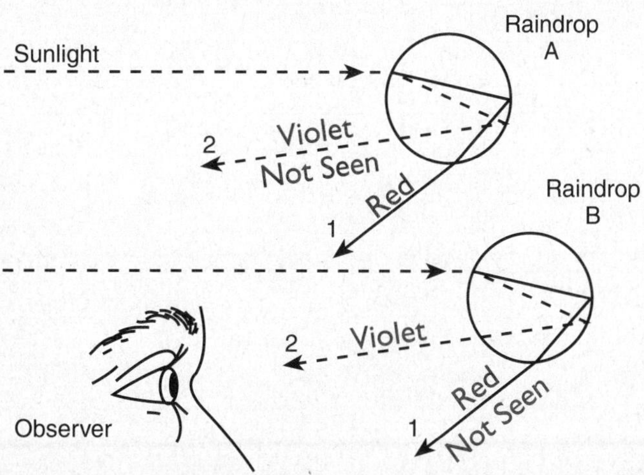

Figure 27.6

Sunlight is refracted upon entering each spherical raindrop. It is then reflected inside one or more times and refracted a second time as it leaves the raindrop. Although each raindrop separates a spectrum of colors, each color actually reaches our eyes from different raindrops.

8. Figure 27.6 illustrates the path taken by sunlight before it reaches our eyes as a rainbow. Raindrop A is high above the ground and raindrop B is closer to the ground. Light rays 1 and 2 are the two colors at either end of the spectrum. What color is ray 1? red Ray 2? violet Which of the two colors from raindrop A will reach the observer? red Why will the observer not see the other color from raindrop A? The violet ray is refracted over the observer's head. Which of the two colors from raindrop B will reach the observer? violet Why will the observer not see the other color from raindrop B? The red ray is refracted to the ground. To the observer, which color will appear at the top of the rainbow? red

Other interesting optical effects can be seen when light passes through clouds of water droplets instead of being reflected or refracted. Light from the sun or moon that passes through a cloud or through mist is diffracted. That is, light rays are bent around individual droplets. Diffraction produces a corona, or ring of colored light, around the image of the sun or moon. On a foggy night, coronas can be seen around streetlights.

CHAPTER

28A

NAME ______

CLASS ______ DATE ______

Prevailing Winds

What controls the weather in your area? In some locales, nearby oceans or mountains affect the local winds that bring in the weather. Local winds in North America include the warm and dry chinooks and Santa Anas of the Rocky Mountains, the cold northerlies of the southern United States, and the wet monsoons of the southwestern United States. Local winds form from prevailing world winds that are changed as they encounter local topography. Prevailing winds are more extensive than local winds. While prevailing winds originate from differences in pressure, their global patterns are further influenced by such factors as the Coriolis effect and the presence of continents. In this activity, you will analyze the patterns of prevailing world winds to determine how these patterns influence global weather patterns.

Map Skills and Objectives

- To **interpret** global wind patterns from the Prevailing World Winds map
- To **evaluate** the relationship between prevailing winds and ocean currents

Materials

- Prevailing World Winds map, Appendix B, page 659 of your text
- Surface Ocean Currents map, Appendix B, page 658 of your text

Procedure

1. Study the Prevailing World Winds map on page 659 of your text and answer Analysis and Conclusions questions 1–9.

2. Compare the Prevailing World Winds map with the Surface Ocean Currents map on page 658 of your text. Answer Analysis and Conclusions question 10.

Analysis and Conclusions

1. During what season in the Northern Hemisphere do the wind patterns and locations shown on the Prevailing World Winds map prevail?

summer

2. List the prevailing winds that are found in the following locations:

(a) between the North Pole and 60° N latitude polar easterlies

(b) between the Equator and 30° N latitude

northeast trades; southwest monsoons

(c) between 30° N latitude and 60° N latitude southwesterlies

(d) between the South Pole and 60° S latitude polar easterlies

3. Winds blow from regions of high pressure to regions of low pressure. With this fact in mind, identify each of the regions below as being a high-pressure region or a low-pressure region:

(a) South Pole high pressure

(b) horse latitudes high pressure

(c) equator low pressure

(d) North Pole high pressure

(e) 60° S latitude low pressure

4. Use information from the map to explain why the doldrums is also known as the intertropical convergence zone. (You may also need a dictionary.)

The doldrums is a tropical (equatorial) region in which the northeast trades and the southeast trades come together, or converge.

5. Explain why the horse latitudes are known as divergence zones.

At the horse latitudes, prevailing winds move apart, or diverge. The trades move toward the equator, and the westerlies move toward the Poles.

6. Explain how the curved arrow directions of the prevailing winds show the influence of the Coriolis effect. Use the southwesterlies and northwesterlies as examples.

In the Northern Hemisphere, prevailing winds are turned to the right of their "natural" direction of flow. The southwesterlies begin by moving north, are deflected east, and then become southwest winds. In the Southern Hemisphere, prevailing winds are turned to the left of their "natural" direction of flow. The northwesterlies begin by moving south, are deflected east, and then become northwest winds.

7. Explain why the trade winds and the westerlies show a much more continuous pattern across the Southern Hemisphere than they do across the Northern Hemisphere.

There is much less landmass to interfere with wind patterns in the Southern Hemisphere.

8. Which prevailing winds are changed to southwest monsoons by the effect of the Indian subcontinent? Explain how the winds are affected in July.

The northeast trades; they are turned around so that they blow from the southwest. The large landmass heats up in summer, creating a large, low-pressure area toward which the winds blow.

9. If the Prevailing World Winds map was for December instead of July, in what ways would you expect the map to appear different near the equator? Over the Indian subcontinent?

The zone where the northeasterlies and southeasterlies converge (ITCZ) would move south over the oceans. Over India, the winds would reverse direction and move out from the landmass.

10. Compare the Prevailing World Winds map and the Surface Ocean Currents map. Name the prevailing winds that influence the following ocean currents:

(a) South Equatorial — southeast trades

(b) North Pacific — southwesterlies

(c) Benguela Current — southeast trades

(d) Gulf Stream — southwesterlies

(e) North Atlantic — southwesterlies

(f) West Wind Drift — northwesterlies

NAME ______________________

CLASS ______________ DATE ______________

CHAPTER 28B

LAB INVESTIGATION

The Foucault Pendulum and the Coriolis Effect

Foucault suspended his pendulum beneath the dome of the Pantheon, a large public building.

In Paris in 1851, Jean Foucault performed the first experiment that proved Earth rotates on its axis. He hung a heavy iron ball on a wire attached to a 61-meter-high ceiling. The ball hung just above the floor, and he set it swinging in a geographic north-south direction. The laws of physics tell us that a swinging pendulum will not change direction, yet Foucault noticed that his pendulum appeared to change direction steadily with time. Its path rotated clockwise at a rate of 11° per hour. After eight hours, the pendulum was swinging along an east-west line. This apparent change in position of the pendulum was in fact caused by the rotation of Earth beneath the pendulum.

The rotation of Earth, demonstrated by Jean Foucault, also influences the paths of large-scale winds and ocean currents. Rotation causes their paths to curve, rather than move along straight lines. This influence on the currents is called the Coriolis effect.

Lab Skills and Objectives

- To **demonstrate** Foucault's experiment concerning Earth's rotation
- To **demonstrate** how Earth's rotation produces the Coriolis effect

Materials

- white cardboard disk with hole in the center
- 5 large washers
- string or monofilament line, about 60 cm
- large paper clip
- colored chalk
- pencil
- ring stand

Make the cardboard disks beforehand. Construct each disk so that the radius is slightly less than the length of the base of a ring stand. The base of the ring stand will then provide a flat surface for rotating and writing on the disk in Part B. Cut a hole about the size of the diameter of the ring stand rod in the center of each disk.

Procedure

Part A The Foucault Pendulum

Set up a Foucault pendulum for the students to observe periodically during the class. Use a heavy bob on a wire and make the wire as long as possible.

1. Make a model of Jean Foucault's pendulum with the above materials. Use a cardboard disk to represent the Northern Hemisphere. Assume you are looking down on Earth from above the North Pole. Therefore, the center of the disk represents the North Pole and the outer edge represents the equator. With chalk, label the North Pole and the equator on the disk. Make a chalk mark a little less than halfway from the center toward the edge of the disk. The mark represents the position of Paris in the Northern Hemisphere. Label Paris and draw a line on the disk from Paris to the North Pole.

2. Make a pendulum by tying a paper clip to one end of the string and sliding five washers onto the string. Tie the free end of the string to the pencil, as shown in Figure 28.1. Hold the pencil so that the pendulum hangs about 5 cm above the floor.

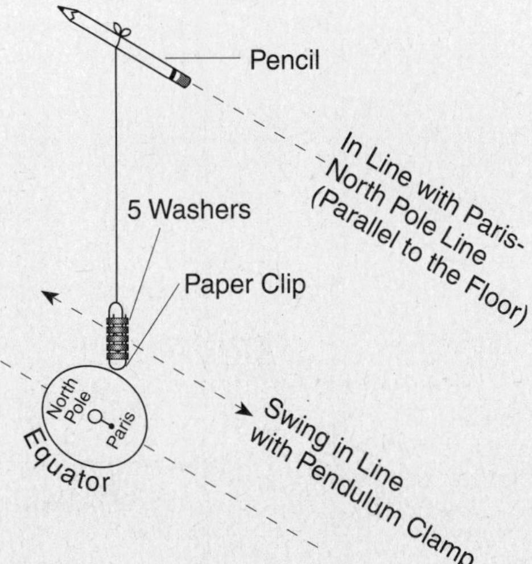

Figure 28.1

3. Place the disk on the floor, with Paris directly below the pendulum. Orient the disk so that the pencil is in line with your Paris-North Pole line (Figure 28.1). Making sure you don't move the pencil, swing the pendulum along that line and you have a model of how Foucault started his experiment. Note the direction in which the pendulum is swinging above Paris. Draw a line through Paris on the disk in Figure 28.2A to show the direction of the pendulum swing.

4. To represent Earth's rotation on its axis, rotate Paris 45° counterclockwise around the North Pole. Then shift the disk slightly to the left (Figure 28.2B), so that the pendulum continues to hang directly above Paris. Swing the pendulum in line with the pencil as you did in procedure step 3. (Earth has rotated, but the pendulum swing has not changed.) Draw a line through Paris on the disk in Figure 28.2B to show the direction of the pendulum swing over Paris.

5. Repeat procedure step 4, rotating the disk a second 45°. Draw a line through Paris in Figure 28.2C to show the direction of pendulum swing over Paris.

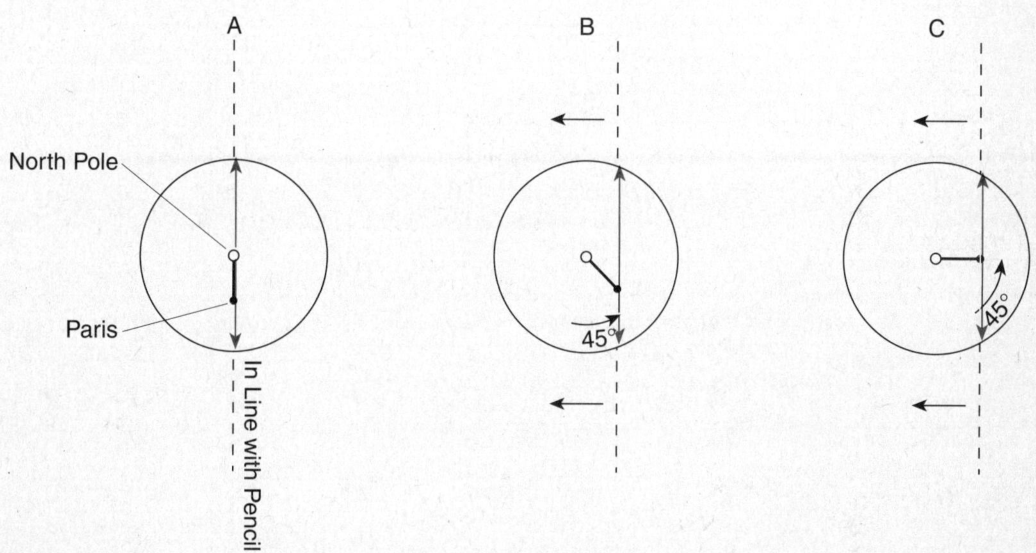

Figure 28.2

Part B The Coriolis Effect

6. Reuse the cardboard disk from Part A to demonstrate the Coriolis effect. Work in pairs. Turn the cardboard disk over to the clean side. Slide it over the ring stand and down to the base.

Students may have to practice rotating and drawing together before they can produce a clear chalk line. Drawing along a straight line will prove very difficult.

7. Assume you are looking down on the Northern Hemisphere, represented by the cardboard disk, from a point above the North Pole. When viewed from this point, Earth appears to rotate counterclockwise. Have one person steady the ring stand and rotate the disk slowly counterclockwise. At the same time, the second person should draw the chalk across the disk straight toward them from the center hole. Be sure to keep moving your hand along a straight line as the disk turns. The chalk line represents an air or water current moving southward from the North Pole. Draw an arrow inside circle A of Figure 28.3 to show the path of the chalk line. Label the arrow in terms of the direction the compass is pointing.

8. Repeat procedure step 7, this time moving the chalk in the opposite direction, from the edge of the disk toward the center. The chalk line represents an air or water current moving northward from the equator. Draw and label the direction of the current in circle B.

Figure 28.3

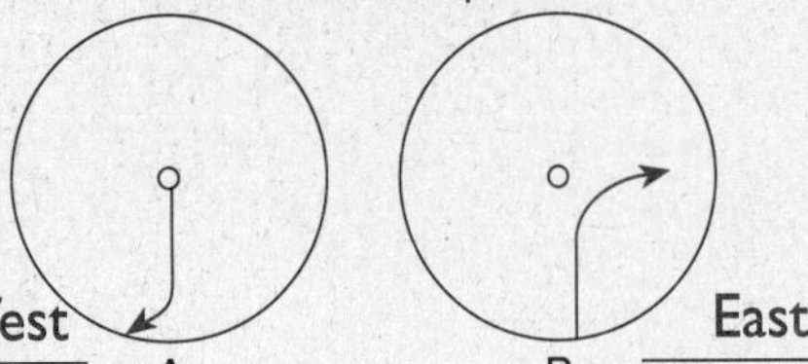

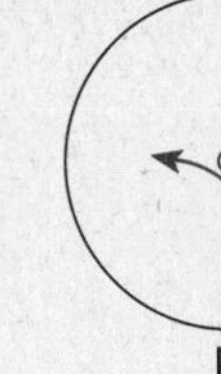

9. Assume you are looking down on the Southern Hemisphere from a point above the South Pole. From this point, the Southern Hemisphere appears to rotate clockwise. Move the disk clockwise to show this rotation. Repeat procedure steps 7 and 8. Draw and label the directions of the chalk lines in circles C and D.

Once they have practiced on the cardboard disks, you can have students try the activity on a globe.

Analysis and Conclusions

1. Look at the line you drew in Figure 28.2A. From the point of view of the people in Paris, in which directions did the pendulum swing?

north and south

2. Compare the first line with the one you drew in Figure 28.2B. In Paris, in which directions did the pendulum swing?

northeast and southwest

3. Look at the line you drew in Figure 28.2C. In which directions did the pendulum swing?

east and west

4. In Foucault's original experiment, how much time elapsed between positions A and B (Figure 28.2)?

4 h

Between positions A and C?

8 h

You might ask students to determine how the pendulum would work at the North Pole and at the equator. (At the North Pole, the pendulum will always swing south (the only direction from the North Pole); at the equator, the pendulum will always swing north and south.)

5. In what direction did the air or water current in circle A begin to move? In what direction did it turn?

The current started south and turned west.

6. In what direction did the air or water current in circle B begin to move? In what direction did it turn?

The current started north and turned east.

7. Compare the movements of the water or air currents in the Southern Hemisphere with those of the Northern Hemisphere.

Currents that start out moving in the same direction turn in opposite directions in the two hemispheres.

8. How is the Coriolis effect illustrated by the map of the ocean currents on page 658 of Appendix B?

The ocean currents tend to move in the directions shown by this activity.

CHAPTER

29

Depending upon your students' knowledge of US geography, this activity can require more than one day of class or lab time.

NAME ____________________

CLASS ____________ DATE ____________

MAP ACTIVITY

Weather Patterns

Air masses are large portions of the troposphere that have the same weather throughout. By studying a weather map, you can locate the boundaries of an air mass and find out about its properties. In this lab, you will construct a weather map using pressure, temperature and rainfall.

Map Skills and Objectives

- To **construct** maps of weather variables
- To **interpret** data on weather maps based on the movement of air masses

Materials

- 2 copies of Figure 29.1
- colored pencils
- lead pencil

Procedure

1. In the space in the lower left corner of a copy of Figure 29.1,write *Air Pressure and Temperature.* Note that isotherms have already been drawn on the map. Study the temperature data that was used to plot the isotherms (Figure 29.2). Locate isotherms for 10, 20, 30, 40, 50, 60, and 70 degrees.

City circles need to be filled in as dark as possible to stand out under the final shading.

2. Using Figure 29.2, identify cities with air pressures in the ranges given below. With a colored pencil, mark cities in Range 1 (992.1–996.0 mb) on Figure 29.2. With a different colored pencil, mark each of the cities in Range 2 on Figure 29.2. In this way, locate all the cities in Ranges 3–7 using a different colored pencil for each range.

Range 1: 992.1– 996.0
Range 2: 996.1–1000.0
Range 3: 1000.1–1004.0
Range 4: 1004.1–1008.0
Range 5: 1008.1–1012.0
Range 6: 1012.1–1016.0
Range 7: 1016.1–1020.0

3. Use the different colors on your map to help you draw lines (isobars) for 996, 1000, 1004, 1008, 1012, and 1016 millibars.

4. Label each isobar.

5. Using the same color as the city circles, lightly shade in each belt between the isobars.

6. On a second copy of Figure 29.1, write *Rainfall and Temperature* in the lower left corner.

7. Using any color, fill in the circle on the map for each city with an R (for rain) in the last column of Figure 29.2.

8. Carefully draw a single smooth line that encloses all of the circles you have colored. Avoid including cities without rain inside your line.

9. Lightly shade the area inside your line.

Analysis and Conclusions

1. Examine the temperature data for cities around the country and the isotherms on the map. Identify the location of three air masses that cover the United States. Determine whether each air mass is warm or cold.

A large, bitter cold air mass is centered on the Canadian border over Montana.

A warm air mass is centered in the southeast. A second cold air mass is centered over the northeast (New England).

 NAME ______________ CLASS ______________ DATE ______________

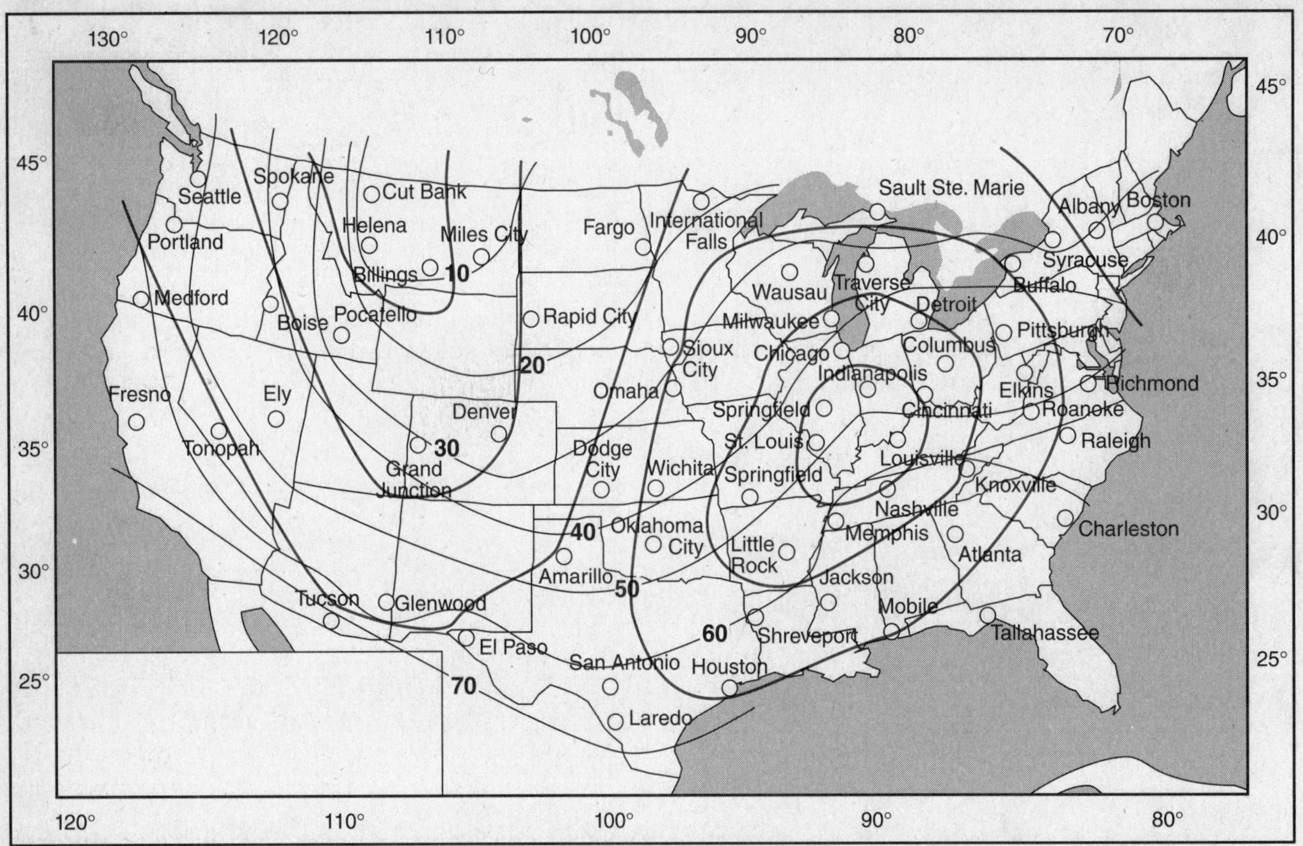

Figure 29.1

2. The boundary between two air masses is called a front. What feature of both maps tells you the directions in which two air masses are moving? Give the direction of each.

The cold front and warm front symbols indicate the direction of the front. A warm front is moving NE. A cold front is moving SE.

3. Explain what happens along cold fronts and along warm fronts such as those seen on your maps. Give evidence from your map that supports your explanation.

Fronts frequently bring precipitation. It is raining ahead of the warm front in Columbus, Cincinnati, and Pittsburgh and in Little Rock, Memphis, and Shrevesport.

4. Cut Bank and Grand Junction are 1080 kilometers from each other and lie on a line perpendicular to the isobar between them. Calculate the pressure gradient between Cut Bank and Grand Junction. The pressure gradient is the difference between the pressures in the two cities divided by the distance between the two cities.

$$\frac{1016.3 \text{ mb} - 1013.2 \text{ mb}}{1080 \text{ km}} = 0.003 \text{ mb/km}$$

5. Indianapolis and Richmond are 790 kilometers apart. Calculate the pressure gradient between Indianapolis and Richmond.

$$\frac{1006.1 \text{ mb} - 995.1 \text{ mb}}{790 \text{ km}} = 0.014 \text{ mb/km}$$

6. The strength of the winds depends upon the local pressure gradient. The stronger the pressure gradient (large number) the stronger the winds. Which pair of cities, Cut Bank and Grand Junction or Indianapolis and Richmond, were having the stronger winds?

Indianapolis and Richmond; The pressure gradient between them is greater than that between Cut Bank and Grand Junction.

City	Temperature (°F)*	Pressure (mb)*	Rain	City	Temperature (°F)*	Pressure (mb)*	Rain
Albany, NY	31	1008.5		Medford, OR	61	1007.9	
Amarillo, TX	41	1007.8		Memphis, TN	61	998.5	R
Atlanta, GA	63	1002.6		Miles City, MT	9	1013.9	
Billings, MT	8	1016.5		Milwaukee, WI	39	998.5	
Boise, ID	42	1011.1		Mobile, AL	68	1003.9	
Boston, MA	35	1008.8		Nashville, TN	62	997.4	
Buffalo, NY	35	1004.5		Oklahoma City, OK	43	1003.1	
Charleston, SC	65	1006.2		Omaha, NE	31	1003.5	
Chicago, IL	43	997.1		Pittsburgh, PA	44	1002.0	R
Cincinnati, OH	49	997.3	R	Pocatello, ID	29	1013.5	
Columbus, OH	45	998.3	R	Portland, OR	58	1008.1	
Cut Bank, MT	8	1016.3		Raleigh, NC	55	1005.1	R
Denver, CO	25	1012.2		Rapid City, SD	17	1011.7	
Detroit, MI	43	1000.1		Richmond, VA	53	1006.1	R
Dodge City, KS	33	1006.5		Roanoke, VA	52	1003.5	R
Elkins, WV	48	1003.1	R	San Antonio, TX	61	1004.8	R
El Paso, TX	62	1007.9		Sault Ste Marie, MI	28	1004.1	
Ely, NV	46	1009.5		Seattle, WA	53	1009.1	
Fargo, ND	17	1008.2		Shreveport, LA	66	1001.8	R
Fresno, CA	65	1007.3		Sioux City, IA	23	1004.2	
Glenwood, KS	57	1008.8		Spokane, WA	37	1012.8	
Grand Junction, CO	31	1013.2		Springfield, IL	45	994.9	R
Helena, MT	9	1016.8		Springfield, MO	44	999.5	
Houston, TX	68	1003.9		St. Louis, MO	46	995.0	R
Indianapolis, IN	48	995.1	R	Syracuse, NY	28	1006.8	
International Falls, MN	16	1007.2		Tallahassee, FL	65	1006.1	
Jackson, MS	67	1001.5		Tonapah, NV	54	1007.8	
Knoxville, TN	61	1000.5		Traverse City, MI	37	1001.5	
Laredo, TX	64	1005.2	R	Tucson, AZ	71	1007.5	
Little Rock, AR	51	999.9	R	Wausau, WI	32	1001.5	
Louisville, KY	58	995.5	R	Wichita, KS	35	1003.7	

Figure 29.2 *The data are presented in units students are most likely to hear in the media.

CHAPTER 30

NAME ____________________

CLASS ____________ DATE ____________

Hurricane Andrew

Like other Atlantic hurricanes, Hurricane Andrew, which moved across southern Florida and into south-central Lousiana in August of 1992, started as a low-pressure system in the tropics off the west coast of Africa. Warm water and moisture-laden air supplied the energy for it to strengthen into an ordinary and average tropical storm. Surface winds began to move the storm westward. Although all tropical storms form and develop in this way, only a few intensify into hurricanes. Most encounter upper air winds moving in the opposite direction from the surface winds. As a result, these storms weaken and soon die out. Tropical storm Andrew, on the other hand, encountered upper air winds moving in the same direction as the surface winds. These reinforcing winds caused Andrew to quickly strengthen into an unusually powerful hurricane. In fact, Andrew may well prove to be one of the most intense Atlantic hurricanes of the twentieth century.

Lab Skills and Objectives

- To **graph** and **interpret** weather data
- To **correlate** the track of a hurricane with weather data

Materials

- colored pencils (minimum of four different colors needed)
- ruler
- straightedge

Times are expressed in Universal time, which precedes EDT by four hours.

A knot is a nautical mile per hour. One nautical mile per hour is equivalent to 1.15 statute (land) miles per hour.

Hurricane Data

Date	Time (hours–24 hr clock)	Air Pressure (millibars)	Wind Speed (knots)
Aug 21	0:00	1014	45
	6:00	1010	45
	12:00	1007	50
	18:00	1004	50
Aug 22	0:00	1000	55
	6:00	994	60
	12:00	981	70
	18:00	969	80
Aug 23	0:00	961	90
	6:00	947	105
	12:00	933	120
	18:00	922	135
Aug 24	0:00	930	125
	6:00	937	120
	9:00	922	125
	12:00	951	110
	18:00	947	115

Hurricane Data

Date	Time (hours–24 hr clock)	Air Pressure (millibars)	Wind Speed (knots)
Aug 25	0:00	943	115
	6:00	948	115
	12:00	946	115
	18:00	941	120
Aug 26	0:00	937	120
	6:00	955	115
	12:00	973	80
	18:00	991	50
Aug 27	0:00	995	35

Figure 30.1

 NAME ______________ CLASS ______________ DATE ______________

Procedure

1. Use the grid in Figure 30.2 to plot with a colored pencil the wind speed versus time from the data table in Figure 30.1. Connect the points using a straightedge and label your graph.

2. Use a different colored pencil to plot air pressure versus time. Note that air pressure is along the right vertical axis of the grid. Connect the points and label the graph.

3. Use the track of Hurricane Andrew in Figure 30.3 to determine the time of landfalls, that is, the instances when Hurricane Andrew hit land. For Andrew, there were two mainland landfalls, one in Florida and one in Louisiana. Draw vertical lines on your graph with a third colored pencil corresponding to the hour of each landfall.

4. In a fourth color, draw a vertical line to indicate when Hurricane Andrew moved off the western coast of Florida into the Gulf of Mexico.

5. Mark on the track of Hurricane Andrew in Figure 30.3, the hours of greatest strength, i.e. greatest wind speed and lowest pressure.

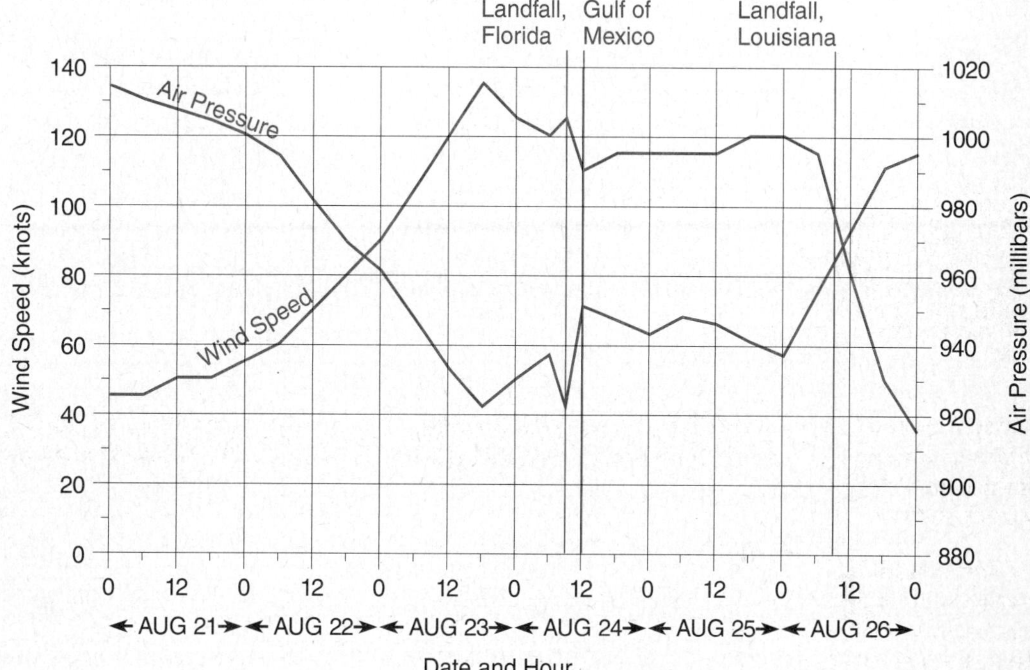

Figure 30.2

Analysis and Conclusions

1. What does your graph show as the general relationship between air pressure and wind speed?

As air pressure decreases, wind speed increases. As air pressure increases, wind speed decreases.

2. What happened to air pressure and wind speed after Hurricane Andrew's landfalls?

Air pressure increased, and wind speed decreased.

3. What happened to air pressure and wind speed after Hurricane Andrew left Florida's west coast and once again moved over water?

Air pressure decreased, and wind speed increased.

4. Explain why air pressure and wind speed are affected by the surface over which a hurricane moves.

A hurricane gets its energy from the heat and the water vapor from the sea surface and from the release of heat by condensing water vapor. When a hurricane moves over land, its energy supply is cut off.

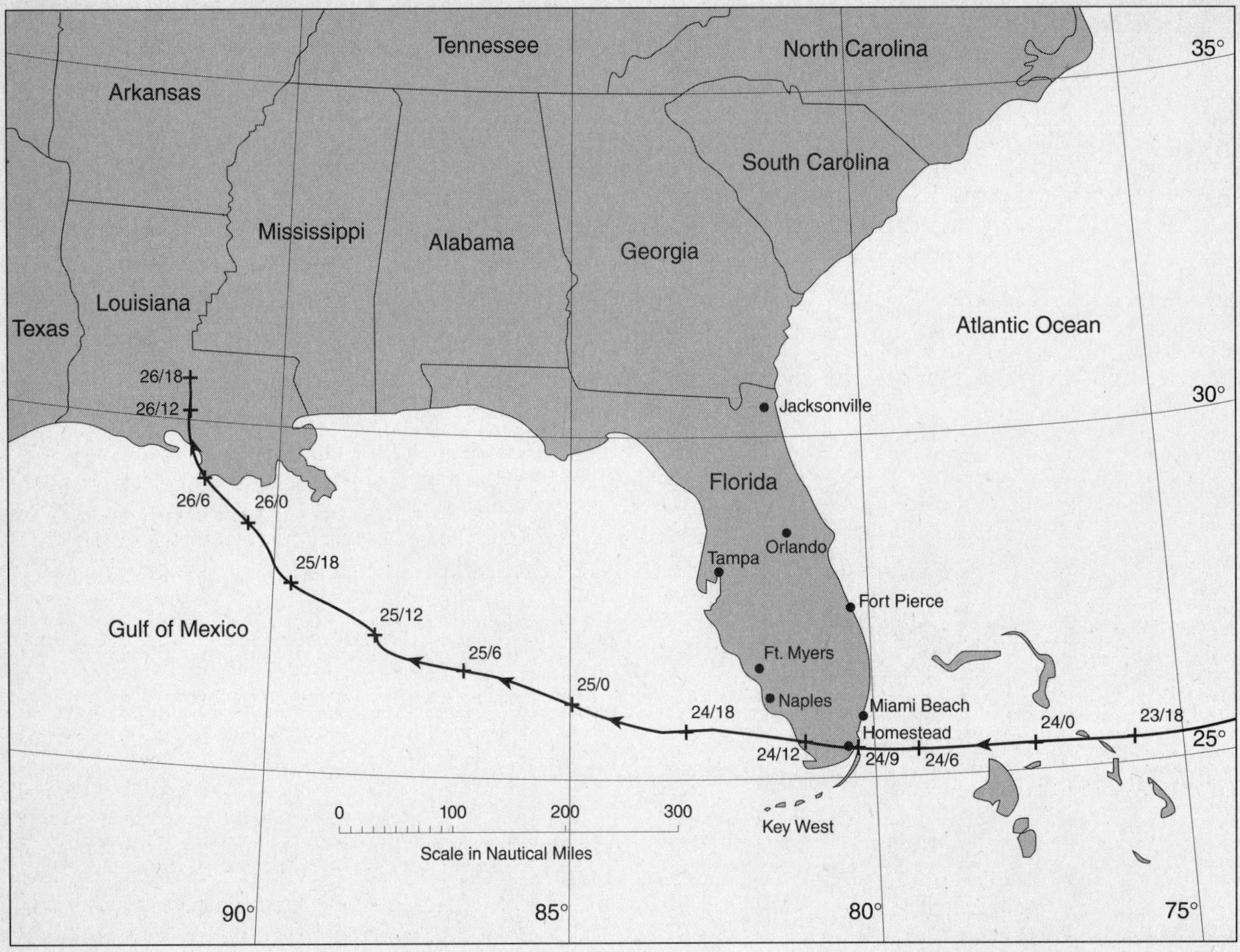

Figure 30.3

5. Of the cities shown on the map in Figure 30.3, Homestead experienced the most damage from Hurricane Andrew. Why?

Homestead was on the hurricane's path.

6. Use the scale on the map and a ruler to estimate the forward speed in knots (nautical miles /hour) of Andrew on August 24 between

(a) 6:00 (24/6) and 9:00 (24/9).

$$\frac{\text{55 nautical miles}}{\text{3 hours}} = \text{18.3 knots}$$

(b) 9:00 (24/9) and 12:00 (24/12).

$$\frac{\text{45 nautical miles}}{\text{3 hours}} = \text{15 knots}$$

7. Based on question 6, how did landfall affect the forward speed of Andrew?

Andrew moved slower over land.

8. A tropical storm officially becomes a hurricane when it attains wind speeds greater than 64 knots. When did Andrew change from a tropical storm to a hurricane? When did it change back to a tropical storm?

Hurricane Andrew changed from a tropical storm to a hurricane on August 22 between 6:00 and 12:00. It changed back to a tropical storm August 26 between 12:00 and 18:00.

NAME ______________________

CLASS ______________ DATE ______________

INQUIRY LAB

Temperatures in a Microclimate

A **microclimate** is a climate in a small, distinct region. The region can be as small as a cubic meter or as large as a major city. Microclimates depend on local climate controls such as altitude, air movement, amount of shade or sunshine, the type of ground surface (since surfaces radiate heat differently), and the distance from a warm or cool surface.

The climate of a small area can influence the selection of construction sites, building materials, and heating or cooling equipment. For example, solar energy analysts need information about temperature variations around a house before they can recommend the most effective kind and placement of solar energy equipment. In this lab, your class will work as a team to record the temperature variations of a microclimate in order to draw isotherm maps. Then you will prepare a plan to determine the optimum location for solar energy equipment at your school.

Lab Skills and Objectives

- To **record** the variations in temperature occurring within the area of a microclimate
- To **record** temperature variations with a small change in elevation
- To **design an experiment** to determine optimum placement of solar energy equipment

Materials

- metric tape measure, at least 5 m long
- approximately 50 m of string
- 36 long nails or wooden stakes
- scissors
- masking tape
- wax marking pencil
- hammer or mallet
- 36 alcohol thermometers

Choose an area outside where there is a boundary between warmer and cooler surfaces. For example, choose an area where shaded and sunlit ground meet (next to the school building) or where grass and asphalt meet (at the edge of the parking lot). Make sure shadows don't move too much within the area while you are making the grid. In the classroom, try orienting the grid square with one side among an outside wall or in the direct sunlight of a window, or with one corner at the doorway.

Procedure

Part A

1. Your teacher will select an area either outdoors or inside your classroom and will select a starting point. With your classmates, you will mark off a block 5 m by 5 m and then divide it into a grid pattern of blocks 1 m by 1 m. If you are outdoors, mark each point in the grid by driving a nail or wooden stake into the ground. Leave at least 3 cm of each nail exposed above the ground and attach a masking-tape label to the nail. If you are indoors, mark each point on the floor with an "X" made of masking tape.

2. Mark the starting point (see Figure 31.1). Use a tape measure to measure 5 m over to the position of the upper right corner point. Mark this point and every 1-m interval between it and the starting point. Label the points A1 through A6 as indicated.

3. Beginning at the starting point, measure down 5 m to the lower left corner point. Mark this point and every 1-m interval between it and the starting point. Label the nails B1 through F1 as indicated. You now have a reference system to identify each point on the grid.

4. Find and mark the lower right corner point (F6 on Figure 31.1) by measuring 5 m over from point F1 and 5 m down from point A6. Mark off the eight remaining points along the outside of the large block.

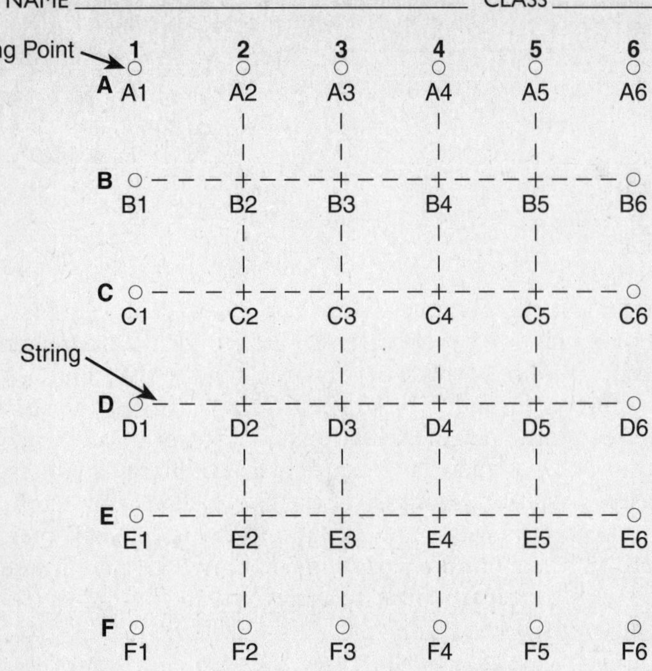

Figure 31.1

5. Cut the string into eight 6-m segments and stretch the strings between the nails as shown in Figure 31.1, so that the strings form a grid pattern of 1-m^2 blocks. Mark the point where the strings intersect and label each point as indicated.

6. Each student should stand with a thermometer at one point on the grid. At your position, hold your thermometer by the top at eye level. Do not handle the bulb of the thermometer. If you are outside, face north and hold the thermometer in your shadow. Wait about 3 min to allow the thermometer to reach air temperature. When your teacher indicates, record air temperature (in degrees Celsius) at the appropriate location on the Eye Level chart in Figure 31.2.

7. Place the thermometer on the ground or floor between your feet. Position the thermometer in your shadow with the bulb pointing north. Wait 3 min. When your teacher indicates, record the temperature in the Ground Level chart in Figure 31.2.

8. Starting with point A1, each student should read off the two temperatures he or she recorded. Fill in the temperatures by the appropriate dots in Figure 31.2.

Students should draw only one isotherm line for a large area of the same temperature. The line should be next to the isotherm for the next lower temperature.

9. Use your temperature data on Figure 31.2 to make two isotherm maps of the area you studied. Remember that isotherms are lines that connect points of equal temperature. Use an isotherm interval of 1° C. With smooth curves, connect points of the same temperature at eye level on Figure 31.2. Do the same for the temperature at ground level. Follow the same guidelines you would use for drawing contour lines on a topographic map. Answer Analysis and Conclusions questions 1–5.

Part B

10. Suppose you were hired to determine the best location for solar energy equipment at your school. On a separate sheet of paper, write the materials you would need, the procedure you would follow, and any data charts you would keep in order to evaluate your school's microclimate. You may wish to review the introduction to this lab to help you get started. Answer Analysis and Conclusions questions 6–9.

Analysis and Conclusions

1. Why did you shield the thermometers from direct sunlight?

In the shade, a thermometer measures true air temperature, but in the sun it measures insolation.

2. Compare the temperatures at ground level and eye level and account for any differences.

Air movement tends to mix air at eye level, causing less temperature variation at that level. At ground level, temperatures tend to vary more because the ground varies in material and therefore in the amount of heat it radiates.

3. Review your isotherms map. How do you account for temperature variations at ground level? At eye level?

Answers will vary and will depend on the individual conditions of shading, surface materials, and air circulation.

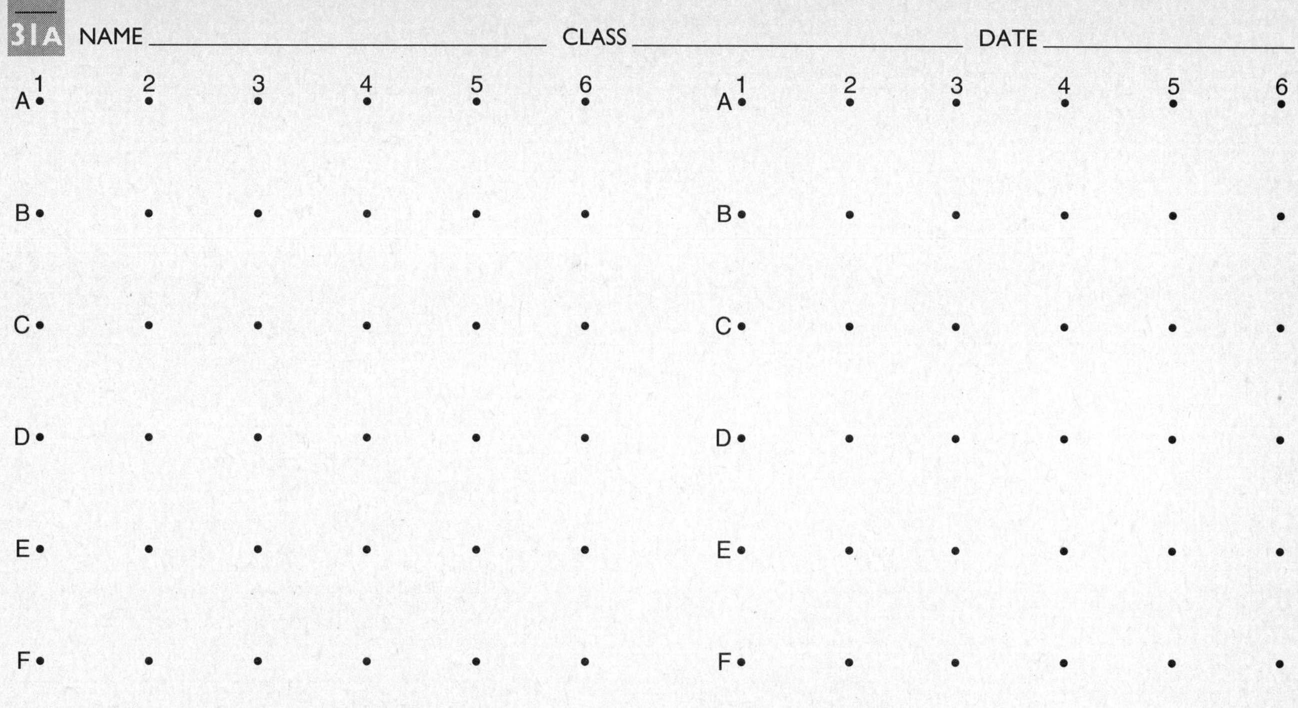

Figure 31.2 Eye Level Ground Level

4. How would air movements through your region affect your temperature values?

In protected areas, wind would mix the air, so there would be less variation in temperature. In open areas, temperature may vary more because warmer or cooler air may blow into these areas.

Sun and shade can cause variations of 10° C or more.

5. Suggest several occurrences in your area that would affect the temperature variation.

A cloud might cover the sun; plants could grow on a bare spot; asphalt may be painted white; the wind could change; and so forth.

6. In your procedure to determine the best location for solar energy equipment, what measurements did you decide should be made?

Answers may include hourly temperature readings at several elevations, the cumulative number of hours of sunlight at each location throughout the day and throughout the year, wind speed measurements, and distance from warm or cool surfaces.

7. Did your procedure include gathering data from all locations around the school? If not, explain.

Students may have eliminated areas if they were known to be north facing, or shaded by trees or tall buildings all year.

8. How will wind affect the amount of energy absorbed by solar energy equipment?

Absorption should not be affected, but heat loss from storage units may be increased.

9. In order to complete your study, how much time do you estimate you would need?

A realistic estimate is one full year to account for seasonal variations in duration of sunlight around the school.

CHAPTER 31B

NAME ____________________

CLASS ____________ DATE ____________

ENVIRONMENTAL LAB

Carbon Dioxide and Global Warming

Is the threat of global warming myth or fact? Many observers look alarmingly to the 1980's—a decade of unprecedented warmth—to confirm their fears that global warming is real. Yet a short-term trend such as this can mean very little. What about global temperatures over the long term? As it turns out, long-term studies verify that global temperatures have indeed been increasing, although sporadically, since the turn of the century.

What's causing global temperatures to rise? Many environmental scientists point to the increasing atmospheric concentrations of greenhouse gases—carbon dioxide (CO_2), water vapor (H_2O), methane (MH_4), nitrous oxide (N_2O), ozone (O_3), and the chlorofluorocarbons (CFC's). A clear, historical link has been established between CO_2 concentrations and global temperature change. By analyzing tiny bubbles of air trapped in ice core samples, scientists have learned that, in the past, when atmospheric CO_2 concentrations increased, so did global temperatures. Periods of markedly low CO_2 concentrations correspond to periods of extreme cold, i.e., the ice ages.

In this lab, you will investigate both short-term and long-term trends in concentrations of CO_2 in the atmosphere and identify some of the causes and effects of global warming.

Ozone in the stratosphere shields living organisms from harmful ultraviolet radiation. CFC's are known to deplete stratospheric ozone. When in the troposphere, both ozone and CFC's contribute to the greenhouse effect.

Lab Skills and Objectives

- To **graph** changes in atmospheric CO_2 concentration and to **interpret** the graph
- To **correlate** trends in CO_2 concentrations with future climate change

Materials

- sharp pencil

Procedure

1. The data in Figure 31.1 are CO_2 concentrations in parts per million (ppm) from 1987–1991. Use the data to plot CO_2 concentrations as a function of date on the graph grid provided in Figure 31.2. Draw a smooth curve between your data points.

Updates of carbon dioxide data can be obtained from Carbon Dioxide Information Analysis Center, Oak Ridge National Laboratory, Building 1000, P. O. Box 2008, MS-6335, Oak Ridge, TN 37831-9984

CO_2 Concentrations (ppm)					
Date	1987	1988	1989	1990	1991
Jan	348.2	350.2	352.7	353.7	354.6
Mar	349.6	352.1	353.7	355.6	357.1
May	351.9	354.2	355.7	357.1	359.0
Jul	349.8	352.6	353.8	354.5	356.1
Sep	346.4	348.8	349.8	351.0	352.2
Nov	347.7	350.1	351.3	352.7	

Figure 31.1

Analysis and Conclusions

1. What two patterns of change in CO_2 concentrations are evident from your graph? During which month of each year were the CO_2 concentrations the highest? the lowest?

an increase and a decrease within each year and an overall increase in the peak value each year; highest in May; lowest in September

The variation in CO_2 concentrations throughout the year is an example of cyclic change.

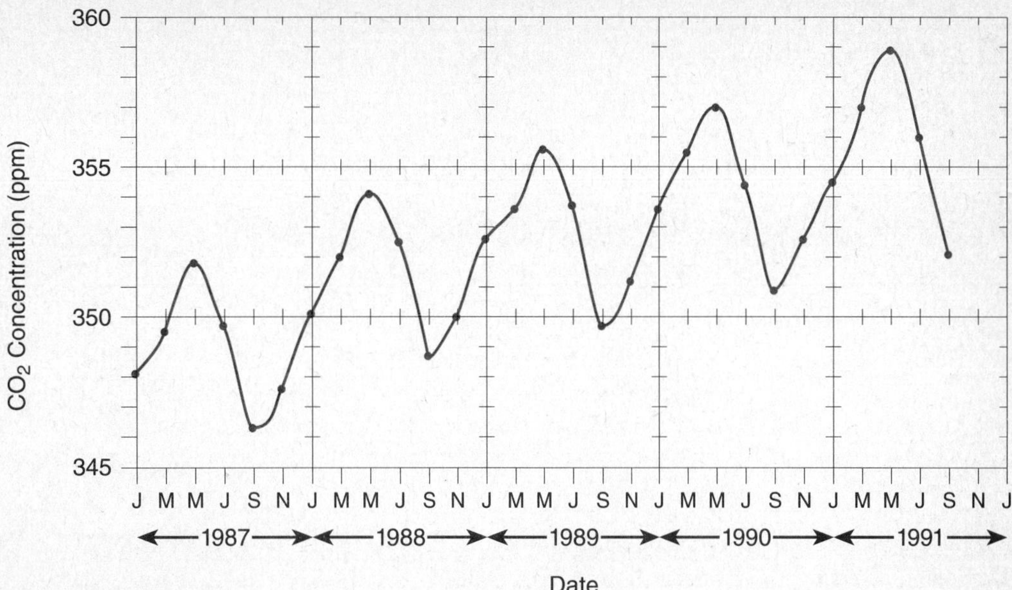

Figure 31.2

2. Based on what you know about the relationship between photosynthesis and CO_2, explain why CO_2 concentrations cycle throughout the year.

Green plants, abundant during the summer, remove CO_2 during the process of photosynthesis. Since green plants are dormant during winter months, the plants cannot remove CO_2 from the atmosphere.

3. Based on what you know about the relationship between the burning of fossil fuels (coal, oil, gasoline) and CO_2, what else accounts for the cyclic nature of CO_2 concentrations throughout the year?

The burning of fossil fuels produces CO_2. Since more fossil fuels are burned during the winter months to heat homes, CO_2 concentrations increase in the winter and decrease in the summer.

4. What effect is the destruction of forests likely to have on atmospheric CO_2 concentrations? Explain your answer.

The concentrations of CO_2 would likely increase. Trees absorb CO_2 during photosynthesis. Fewer trees would mean less absorption and a greater build-up of CO_2 in the atmosphere.

5. What are two ways that the rate of change in atmospheric CO_2 concentration could be reduced?

Plant trees to replace those lost to deforestation; reduce reliance on fossil fuels through conservation and the use of alternative sources of energy.

6. If, as predicted, increased concentrations of CO_2 in the atmosphere lead to global warming, what might happen to the polar ice caps? sea levels? coastal communities?

melt; rise; flooding

CHAPTER 32

NAME ____________________

CLASS __________ DATE __________

INQUIRY LAB

Making a Geologic Time Line

A geologic timetable on page 600 in your text, lists the eras, periods, and epochs into which Earth's history is divided. It is difficult, however, for a geologic timetable to show the relative lengths of the eras and periods. You can draw a geologic time line to help you better understand the duration of geologic events.

Lab Skills and Objectives

- To **compare** and **contrast** the relative lengths of the geologic eras and periods

Materials

- 5-meter length of adding machine tape
- meter stick
- pencil

Students may need help in realizing that there are 1000 millions in 1 billion and, therefore, 1 mm of tape represents 1 million years.

Procedure

1. Obtain a piece of adding machine tape about 5 m long. Measure 10 cm from one end of the tape and draw a line across the tape. Write your name in the 10-cm space.

2. Label the line at 10 cm *Now.* Write this label on the 10-cm side of the line. All of your other measurements will be made from this line that locates the present.

3. Measuring from your *Now* line, mark off your tape in 1-m intervals. At each interval, make a line on the tape. Label the lines 1 Billion (the mark nearest the *Now* line), 2 Billion, 3 Billion, and 4 Billion.

4. Measuring from the *Now* line and using the scale 1 m = 1 billion years, plot on your tape the events listed in Figure 32.1. At each measurement, draw a straight line across the tape. Label each line with the number of years and the name of the event. For example, the oldest event listed in Figure 32.1 is the origin of Earth 4.6 billion years ago. To plot it on your tape, measure 460 cm (4 m + 60 cm) from the *Now* line. Draw a line across the tape and label it 4.6 Billion—Origin of Earth. Answer Analysis and Conclusions questions 1–4 before continuing.

5. Other scales can be used to gain an appreciation for geologic time. Develop a time scale in which the 4.6 billions of years of geologic time is compressed into one day. On such a scale, Earth would have originated twenty-four hours ago at approximately the hour shown on your classroom clock. Use your scale to calculate the time and date of occurrence of the first known animals, the first bird, the hominid footprints in footprint tuff and the end of the Ice Age. Mark on your tape the time and date of occurrence of these and any five other events. Assuming a time of 11:00 A M. on April 26, the time of the first animals would be 4:44 A.M., April 27; first bird at 9:49 A.M., April 27; the first mammals at 9:57 A.M., April 27; the hominid footprints in footprint tuff at 10:59 A.M., April 27; the end of the Ice Age at 0.2 seconds before 11:00 A.M., April 27.

Analysis and Conclusions

1. Which two events on your tape are separated by the longest duration of geologic time? By how many years are they separated?

The longest duration is from the start of the Proterozoic, 2.5 billion years ago, to the first known animals, 1.2 billion years ago. The difference is 1.3 billion years.

2. From your tape, determine the duration of each of the following:

(a) Archeozoic Era 1.3 billion

(b) Proterozoic Era 1940 million

(c) Paleozoic Era 330 million

(d) Mesozoic Era 183 million

(e) Cenozoic Era 65 million

3. Which of the eras listed in question 2 was the longest? Which was the shortest?

The Archeozoic Era was the longest; the Cenozoic the shortest.

4. Dinosaurs lived only during the Mesozoic Era. If geologic time started 4.6 billion years ago, during what percentage of geologic time did dinosaurs exist?

$$\frac{165 \text{ million}}{4.6 \text{ billion}} \times 100 = \frac{165\,000\,000}{4\,600\,000\,000} \times 100 = 3.7 \text{ percent}$$

5. On the time scale you developed in procedure step 5 (4.6 billion years equals 24 hours), how many seconds elapsed since humans appeared on Earth?

66 seconds

Geologic Eras, Periods, and Epochs

Number of Years Ago	Event
11 thousand	end of the Ice Age
2 million	beginning of Pleistocene Epoch
3.5 million	hominid footprints in Footprint Tuff
5 million	beginning of Pliocene Epoch
23 million	beginning of Miocene Epoch
38 million	beginning of Oligocene Epoch
53 million	beginning of Eocene Epoch
65 million	beginning of Cenozoic Era and Paleocene Epoch
135 million	beginning of Cretaceous Period
200 million	first mammals
213 million	beginning of Jurassic Period
225 million	first bird
248 million	beginning of Mesozoic Era and Triassic Period
290 million	beginning of Permian Period
320 million	beginning of Pennsylvanian Period
350 million	beginning of Mississippian Period
410 million	beginning of Devonian Period
435 million	beginning of Silurian Period
485 million	beginning of Ordovician Period
560 million	beginning of Paleozoic Era and Cambrian Period
1.2 billion	first known animals
2.5 billion	beginning of Proterozoic Era
3.5 billion	oldest known rocks
3.8 billion	beginning of Archeozoic Era
4.6 billion	origin of Earth

Figure 32.1

CHAPTER

33

NAME ______________________

CLASS ____________ DATE ____________

Rock Correlation

Cayuga Lake is one of the scenic Finger Lakes of central New York State. The Cayuga Lake Basin is the valley occupied by Cayuga Lake. During the Devonian Period, this area was under a warm, shallow sea. Various kinds of sedimentary rocks were deposited on the floor of this sea. Today, these sediments can be seen as over 1200 meters of sedimentary rock. Many quarries, road cuts, and spectacular gorges make it possible to study these rock layers. By correlating the rocks of one outcrop with those of another outcrop, geologists have been able to determine the order in which the rocks were deposited. A **stratigraphic column** shows all the rocks in an area in this order. In this laboratory, you will construct a stratigraphic column for the Cayuga Lake Basin, using information from nine "outcrops."

Lab Skills and Objectives

- To **construct** a stratigraphic column by correlating rock outcrops

Materials

- scissors
- pencil
- paste or glue
- construction paper, 1 piece 40 cm long

Procedure

1. Figure 33.1 shows cross sections of nine outcrops in the Cayuga Lake Basin. Study the cross sections and identify the kinds of sedimentary rocks that occur in each.

2. Turn to the blank back of the page with the cross sections. On the back of each cross section, draw an arrow pointing to the top of the page. (You will need the arrow to identify which way is "up.")

3. **CAUTION: Use care when working with scissors.** Turn the page back over and carefully cut out each cross section.

4. Lay the cross sections on your desktop and move them around to match the rocks of one "outcrop" with similar rocks in other "outcrops."

You may want to check students' correlations before they paste the sections on the construction paper.

5. Once you have matched all of the cross sections, paste them to the construction paper to form a single column. The cross sections will overlap each other where layers are duplicated. Your single column is a stratigraphic column for the Cayuga Lake Basin.

6. The table in Figure 33.2 describes and names the rock layers in your stratigraphic column. The oldest rock units are at the bottom of the table, and the youngest are at the top. Use the table to label each of the rock units in your column. (Use the thicknesses given in Figure 33.2 to determine the relative thicknesses of the layers in your stratigraphic column.)

7. Answer Analysis and Conclusions questions.

Analysis and Conclusions

1. Which three rock units are entirely limestone? Manlius, Onondaga, Tully

2. Which two rock units are entirely shale? Ludlowville, Geneseo

3. Which two rock units are shale with limestone at the top? Marcellus, Skaneateles

4. One of the rock units in this stratigraphic column is thought to have originally been a beach sand that was spread across what are now New York and Pennsylvania during the Middle Devonian. Which rock unit is most likely to have originated as a beach? Why?

The Oriskany; A Devonian beach sand would be a sandstone today.

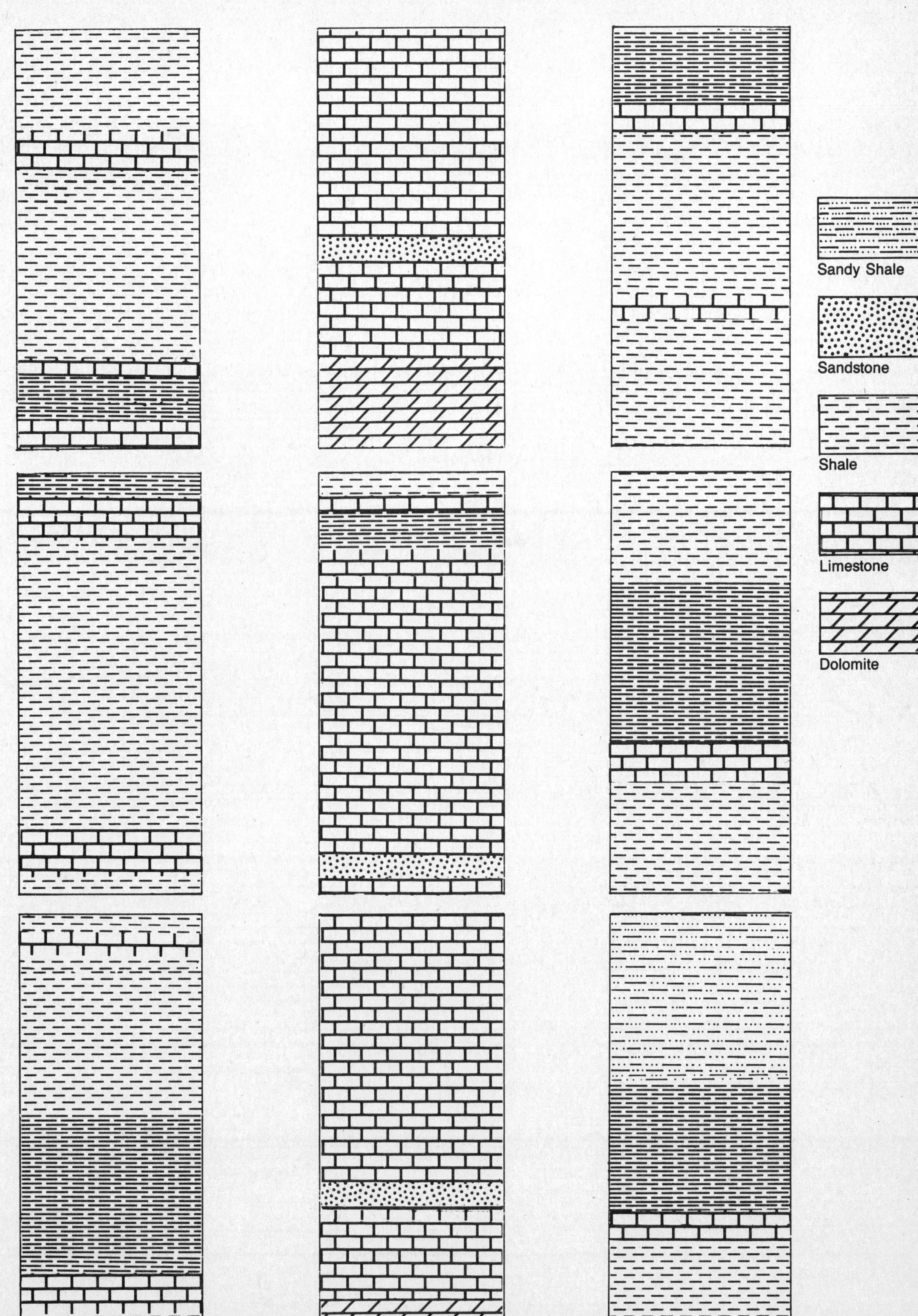

Figure 33.1

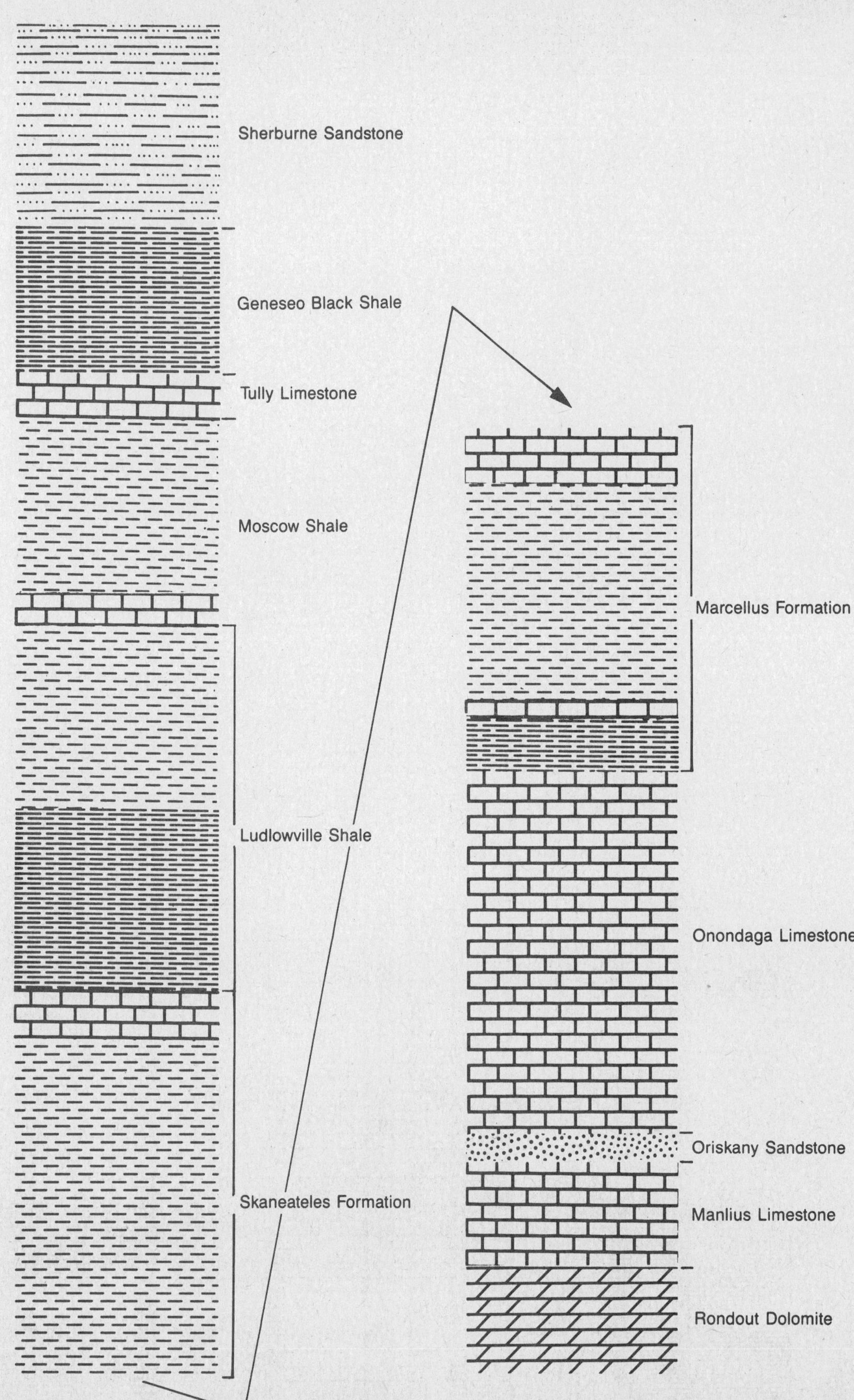

Figure TAE 33.1

Devonian Rock Units of the Cayuga Lake Basin	
Name	**Description**
Sherburne	shale with increasing sand
Geneseo	black shale, about 10 m thick
Tully	limestone, about 3 m thick
Moscow	shale with limestone at base, about 15 m thick
Ludlowville	shale, about 25 m thick
Skaneateles	shale with limestone at top, total thickness about 28 m
Marcellus	primarily shale, black shale at base, then thin limestone, nearly 4-m thick limestone at top, total thickness nearly 25 m
Onondaga	limestone, over 25 m thick
Oriskany	sandstone, about 1.2 m thick
Manlius	limestone, about 7.6 m thick
Rondout	dolomite, about 7.6 m thick

Figure 33.2

5. The Tully is a prominent rock layer of the Cayuga Lake Basin. It stands out visibly between the Moscow below it and the Geneseo above it. What could cause this difference in the appearance of the rock layers?

The Tully is a limestone; the Moscow and Geneseo are shales. The Tully must be more resistant to erosion.

6. Sand is deposited nearer to the shore than silt and clay. Refer to the description of the Sherburne formation in Figure 33.2. How was the distance between the area where this layer was deposited changing during the time the Sherburne was being deposited? Explain your answer.

The amount of sand increases from the bottom to the top of the unit. Therefore, the shoreline must have been approaching the area (the distance was decreasing).

7. The upper layers of the Onondaga limestone contain some volcanic ash. What was the most likely location of the volcanoes from which this ash came? (Use your textbook for help.)

The Acadian Orogeny occurred at the end of the Devonian; therefore, the volcanic ash most likely came from New England.

8. The Onondaga contains an abundance of coral fossils, along with crinoids, brachiopods, and trilobites. Why are fossils of ferns, rushes, and primitive conifers unlikely to be found in these rocks?

Corals, crinoids, brachiopods, and trilobites are marine animals; ferns, rushes, and conifers are land plants.

9. Lime obtained from limestone is an important ingredient in the manufacture of cement. Would the Cayuga Lake Basin be a good or poor location for a cement-making plant? Why?

A good location; several limestones occur in the stratigraphic column.

NAME ______________________________

CLASS ______________ DATE ______________

CHAPTER 34

LAB INVESTIGATION

Using Fossils

Fossils are the remains of past life. Groups of fossils, called **fossil assemblages,** can often be used to determine the age of the rock in which the fossils are found.

Lab Skills and Objectives

- To **identify** several kinds of fossils
- To **compare** the ages of the fossils
- To **identify** the geologic age of the rock containing the fossils

Materials

- 5 fossil assemblages

The fossils contained in each assemblage are:
I – *Athyris, Favosites, Phacops, Flexicalymene*
II – *Turritella, Gryphaea, Phylloceras*
III – *Pentremites, Favosites, Hydnoceras*
IV – *Exogyra, Phylloceras, Terebratula*
V – *Neospirifer, Athyris, Pentremites*

Procedure

1. In Figure 34.1 note the names of some fossils (italicized) and the groups to which they belong (boldface). Also note the geologic periods during which each organism lived. Use Figure 34.2 to summarize the information in Figure 34.1. For each group listed in the table, write the name of a fossil and block out the periods in which the organism lived. For example, the *Favosites* in the **Coral** group lived from the Ordovician through the Permian period. In the first row of Figure 34.2, the spaces under all headings from ORD through PER have been blocked out. If actual fossil specimens are not available, make copies of Figure 34.1, cut out the illustrations, and put them together in the fossil assemblages required.

2. Answer Analysis and Conclusions questions 1–5.

3. Obtain Fossil Assemblage I. Using the fossil illustrations in Figure 34.1 as a guide, identify each of the fossils in the assemblage. Then block in the time range for each organism in Figure 34.3, just as you did in Figure 34.2. Answer Analysis and Conclusions question 6.

4. Obtain Fossil Assemblage II and complete Figure 34.4. Answer Analysis and Conclusions question 7.

5. Obtain Fossil Assemblages III, IV, and V. Fill in the time range for each assemblage in the appropriate figure. Answer the Analysis and Conclusions question for each assemblage.

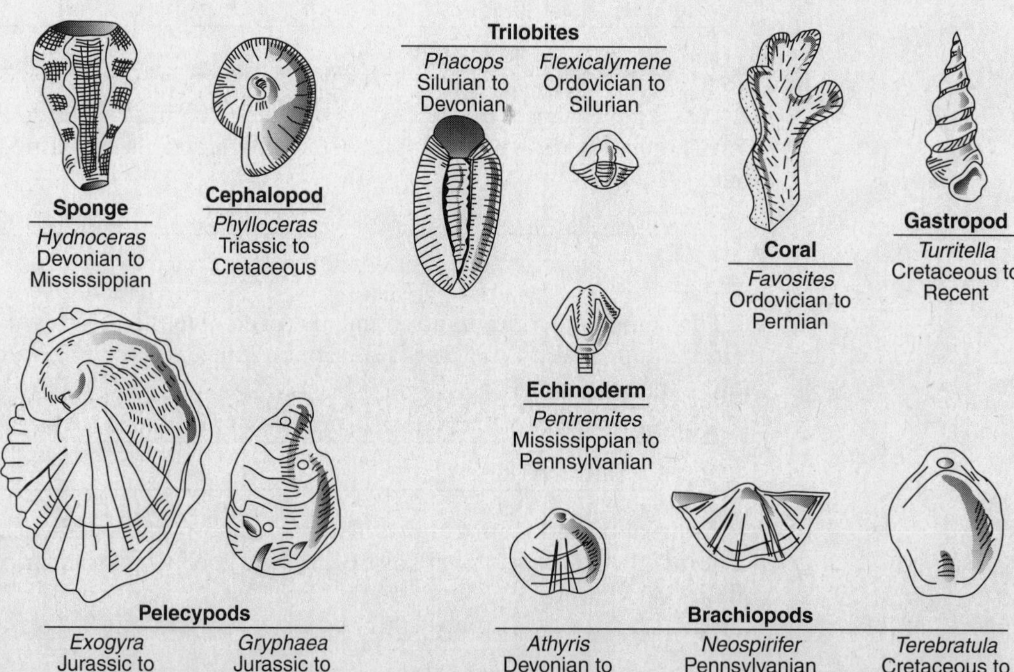

Figure 34.1

*CAM = Cambrian
ORD = Ordovician
SIL = Silurian
DEV = Devonian
MIS = Mississippian
PEN = Pennsylvanian
PER = Permian
TRI = Triassic
JUR = Jurassic
CRE = Cretaceous
TER = Tertiary
QUA = Quaternary

Data Table

		Period*											
Group	**Name**	CAM	ORD	SIL	DEV	MIS	PEN	PER	TRI	JUR	CRE	TER	QUA
coral	*Favosites*		■	■	■	■	■	■					
sponge	*Hydnoceras*				■	■							
brachiopod	*Athyris*				■	■	■	■	■				
brachiopod	*Neospirifer*						■	■					
brachiopod	*Terebratula*										■	■	
pelecypod	*Exogyra*									■	■		
pelecypod	*Gryphaea*									■	■	■	
gastropod	*Turritella*										■	■	■
cephalopod	*Phylloceras*								■	■	■		
echinoderm	*Pentremites*					■	■						
trilobite	*Flexicalymene*		■	■									
trilobite	*Phacops*			■	■								

Figure 34.2

Fossil Assemblage I

Group	**Name**	CAM	ORD	SIL	DEV	MIS	PEN	PER	TRI	JUR	CRE	TER	QUA
brachiopod	Athyris				■	■	■	■	■				
coral	Favosites		■	■	■	■	■						
trilobite	Phacops			■	■								
trilobite	Flexycalymene		■	■									

Figure 34.3

Fossil Assemblage II

Group	**Name**	CAM	ORD	SIL	DEV	MIS	PEN	PER	TRI	JUR	CRE	TER	QUA
gastropod	Turritella										■	■	■
pelecypod	Gryphaea									■	■	■	
cephalopod	Phylloceras								■	■	■		

Figure 34.4

Fossil Assemblage III

Group	**Name**	CAM	ORD	SIL	DEV	MIS	PEN	PER	TRI	JUR	CRE	TER	QUA
echinoderm	Pentremites					■	■						
coral	Favosites		■	■	■	■	■	■					
sponge	Hydnoceras				■	■							

Figure 34.5

Fossil Assemblage IV													
Group	**Name**	**CAM**	**ORD**	**SIL**	**DEV**	**MIS**	**PEN**	**PER**	**TRI**	**JUR**	**CRE**	**TER**	**QUA**
pelecypod	Exogyra									■	■		
cephalopod	Phylloceras								■	■	■		
brachiopod	Terebratula										■	■	

Figure 34.6

Fossil Assemblage V													
Group	**Name**	**CAM**	**ORD**	**SIL**	**DEV**	**MIS**	**PEN**	**PER**	**TRI**	**JUR**	**CRE**	**TER**	**QUA**
brachiopod	Neospirifer						■	■					
brachiopod	Athyris				■	■	■	■	■				
echinoderm	Pentremites					■	■						

Figure 34.7

Analysis and Conclusions

1. Which organism listed in Figure 34.2 lived for the greatest number of geologic time periods? To what group does it belong? List the periods during which it lived.

The coral *Favosites* lived for the greatest number of geologic periods—Ordovician, Silurian, Devonian, Mississippian, Pennsylvanian, and Permian.

2. Using Figure 34.2, list the fossils that could be found in rocks of Devonian Age. Name the group to which each belongs.

Phacops (trilobite), *Athyris* (brachiopod), *Favosites* (coral), *Hydnoceras* (sponge)

3. Using Figure 34.2, list the fossils that could be found in rocks of Jurassic age. Name the group to which each belongs.

Exogyra (pelecypod), *Gryphaea* (pelecypod), *Phylloceras* (cephalopod)

4. Could fossils of the trilobite *Flexicalymene* and the coral Favosites be found in the same rock layer? Explain your answer.

Yes. Both could be found in Ordovician and Silurian rocks.

5. Could fossils of the trilobite *Phacops* and the brachiopod *Terebratula* be found in the same rock layer? Explain your answer.

No. There is no geologic period when both were living.

6. Identify the age of the rocks from which Fossil Assemblage I could have been obtained.

The fossils in Fossil Assemblage I can only be Devonian.

7. Identify the age of the rocks from which Fossil Assemblage II could have been obtained.

The fossils in Fossil Assemblage II can only be Cretaceous.

8. Identify the age of the rocks from which Fossil Assemblage III could have been obtained.

The fossils in Fossil Assemblage III can only be Mississippian.

9. Identify the age of the rocks from which Fossil Assemblage IV could have been obtained.

The fossils in Fossil Assemblage IV can only be Cretaceous.

10. Identify the age of the rocks from which Fossil Assemblage V could have been obtained.

The fossils in Fossil Assemblage V can only be Pennsylvanian.

CHAPTER 1

LAB ACTIVITY

NAME ____________________

CLASS ______________ DATE ______________

Collecting and Interpreting Data

Data Table A	
Pour #	Distance (cm)
1	3.6
2	5.2
3	6.2
4	7.0
5	7.7
6	8.4
7	9.0
8	9.5
9	9.9
10	10.3

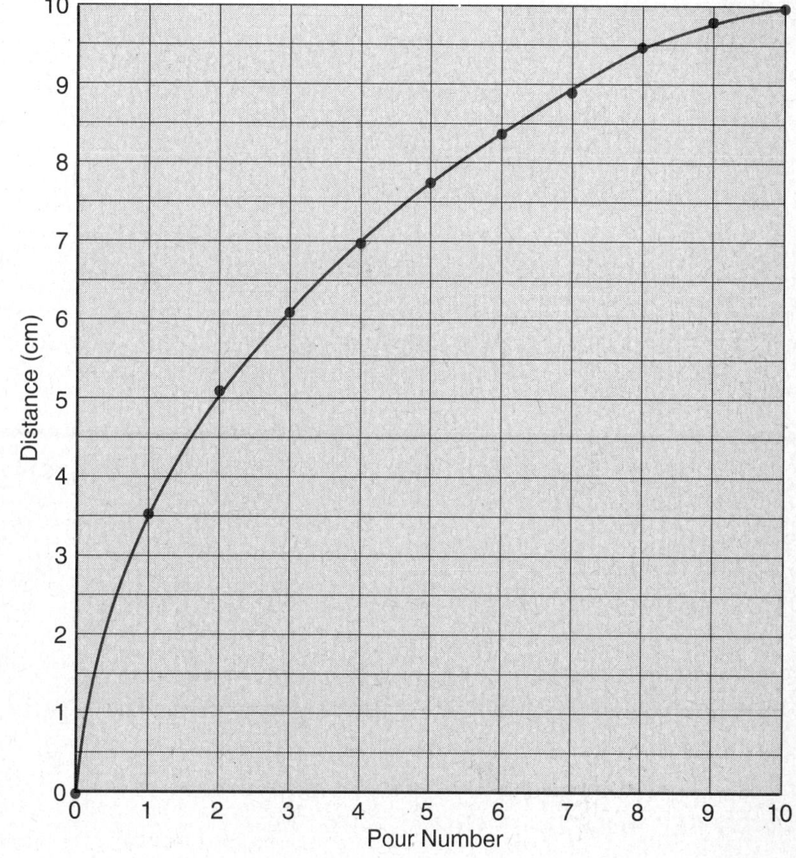

Figure 1.11

Analysis and Conclusions

1. How did the spacing between the lines on the funnel change as more water was added to the funnel? Why did the change occur in that way?

The spacing between the lines decreased because the funnel became wider.

2. If the funnel was sealed at the wide end, inverted, and filled 50 mL at a time from the narrow end, what would you expect to happen to the spaces between the lines as the funnel was filled?

The spaces between the lines would increase.

3. If you lived on a lake with a funnel-shaped bottom, would you be more concerned about a heavy rain causing the lake to flood its banks if the funnel was wide side down or wide side up (assuming it could occur either way)?

Flooding would be a greater concern if the lake were wide side down.

4. Locate the graphs on pages 15, 189, 269, and 608 of your textbook. Which graph is shaped most like your graph? Identify one way in which each of the other graphs is shaped differently from your graph.

The graph on page 189; The graph on page 15 goes up sharply to the right. The graph on page 269 is a straight line. The graph on page 608 goes down to the right.

5. If the distance between the lines on the funnel had been measured instead of the total distance to each line and then plotted on a graph, which one of the same four graphs would most closely resemble the results? (Plot a new graph by recalculating the new distances.)

The greatest distance between the lines occurred at the start and then decreased. This resembles the graph on page 608.

6. If instead of a funnel a large beaker had been filled 50 mL at a time and the results plotted on a graph, which of the four graphs would most closely resemble the results?

If a beaker had been used, the spaces between marks would have been uniform. This resembles the graph on page 269.

NAME ______________________

CLASS ____________ DATE ____________

CHAPTER 2

LAB ACTIVITY

TEXT ACTIVITY

DATA SHEET

Eratosthenes and Earth's Circumference

Analysis and Conclusions

Data Table A
Angle used (°) = ______________
Length arc AB (cm) = ______________ (distance along circle)
Length AC (cm) = ______________ (radius of circle)

1. What fractional part of the whole circle is your angle? (Remember that there are 360° in a circle and that 180° is ½ circle, 90° is ¼ circle, and so on.)

Answers will vary depending upon student drawings. If, for example, the angle is 36°, 36° is 1/10 of a circle.

2. Use your answer to question 1 and your value for the length of arc AB to determine the circumference of your circle to the nearest tenth of a centimeter. For example, if the angle in question 1 is one tenth of the circle, the circumference will be ten times the length of arc AB. This is the method Eratosthenes used to calculate the circumference of Earth.

Student answers will depend upon student data. If 1/10 of the circle is 6.2 cm, then the whole circle must be 10 × 6.2 or 62.0 cm.

3. A standard formula for determining the circumference of a circle is $C = 2\pi r$. Using that formula, determine the circumference of your circle again. (Use $\pi = 3.14$.)

If, for example, the length of AC is 9.8 cm, then $2\pi r = 2 \times 3.14 \times 9.8 = 61.5$ cm (to the nearest tenth).

4. By what percent do your answers to questions 2 and 3 differ? To calculate the difference, subtract the smaller circumference from the larger circumference, then divide the difference by your circumference value in question 3 and multiply the result by 100.

$$62.0 - 61.5 = 0.5; \quad \frac{0.5}{61.5} \times 100 = 0.8\%$$

With any care at all, students' values can come within 1 or 2 percent of one another.

5. What part of a whole circle is the angular distance from E to F? Use the same method as in question 1.

20° is 1/18 of the circle.

Figure 2.6

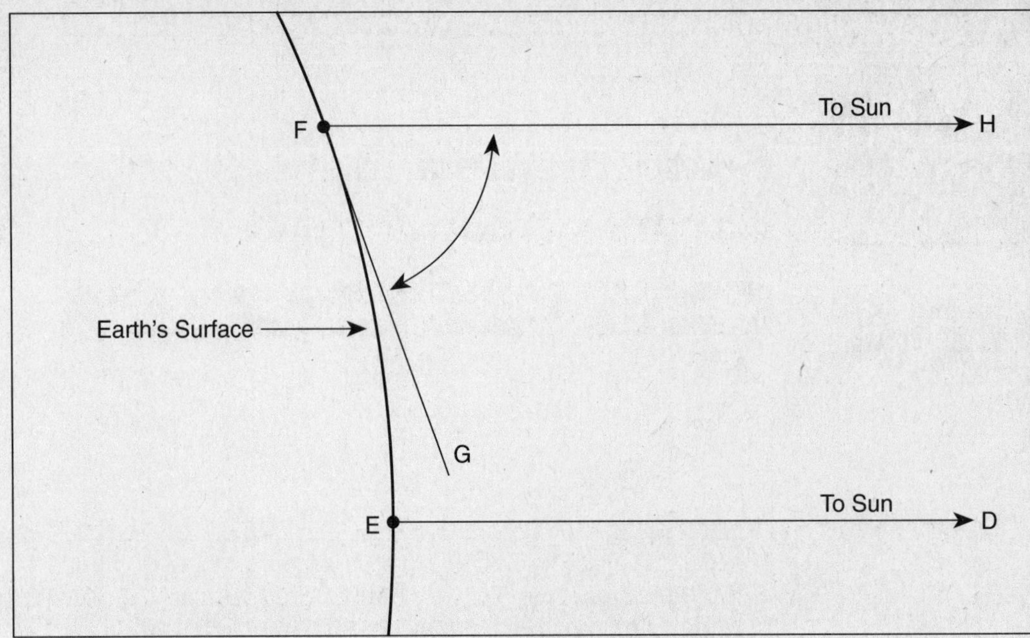

Data Table B	
Angle GFH (°) =	______
Distance for arc E to F (°) =	______
Measured length of arc EF (cm) =	______ (distance along circle)
Distance from E to F (km) =	______

6. Use your answer to question 5 and the distance in kilometers from E to F to determine the circumference of Earth.

$2200 \times 18 = 39\,600$ km

7. Assume Earth's actual circumference is 40 000 kilometers. Determine the percent by which your value from question 6 differs from the actual circumference. Use the same technique as in question 4 but divide by 40 000 before multiplying by 100.

$$\left(\frac{40\,000 - 39\,600}{40\,000}\right) \times 100 = 1\%$$

NAME ______________________

CLASS ______________ DATE ______________

Growing Crystals

Procedure

Use the spaces provided to make sketches of the suspended crystal on each day of observation.

Day 1

Day 2

Day 3

Day 4

Day 5

Day 6

Day 7

Analysis and Conclusions

1. Why was the piece of paper towel placed over the beaker? Identify at least two functions that it served.

The paper towel slowed the rate of evaporation and prevented dust from contaminating the solution.

2. What would have happened to the seed crystal if it had been placed in the warm solution the first day?

The seed crystal would have dissolved.

3. What was the source of material for the crystal?

The source of crystal material was the solution that contained dissolved ammonium alum.

4. A cube is a six-sided figure in which each of the sides are squares. As your crystal grew, did it resemble a cube on any day?

Depending upon the shape of the seed crystal, some students may have seen cubes as the crystal formed.

5. An octahedron is an eight-sided figure in which each side is a triangle. How closely did your final crystal resemble an octahedron?

Over time, the crystal should become more octahedral. Preliminary phases might resemble cubes with flat corners where the octahedron surfaces are starting to form.

6. Seed crystals grown in the bottom of a beaker are often only the top half of a crystal. Why wouldn't the other half grow?

Each crystal is free to grow only upward and sideways. Since they cannot grow downward, only half of each crystal can form.

CHAPTER 4

LAB ACTIVITY

NAME ______________________

CLASS ____________ DATE ____________

Identification of Minerals

Analysis and Conclusions

Data Table							
Mineral Number	Color	Streak	Cleavage/ Fracture	Hardness	Luster	Special Properties	Mineral Name

1. Some minerals can be identified by a single property. Sulfur is one example. What property is most useful for the identification of sulfur?

   The most useful property for the identification of sulfur is its bright yellow color.

2. What color is biotite? List two other properties that are useful in identifying biotite.

   Black, brown, or dark green; Biotite has excellent cleavage in one direction and the pieces that cleave (peel off) are thin, elastic films.

3. There is a second mineral that belongs to the same mineral group as biotite. (It does not occur in your mineral set.) What is this mineral and its mineral group? How does its color compare to that of biotite?

The mineral is muscovite, and it is a mica. Muscovite is lighter in color than biotite.

4. Explain why the feel of gypsum and talc can be used to distinguish between the minerals.

Talc has a greasy feel; gypsum does not.

5. Explain how cleavage and fracture can be used to distinguish between quartz and feldspar.

Feldspar has good, two-directional cleavage, and quartz has conchoidal fracture.

6. Explain how cleavage can be used to distinguish between halite and calcite.

Although both have excellent, three directional cleavage, their cleavage planes meet at different angles. The cleavage planes in halite meet at right angles, and those in calcite do not meet at right angles.

7. What are the three most useful properties for the identification of halite? Olivine?

Taste, cleavage, and hardness; Olivine has a yellowish and greenish color, a white to light green streak, and a glassy and granular appearance.

NAME ______________________

CLASS ____________ DATE ____________

CHAPTER 5

LAB

ACTIVITY

TEXT ACTIVITY

DATA SHEET

Studying Rocks in Thin Sections

Analysis and Conclusions

1. Grain or crystal size can provide clues to rock types. Typically, sedimentary grains are rounded and found in a cement matrix. Igneous grains fit together in a jigsaw puzzle fashion. Metamorphic grains exhibit linear patterns and foliation. (Foliation is a parallel arrangement of minerals such as alternating layers of dark and light minerals.) Look at rocks A to D on page 81 of your text. Which of the rocks shown is sedimentary? Metamorphic? Igneous?

Rock C is sedimentary; Rock D is metamorphic; Rock A and Rock B are Igneous.

2. Determine the *actual* size of an average grain of Rock C. The actual diameter of the rock sample shown in each diagram is 0.5 centimeters. Use your average grain diameter data and the magnified diameter you recorded. Show your work.

The average grain diameter is approximately 0.5 cm. Therefore, the actual diameter of the rock sample is

$$\frac{0.5 \text{ cm}}{4.0 \text{ cm}} = \frac{X \text{ cm}}{0.5 \text{ cm}}$$

$$X = 0.06 \text{ cm}$$

3. Using your answer to question 2, determine the name of the average grain size in Rock C. The diameter of clay-sized grains ranges from 0.00001 to 0.0004 cm, silt 0.0004 to 0.006 cm, sand 0.006 to 0.2 cm, and pebbles 0.2 to 6.4 cm. Which kind of sedimentary rock is Rock C? Explain your answer.

The grain size is 0.06 cm, which according to the ranges makes the sedimentary rock sandstone.

4. In Rock A, which two minerals did you estimate make up over 50% of the rock? Which minerals make up the remainder of the rock?

Quartz and orthoclase feldspar; amphibole, biotite mica, and plagioclase feldspar

5. In Rock B, which two minerals did you estimate make up over 50% of the rock? Which minerals make up the remainder of the rock?

Plagioclase feldspar and amphibole; pyroxene, biotite mica, olivine and quartz

6. Turn to the graph on page 61 of your text. Which rock in the graph most nearly matches the mineral composition of Rock A? Which rock in the same graph most nearly matches the mineral composition of Rock B? Explain your answers.

Rock A is granite because quartz and feldspar are over 50% of a granite while other minerals make up much less. Rock B is gabbro because plagioclase and amphibole are most abundant in that rock.

7. Igneous rocks are commonly grouped into mafic rocks and felsic rocks based on their chemical composition. Mafic rocks are dark in color because they contain a number of dark minerals such as amphibole, pyroxene, olivine, and biotite, as well as plagioclase feldspar. Felsic rocks are light in color and contain minerals such as quartz and orthoclase feldspar as well as some dark minerals such as biotite and amphibole. Based on these definitions, which rock, A or B, is mafic? Which rock is felsic? Explain your answer.

Rock B, or the gabbro, is mafic. It contains dark minerals such as amphibole, olivine, biotite. Rock A, or the granite, is felsic. It contains the lighter colored minerals such as orthoclase feldspar and quartz.

8. Compare the diagrams for Rock C and Rock D. Look at each rock's texture (i.e. size, shape, orientation, and contact points with other crystals). How does the texture differ in the two rock samples?

Rock C has rounded grains of quartz, with calcite between the minerals. Rock D has interlocking grains of quartz, elongated in a planar pattern.

9. Look at the diagram of Rock E. Is it sedimentary, metamorphic, or igneous? Explain your answer.

Rock E is metamorphic, evidenced by the foliation and linear patterns of the grains.

NAME ______________________________

CLASS ______________ DATE ______________

TEXT ACTIVITY

DATA SHEET

Measuring Particulate Air Pollution

Analysis and Conclusions

Data Table A							
	Slide 1	Slide 2	Slide 3	Slide 4	Slide 5	Slide 6	Slide 7
Days Exposed							
Field 1							
Field 2							
Field 3							
Field 4							
Average Count							
Average Count – Average Count Control							
Particulates per cm^2							
Particulates Deposited per Day							

1. Compare the number of particulates deposited in each area. Where did you find the most particulates? Where did you find the least? How did the numbers compare to your predictions?

Answers will vary.

2. Based on your description of the particulates, did the types of particulates differ from place to place? Were there significant differences in the particulate levels indoors and outdoors? Explain your answer.

Answers will vary based on the locations of the slides.

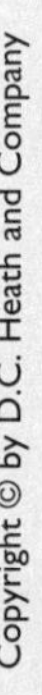

3. What do you think are sources for particulates?

Indoor sources include dirt and dust that has been brought in from outside, insulation, and furnaces. Outdoor sources include pollen from plants, dust from soil, and particulates from factory and power plant emissions.

4. What do you think would lead to high particulate levels indoors?

Answers may include older buildings that lack filtering systems, open windows, poorly maintained furnaces, and whether the building is cleaned regularly.

5. The severity of outdoor air pollution often depends on weather conditions. Explain how weather conditions might affect the particulate levels from day to day.

Dry weather increases dust and other particulates in air. Wind can either disperse particulates from an area or bring in particulates from other areas.

NAME ______________________

CLASS ______________ DATE ______________

Latitude and Longitude

Procedure

1. Use the Earth's Climates Map on page 664 of your text to identify the city nearest to the following rounded latitudes and longitudes.

(a) 41°N, 74°W New York

(b) 56°N, 38°E Moscow

(c) 12°S, 77°W Lima

(d) 34°S, 151°E Sydney

(e) 42°N, 12°E Rome

(f) 26°S, 28°E Johannesburg

(g) 71°N, 24°E Hammerfest

(h) 6°S, 107°E Jakarta

(i) 40°N, 116°E Beijing

(j) 1°S, 37°E Nairobi

(k) 35°S, 59°W Buenos Aires

(l) 61°N, 150°W Anchorage

Students' answers may vary by 2° or 3°.

2. To the nearest whole degree, estimate the latitude and longitude of the following cities. Be sure to include the correct compass directions (N, S, E, W) in your answer.

(a) Manaus (South America) 2°S, 60°W

(b) Tokyo (Asia) 36°N, 140°E

(c) Barrow (North America) 71°N, 155°W

(d) Melbourne (Australia) 39°S, 146°E

(e) Singapore (Asia) 1°N, 104°E

3. Turn to the Physical United States map on pages 654–655 of your text. Determine the city nearest to each of the following rounded latitudes and longitudes. Include the state in your answer.

(a) 37°N, 122°W Tallahassee, FL

(b) 42°N, 71°W Boston, MA

(c) 30°N, 95°W Houston, TX

(d) 30°N, 84°W San Jose, CA

(e) 44°N, 70°W Augusta, ME

(f) 33°N, 117°W San Diego, CA

(g) 46°N, 123°W Portland, OR

(h) 40°N, 80°W Pittsburgh, PA

(i) 40°N, 105°W Denver, CO

Analysis and Conclusions

1. Copenhagen is approximately 13° due north of Rome. Using the conversion given on page 111 of your text, determine the distance in kilometers between the two cities.

From Topic 2, 1° of latitude = 112 km. Therefore, 13° of latitude = 13 × 112 or 1456 km.

2. Is it possible for a city to be located at 120°S, 30°W? Explain your answer.

No; Latitude cannot be greater than 90°.

3. How many degrees of latitude separate New Orleans and Philadelphia? Express your answer in minutes of latitude.

10° or 600′

4. Would you travel farther if you drove 2° due east from Bismarck, North Dakota, or from Austin, Texas? Explain your answer.

Austin; The distance between longitude lines increases toward the equator.

5. What is the approximate latitude and longitude of your school?

Answers will depend upon the school's location.

6. The antipode is the location directly on the opposite side of Earth from your location. It is the same distance south of the equator as you are north and on the same north-south great circle. Determine the latitude and longitude of your antipode.

Indian Ocean for most of the United States

CHAPTER 7

MAP ACTIVITY

NAME ____________________

CLASS ____________ DATE ____________

Reading a Topographic Map

Procedure

1. Study the Harrisburg map on page 652 of your text and locate the following features: the Susquehanna River, Peters Mountain (only the letters PETE and the bottom of the letter R appear on the map), Third Mountain, Second Mountain, Cove Mountain, Blue Mountain east of the river, and Blue Mountain west of the river. Based on your observations, which of these mountain ridges appear to have been connected before the Susquehanna River cut through them?

Cove, Second, and Blue

2. How does the spacing between contour lines on the ridges differ from the spacing between contour lines in the valleys? (A magnifier may help.) What does this spacing tell you about the steepness of the land in these areas?

Contour lines are closer together on the ridges, farther apart in the valleys. Ridges are steeper.

3. The contour interval of the map is 20 feet. What is the elevation of the highest contour line shown on Cove Mountain? Second Mountain? Third Mountain?

Cove: 1300 feet; Second: 1380 feet; Third: 1320 feet

4. Locate Fishing Creek on the west side of the Susquehanna River. Look closely at the contour lines along the creek. (A magnifier may help here, also.) How do the contour lines show that Fishing Creek flows into the Susquehanna River?

Contours increase away from the river. Contours crossing the creek point away from the river.

5. Locate the Rockville Bridge in the lower center of the map. How wide is the Susquehanna River at the Rockville Bridge? (Hint: Lay the edge of your report sheet along the bridge and mark off both ends of the bridge. Use the map scale on page 650 of your text like a ruler to measure the distance.)

between 0.6 and 0.7 mile

Analysis and Conclusions

1. How does color on the map distinguish the ridges from valleys? What does this color difference indicate? What is the cause of this difference?

The ridges are green while the valleys are white, indicating that the ridges are wooded. People have probably cleared more trees from the valley areas. (Accept any reasonable explanation.)

2. If you were standing on the contour line at the base of the Water Gap Observation Tower (upper shore of the Susquehanna River near the left edge of the map), could you see the Rockville Bridge on a clear day? Could you see the village of Heckton (east side of the river near the middle of the map)? Explain your answers.

No, the Rockville bridge is not visible because the tip of Cove Mountain blocks the view. Yes, Heckton could be seen because no mountains block the view.

3. (a) Locate the highway that crosses Peters Mountain. Why does the highway jog to the east (toward the Airway Beacon) instead of going straight over the mountain?

The mountain is too steep. By jogging the highway toward the beacon, the elevation changes more gradually.

(b) What is the straight line distance, in miles, between the point where the highway crosses Clark Creek and the point where it crosses the Appalachian Trail near the beacon? (Hint: Use the edge of your report sheet as in Procedure step 5.)

between 1.7 and 1.8 miles

(c) What is the distance along the highway between these same two points? (Hint: Move the edge of your report sheet along the highway.)

between 2.2 and 2.3 miles

CHAPTER 8
LAB ACTIVITY

NAME ______________________________

CLASS ______________ DATE ______________

Temperature and Chemical Weathering

Analysis and Conclusions

Data Table A: Actual Data		
Beaker Number	Temperature (°C)	Time (seconds)
1		
2		
3		
4		
5		

Data Table B: Theoretical Data		
Beaker Number	Temperature (°C)	Time (seconds)
1		
2		
3		
4		
5		

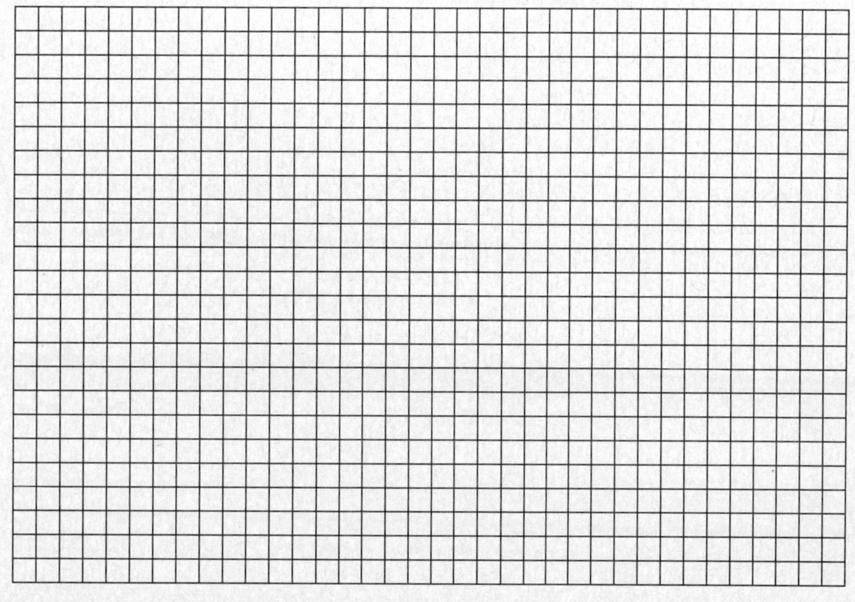

1. (a) In which beaker did the reaction occur most slowly? Beaker 1

(b) In which beaker did the reaction occur most rapidly? Beaker 5

(c) What is the relationship between the temperature and the rate of a reaction?

As temperature increases, the rate of the reaction increases.

2. Based upon your observations, what do you think is the relationship between the temperature and the rate of natural chemical weathering?

As temperature increases, the rate of chemical weathering increases.

3. Are all the temperatures you recorded likely to occur on Earth's surface? Explain.

The highest temperature is unlikely to occur in nature.

4. Turn to the map of Earth's Climates on page 664 of your text. Locate Rio de Janeiro in South America and Seattle in North America. The map key indicates that both cities have climates with abundant moisture.

(a) Recall what you know about carbonic acid in rain and in groundwater. Compare the weathering rate of a limestone in Rio de Janeiro with that of a limestone in Seattle. Is there a difference? Explain your answer.

A limestone should weather faster in Rio de Janeiro because the climate there is hotter.

(b) Which of the two locations is likely to have thicker soil?

The soil would be expected to be thicker in Rio as well.

5. Now locate Barrow, Alaska, on the map. Why is a limestone in Barrow likely to weather very slowly?

The climate at Barrow is cold and dry, which would slow down the chemical reactions.

6. (a) How would the rate of the reaction have been different if the tablets had been ground into a powder before they were dropped into the water? Why?

The rate of the reaction would have increased. Grinding the tablet into pieces increases the surface area, making more surfaces available to chemically react.

(b) Would a graph for such a reaction result in a curve above or below the line of your actual data? Why?

The curve would be below the actual data curve because the reaction would occur in less time.

7. (a) On your graph, is the line for the theoretical data above, below, or the same as your line for the actual data?

below

(b) What does this mean about the rate of the reaction you observed compared with the theoretical rate of reaction?

The observed reaction was slower.

(c) What change in the procedure might have made your actual results more like the theoretical results?

Grinding the sample would have speeded up the reaction and might have made it more like the theoretical curve.

NAME ______________________________

CLASS ______________ DATE ______________

CHAPTER 9

LAB ACTIVITY

TEXT ACTIVITY

DATA SHEET

Interpreting Water Budgets

Analysis and Conclusions

Month	JAN	FEB	MAR	APR	MAY	JUN	JUL	AUG	SEP	OCT	NOV	DEC
Supply	108	131	125	95	96	115	155	142	88	61	60	99
Need	15	19	45	76	124	165	181	166	129	73	26	17
Supply Minus Need	+93	+112	+80	+19	–28	–50	–26	–24	–41	–12	+34	+82
Water Budget Section	S	S	S	S	U	U	U/D	D	D	D	R	R/S

Water budget data for Albany, Georgia (mm water)

Month	JAN	FEB	MAR	APR	MAY	JUN	JUL	AUG	SEP	OCT	NOV	DEC
Supply	62	64	75	72	84	102	82	88	69	61	54	64
Need	0	1	13	48	93	128	145	126	89	48	15	2
Supply Minus Need	+62	+63	+62	+24	–9	–26	–63	–38	–20	+13	+39	+62
Water Budget Section	S	S	S	S	U	U	U	U/D	D	R	R	R

Water budget data for Cumberland, Maryland (mm water)

Month	JAN	FEB	MAR	APR	MAY	JUN	JUL	AUG	SEP	OCT	NOV	DEC
Supply	27	25	39		79	103	95	84	80	53	41	27
Need	0	0	0	24	66	98	127	113	75	37	0	0
Supply Minus Need	+27	+25	+39	+30	+13	+5	–32	-29	+5	+16	+41	+27
Water Budget Section	R/S	S	S	S	S	S	U	U	R	R	R	R

Water budget data for Duluth, Minnesota (mm water)

Month	JAN	FEB	MAR	APR	MAY	JUN	JUL	AUG	SEP	OCT	NOV	DEC
Supply	44	40	41	24	10	3	0	0	4	13	22	40
Need	13	20	37	63	99	139	180	165	114	70	31	12
Supply Minus Need	+31	+20	+4	−39	−89	−136	−180	−165	−110	−57	−9	+28
Water Budget Section	R	R	R	U	U/D	D	D	D	D	D	D	R

Water budget data for Fresno, California (mm water)

1. How are Albany and Cumberland similar in terms of water usage, deficit, recharge, and surplus?

Both have all four water budget sections.

2. Which part of the water budget (usage, deficit, recharge, or surplus) occurs in Albany but does not occur in Fresno? Which occurs in Albany but not in Duluth?

Surplus occurs in Albany but not in Fresno. Deficit occurs in Albany but not in Duluth.

3. Which city is located in the driest climate? Explain your answer in terms of the duration of periods of deficit and surplus.

Fresno; no surplus and over 6 months of deficit.

4. Which city has the wettest climate? Explain your answer.

Duluth; has no deficit but has 5 months of surplus

5. Compare the water budget data for the four cities in this activity with the three cities in Topic 4 (Figures 9.4 and 9.5 on pages 151 and 152 of your text). Of the four cities in the activity, which is most like Phoenix? Which is most like Little Rock? Which is most like Hartford? Explain your answers.

Fresno is most like Phoenix because neither has a surplus period and both have long deficit periods. Albany and Cumberland are most like Little Rock because each has all four water budget sections. Duluth is most like Hartford because neither has a deficit period and both have long surplus periods.

NAME ____________________

CLASS __________ DATE __________

Stream Divides and River Systems

Analysis and Conclusions

Use the map in Figure 10.19 on page 166 to draw and label the Continental Divide and the Mississippi, Colorado, Columbia, Rio Grande, and St. Lawrence River systems.

1. In the continental United States, what happens to rain that falls west of the Great Continental Divide? Rain that falls east?

Rain falling west flows into the Pacific Ocean; rain falling east flows into the Atlantic Ocean.

2. The headwaters of three river systems are located in Colorado along the Great Continental Divide. Identify the three systems.

Colorado, Rio Grande, Mississippi

3. Identify the river system in which each of the following rivers are found.

(a) Snake River Columbia

(b) Platte River Mississippi

(c) Green River Colorado

(d) Wabash River Mississippi

(e) Cumberland River Mississippi

(f) Gila River Colorado

4. What is the source of the water in the St. Lawrence River? In what general direction does the river flow?

The Great Lakes; flows northeast

5. Identify 3 rivers for which the Mississippi River is the base level.

any river that flows into the Mississippi river such as the Ohio, Missouri, Arkansas, Illinois, Wisconsin, and Red

6. Identify the bay, sound, or gulf that serves as base level for

(a) the Sacramento and San Joaquin rivers. San Francisco Bay

(b) the Alabama River system. Mobile Bay

(c) the Connecticut River system. Long Island Sound

7. Locate and label the James, Roanoke, and Savannah rivers. In what topographic feature do these rivers originate?

Appalachian Mountains

8. Name the largest river that flows through the area where you live. Where does that river originate and what is its base level? Is the river part of any of the river systems shown on the map? If so, which one?

Answers will vary.

9. Locate the rivers shown in central Nevada. Why are these rivers not part of a larger river system?

These rivers do not drain into an ocean.

 NAME ______________________ CLASS ______________________ DATE ______________________

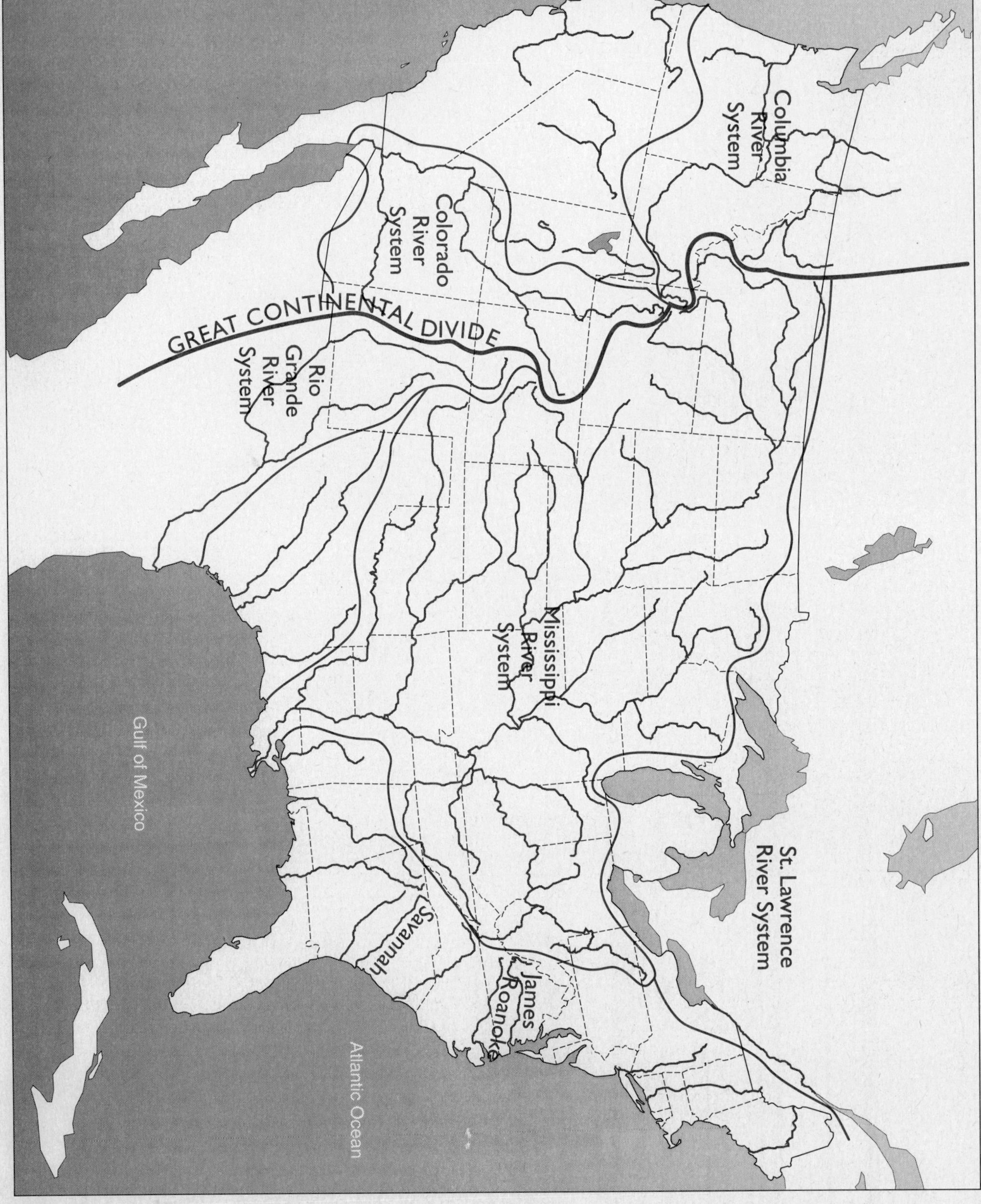

10.19 Major rivers of the United States

CHAPTER 11
MAP ACTIVITY

NAME ______________________

CLASS ______________ DATE ______________

Glacial Rebound

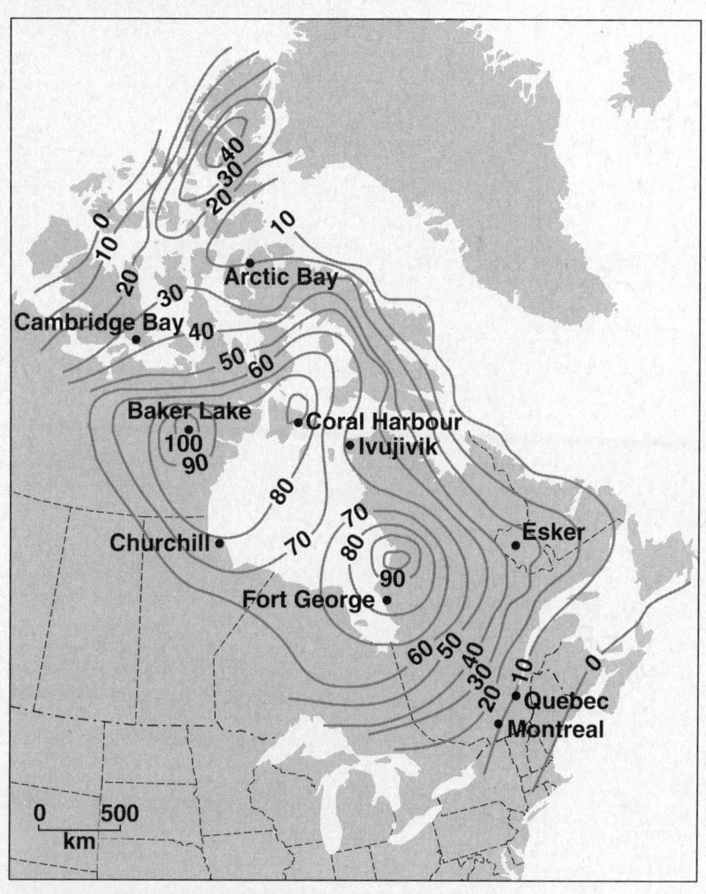

Figure 11.8
Contour map of glacial rebound (contour interval = 10 m)

Data Table		
Canadian City/Town	**Amount of Rebound (meters)**	**Duration of Rebound (years)**
Arctic Bay	20	3700
Cambridge Bay	30	4300
Coral Harbour	89	5800
Baker Lake	100	6000
Churchill	80	5600
Ivujivik	58	5300
Fort George	82	5700
Esker	38	4600
Montreal	13	3100
Quebec	10	2700

Procedure

1. On the map above, use colored pencils to shade the areas between the contours for 10, 30, 50, 70, and 90 meters of rebound. Do not color areas beyond the contours shown on the map.

(a) What is the value of the highest rebound contour shown?

100 m

(b) Relative to Hudson Bay, where are the areas of greatest rebound located?

One area is just west of Hudson Bay, and the other is on the eastern shore of the bay.

3. Use the grid on page 168 to graph the amount of rebound (in meters) you determined from the map versus the duration of rebound (in years). Complete the graph by drawing a smooth curve as near to as many of the points as possible (a "best-fit" curve). Extend the curve to the graph origin (0,0).

Analysis and Conclusions

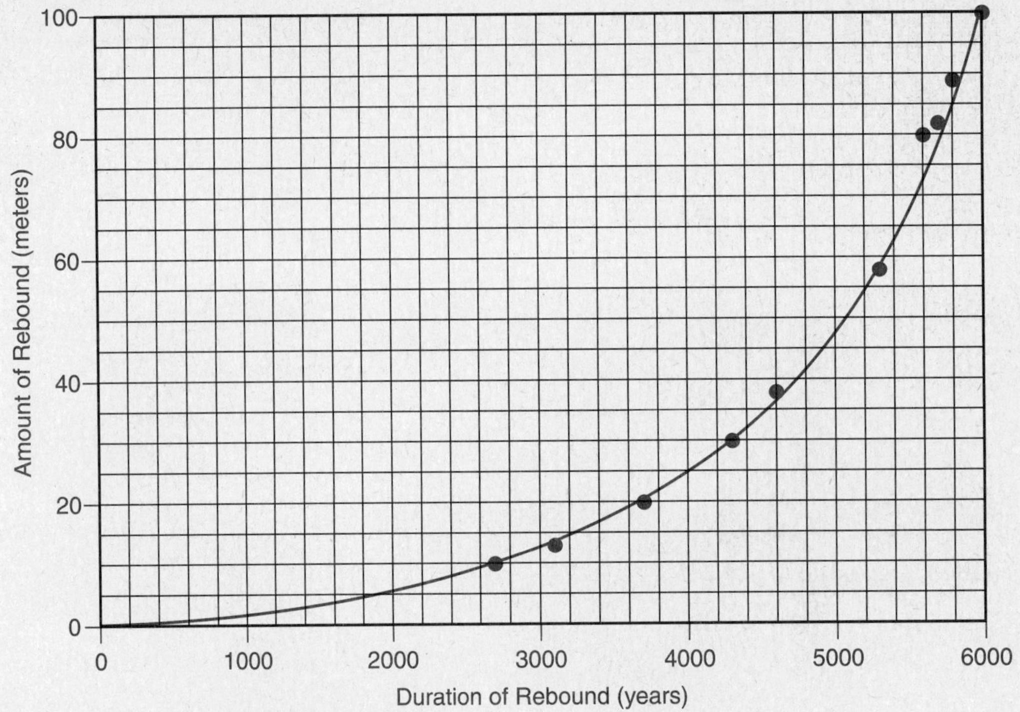

1. The areas on the map with greatest rebound contours are called *rebound centers.* Turn to the map on page 203 of your text and find the locations of the rebound centers identified in Procedure question 1. What are these same areas called on the map?

Keewatin Center and Labrador Center

2. What is the probable relationship between the rebound centers and the thickness of ice in Canada?

The centers of rebound are probably places where the ice is thickest.

3. What is the probable relationship between the rebound centers and the locations where ice first accumulated?

The centers of rebound are probably the places where the ice first accumulated.

4. (a) According to your graph, by what amount did the map area rebound during the first 1000 years shown on the graph (from 6000 to 5000 years ago)?

This value will depend on student graphs but will probably be about 50 meters.

(b) By what amount has the area rebounded in the last 1000 years?

probably less than 5 meters

(c) Has the rate of uplift been constant? Explain.

The rate of uplift has not been constant. It was faster 5000 to 6000 years ago—just after the ice left the area—than it is today.

5. Which of the following would cause the crust to subside and which to rebound?

(a) the formation of a large delta subside

(b) the erosion of a mountain range rebound

(c) the formation of a large lake behind a dam subside

(d) the accumulation of sediments in a large sea subside

(e) the building of a skyscraper subside

CHAPTER 12
LAB
ACTIVITY

NAME ______

CLASS ______ DATE ______

Beach Erosion and Deposition

Procedure

Use the spaces provided to make cutaway sketches of each of the four model beaches.

Student sketches will vary.

Analysis and Conclusions

1. Based on your models, describe how the rate at which waves strike a shoreline affects the erosion of a gradually-sloping model beach.

The rate of beach erosion increases as the rate of wave action increases.

2. How does the initial slope of the beach affect erosion?

The steep-sloping beach erodes more rapidly than the gently sloping beach. Erosion on a steeply sloped beach leaves a cliff-like feature.

3. Describe the distribution of the sand versus the distribution of the gravel in each of your four trials. Why is there a difference?

The smallest particles are eroded from the beach and transported just offshore, where they are deposited. Because gravel is heavier, it is not moved as far by the waves. Instead, the gravel is left exposed on the shore.

4. Explain how the composition of a beach affects beach erosion. Give evidence for your answer.

The more gravel in the beach, the less erosion will occur.

5. Describe any depositional features formed as a result of wave action on your model beaches. In which trial was deposited material most noticeable?

The only apparent depositional feature is the low mound of sand just offshore. The deposited sand may be more noticeable with the steeply sloped beach.

6. Describe how a large storm could significantly change the features of a beach.

A storm produces larger waves at a greater frequency. The waves reach high up on the beach, causing rapid erosion.

7. Beach erosion is a significant problem for many seaside communities. Suggest ways to stabilize shorelines in order to prevent erosion.

Answers may include building sea walls that prevent large waves from reaching the shore. Ideal material to stabilize a beach might include large rocks that would not be washed away.

CHAPTER 13

LAB ACTIVITY

NAME ______________________________

CLASS ______________ DATE ______________

Convection Currents

Procedure

Use the spaces provided to make sketches of the path of the food coloring for each situation.

Student sketches will vary.

Analysis and Conclusions

1. In comparison to Earth's structure, what does each of the following represent in the model: the shoebox? the water? the cup full of hot water?

The shoebox represents Earth's asthenosphere, the water represents the molten material within the asthenosphere, and the cup of hot water represents the heat source from Earth's core.

2. What could be used to represent lithospheric plates in the model?

Any flat object that floats in water could be used to represent the lithospheric plates floating on the asthenosphere.

3. Explain the motion of the food coloring in Part A of this experiment. Use changes in density as the basis of your explanation.

In the first part of the experiment, the food coloring moved about in a random manner. When heat was added, the particles within the food coloring gained energy and their speed increased. The particles then collided more frequently and violently, and as a result, moved farther apart. The food coloring became less dense and rose toward the surface of the water. At the surface, the substance cooled, its particles lost energy, and moved closer together again. The substance then became more dense and sank back toward the bottom of the box.

4. In Part B of this experiment, what did you observe occurring in the region between the hot cups?

Between the two cups, the food coloring from each cup moved toward the center, cooled, and sank back toward the bottom of the box.

5. In comparison to Earth's structure, what kind of plate boundary does each of the following represent: the region directly over the cups of hot water? the region between the two cups of hot water?

The region over the hot water represents a diverging boundary. The region between the two cups represents a converging boundary.

6. Describe another example of a convection current in a natural system. How does it differ from convection currents in the asthenosphere?

Students' answers will vary but may include heated air that rises, cools, and forms clouds or heated water currents that cool at the surface and sink. Differences between students' answers and the asthenosphere should include composition of material, speed of the convection, and source of heat.

7. What kind of boundary separates the North American Plate from the Eurasian Plate? the Eurasian Plate from the Pacific Plate?

diverging boundary; converging boundary

8. If new material is always emerging from a diverging boundary, are the plates continually growing bigger? Explain your answer.

No; While new material emerges from diverging boundaries, old material can be subducted at converging boundaries.

NAME ______________________

CLASS ______________ DATE ______________

CHAPTER 14

LAB ACTIVITY

Patterns of Volcanism

Analysis and Conclusions

1	2	3	4	5	6	7	8	9
Volcano Belt	Length (km)	Volcanoes in Belt	Volcanoes per 100 km	Volcano-Years	Volcano years per 100 km	Explosive Eruptions	Explosive Eruptions per 100 km	Symbol
Italy	352	7	2.0	241	68.5	21	6.0	*
Kermadecs	530	5	0.9	5	0.9	0	0	•
Bismark-West	477	11	2.3	123	25.8	15	3.1	*
Tonga	686	10	1.5	29	4.2	2	0.3	•
Aleutians	1457	40	2.7	132	9.1	13	0.9	+
Mexico	1043	22	2.1	78	7.5	4	0.4	•
Honshu	732	36	4.9	143	19.5	11	1.5	+
Taiwan	501	7	1.4	1	0.2	0	0	•
Halmahera	162	9	5.6	84	51.9	1	0.6	+
Hikkaido	556	15	2.7	72	12.9	6	1.1	+
Kamchatka	716	47	6.6	203	28.4	26	3.6	*
Cascades	1152	38	3.3	8	0.7	2	0.2	•
Central America	1254	79	6.3	337	26.9	30	2.4	*
Peru-Chile-North	1363	63	4.6	43	3.2	1	0.1	•
Sunda	965	30	3.1	112	11.6	6	0.6	+

Figure 14.17 Volcanic belt activity during the past 100 years.

1. Of the 15 volcanic belts, which is the longest? How long is it? Does the longest belt have the greatest total number of volcanoes? Explain your answer.

The Aleutian belt is the longest at 1457 km. The Central America belt has the greatest number of volcanoes (79).

2. If each of the 7 volcanoes in the Taiwan belt had been active every year during the past 100 years, what number would appear in column 5 for the Taiwan belt?

$7 \times 100 = 700$

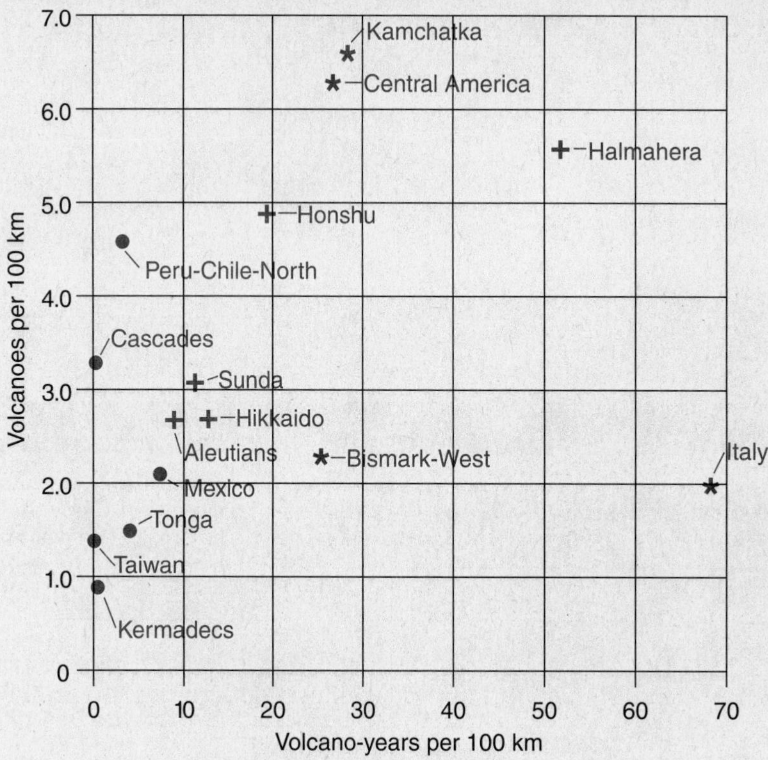

3. During the past 100 years, in which belt have volcanoes been active the greatest number of years? The least number of years?

The volcanoes in the Central America belt have been active the greatest number of years; those of the Taiwan belt, the least.

4. In which belt have the greatest number of explosive eruptions occurred within the past 100 years? How many were there?

The Central America belt; 30

5. Based on your graph, what is the relationship between the number of years in which volcanoes in a belt erupted, the number of volcanoes in the belt, and the number of explosive eruptions over the past 100 years that averaged over 100 km?

Belts with greater total numbers of volcanoes have greater numbers of years of volcanic activity and a greater number of explosive eruptions per 100 km.

6. Does the data for the Halmahera belt correspond with your answer to question 5? What can you infer about eruptions in the Halmahera belt?

The Halmahera belt should have a high number of explosive eruptions, but it does not. Apparently most eruptions along this belt are smooth.

7. The amount of volcanism in a belt is thought to be related to the rate at which the lithospheric plates are coming together. According to your graph, which belt would you expect to have the most rapid rate of convergence? Use Figure 13.1 on page 233 of your text to determine which plates cause the volcanic activity.

The point for the Italy belt is farthest to the right; therefore, the Italy belt should have the highest rate of convergence. It is the result of subduction of the African Plate beneath the Eurasian Plate.

CHAPTER 15
LAB ACTIVITY

NAME ______________________________

CLASS ____________________ DATE ____________________

Earthquakes and Subduction Boundaries

Analysis and Conclusions

Data Table B			
Earthquake Type	**Focus Depth (km)**	**Tonga Total**	**Chile Total**
Shallow	< 70	11	7
Intermediate	70–300	8	25
Deep	> 300	22	3
Total Number of Quakes		41	35

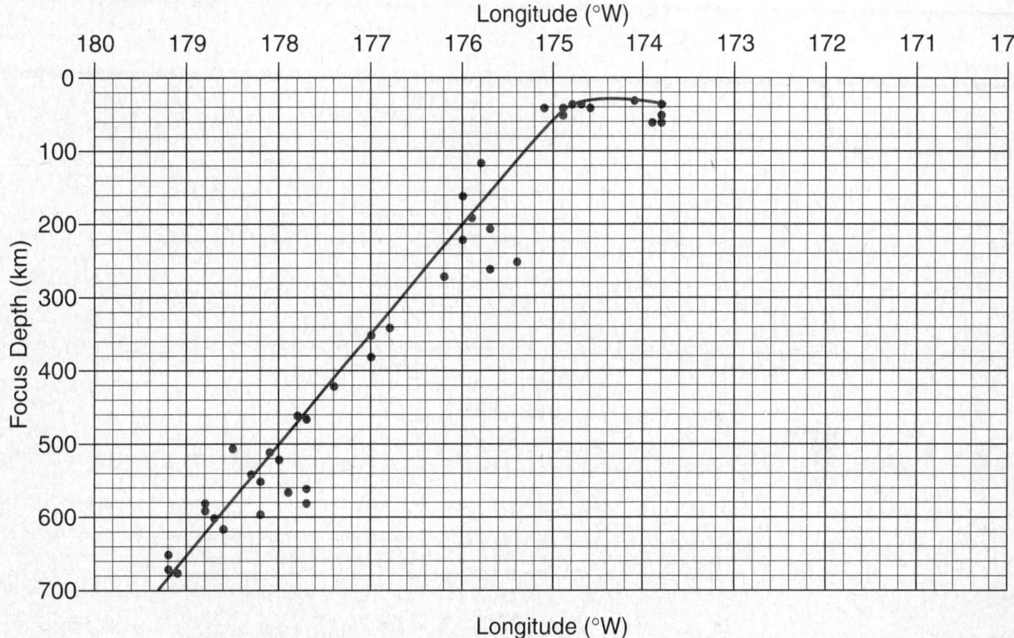

Figure 15.17 Longitude versus focus depth, Tonga area

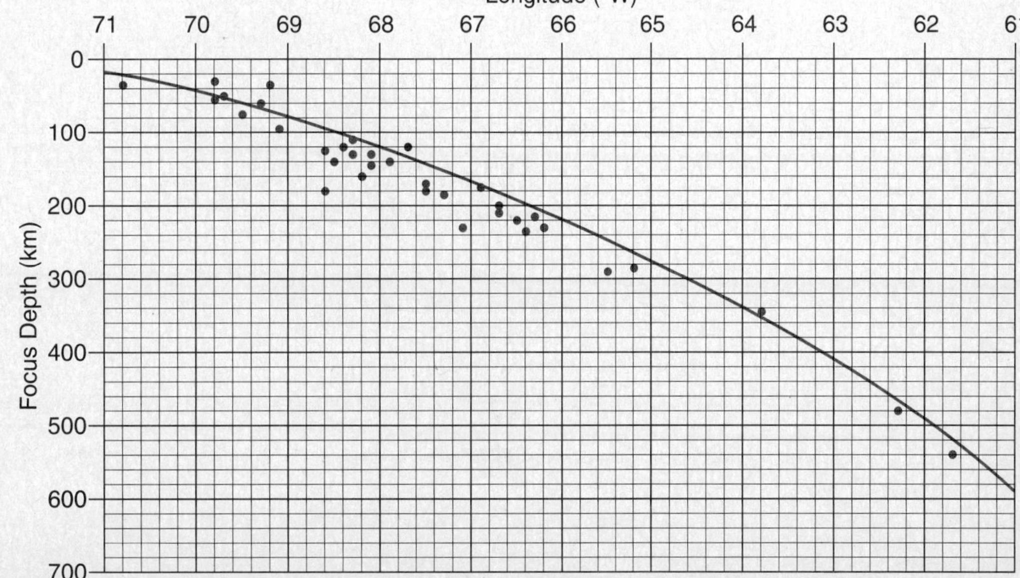

Longitude versus focus depth, Chile area

1. Locate the Tonga and the Chile areas using the maps on pages 233, 656 – 657, and 664 of your text. What plate is subducting in each location? Under which plates are those plates subducting?

For the Tonga area, the Pacific Plate is subducting and the Indian Plate is overriding. For the Chile area, the Nazca Plate is subducting and the South American Plate is overriding.

2. Locate the East Pacific Rise on the map on pages 656 and 657 of your text.

(a) Compare the distance of the Tonga area from the East Pacific Rise with the distance of the Chile area from the East Pacific Rise.

The Tonga area is farther from the East Pacific Rise than the Chile area.

(b) Mid-ocean ridges are the source of oceanic crust. If the East Pacific Rise is the source of the subducting crust in both areas, how do the ages of the two subducting plates compare?

The subducting plate at Tonga must be older than the subducting plate at Chile.

3. Look at your values in Data Table B. Compare the focus depth of the majority of the earthquakes at Tonga with those at Chile.

At Tonga, most earthquake foci are deep (>300 km), while at Chile, most earthquake foci are intermediate (70-300 km) in depth.

4. Now look at the profiles you have drawn for the two areas.

(a) For which area is the subducting plate moving westward? Tonga

(b) Which plate is subducting at a steeper angle? Chile

(c) What does this mean about the type of plate beneath which each plate is being subducted? Explain your answer fully.

The plate at Chile is subducting beneath a continent; the plate at Tonga is subducting beneath an oceanic plate.

5. For the Chile data, the deepest earthquake occurred at longitude 61.7°W and at a depth of 540 kilometers. If the rocks started subducting (left the surface) 10 million years ago and the distance down the subducting plate to the present location is 1000 kilometers, what is the plate's rate of descent, in centimeters per year?

$$\frac{1000\text{ km}}{1} \times \frac{1000\text{ m}}{\text{km}} \times \frac{100\text{ cm}}{\text{m}} \times \frac{1}{10\,000\,000\text{ yr}} = 10\text{ cm/yr}$$

6. Would you expect the subduction rate at Tonga to be more or less than the Chilean rate? Why?

More, because the subducting plate at Tonga is older and therefore denser.

7. Summarize the differences between the subducting plate at Tonga and the subducting plate at Chile by comparing their (a) distance from assumed source of lithosphere, (b) age, (c) angle of descent, (d) rate of descent, and (e) number of deep focus earthquakes.

The subducting plate at Tonga is farther from the source, older, steeper, faster, and has more deep focus earthquakes than the subducting plate at Chile.

NAME ______________________

CLASS ____________ DATE ____________

Mountains and Plate Boundaries

Procedure

1. Use the Physical World map on pages 656 and 657 of your text to locate the Rocky, Appalachian, Andes, Atlas, Alps, and Himalayan mountains.

2. Turn to Figure 13.1 on page 233 of your text. Identify and list the plate (North American, Eurasian, African, etc.) on which each mountain range is located.

Rockies and Appalachians on North American Plate, Andes on South American Plate, Atlas on African Plate, Alps and Himalayas on Eurasian Plate

3. How many of the mountain ranges named in Question 1 are directly on or beside a plate boundary? Name the mountain range and identify the two plates that meet at that plate boundary.

Andes at the Nazca/South American plate boundary; Atlas and Alps at the African/Eurasian plate boundary; Himalayas at the Indian/Eurasian plate boundary

4. Review the definitions *of active continental margin* and *passive continental margin* on page 291 of your text. Which of these margin types is associated with each of your answers to Question 3?

All are at active continental margins.

5. Use the Physical World map to locate the mid-Atlantic Ridge, the East Pacific Rise, the Southeast Indian Ocean Ridge, and the Southwest Indian Ocean Ridge. Each of these mid-ocean ridges is an underwater mountain range.

6. Review the definitions of *diverging boundary* and *converging boundary* on pages 240 and 242 of your text. Which term applies to the mountains identified in your answer to Question 3? Which term applies to mid-ocean ridge systems? What is the basic difference in plate motions between the formation of mountain chains on continents and the formation of mountain chains on the sea floor?

Active continental margins are converging boundaries. Mid-ocean ridges occur at diverging boundaries. The mountain chains on continents are the result of plates coming together; mountains form from the folding and faulting of the rocks due to compression. The mountains of the seafloor are the result of plates pulling apart and associated volcanism.

Analysis and Conclusions

1. The Andes Mountains are younger than the Appalachian Mountains. What evidence is there on the Physical World map that supports this statement?

The Andes are on an active continental margin and are therefore still forming. The Appalachians are on a passive continental margin. They were formed long ago when the eastern coast of North America was also an active continental margin. The Appalachians are smaller because of weathering and erosion over millions of years.

2. Would you expect to find extensive mountain building taking place in Australia? Explain your answer.

No; Australia is in the center of a plate and is surrounded by passive continental margins.

3. Which mountain range is more likely to have active volcanoes, the Andes or the Rockies? Explain your answer.

The Andes. The Andes are presently on an active continental margin; volcanoes are often associated with such margins. The Rockies are not near a plate margin.

4. Active continental margins are also called *seismic* continental margins, while passive continental margins are called *aseismic* continental margins. To what occurrence does the term *seismic* usually refer? What must *aseismic* mean? Explain why these are appropriate terms to apply to their respective plate boundaries.

Students know that *seismic* means that the boundary must be associated with earthquakes. Therefore, an aseismic boundary must lack earthquakes. *Seismic* is appropriate for active plate boundaries because they have earthquakes. *Aseismic* is appropriate for passive plate boundaries since they would not be expected to have earthquakes.

CHAPTER 16

MAP ACTIVITY

NAME ______________________

CLASS ____________ DATE ____________

TEXT ACTIVITY

DATA SHEET

Folded Mountains

Procedure

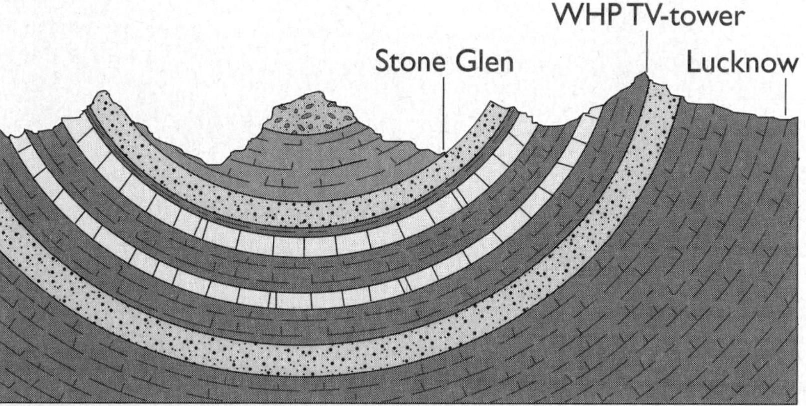

Figure 16.10 Cross section, Harrisburg area

1. Turn to the Physical Map of the United States on pages 654 and 655 of your text. Locate Harrisburg on the map. In what mountain range is Harrisburg located?

Harrisburg is located in the Appalachian Mountains.

2. Now turn to the topographic map of the Harrisburg area on page 652 of your text. Compare the map with the geologic cross-section shown in Figure 16.10. List the four mountains that occur on both the map and the cross-section. In what general map or compass direction was the cross-section drawn (i.e., N-S, E-W)?

Peters, Third, Second, and Blue Mountains appear on both the map and cross-section. The cross-section was drawn in a mostly N-S direction.

3. Look at the cross-section. Two of the mountains shown on the cross-section are formed from the same rock formation. Identify those two mountains. What is the name of the rock formation?

Peters and Second Mountains are both formed from the Pocono Sandstone.

4. Look at the figures in Chapter 16 between pages 294 and 300 of your text. Locate the figure or part of the figure that most resembles the structure shown in the cross-section. What is this structure called?

The overall structure is a syncline.

5. Compare the composition of the ridges in the Harrisburg area with the composition of the valleys. Which rock types form ridges and which rock types form valleys?

The ridges are made of sandstone and conglomerate, while the valleys are made of limestone and shale.

6. Locate Stone Glen on the topographic map on page 652 of your text. Determine where Stone Glen would be located on the cross-section above and label this spot. Repeat this procedure for the community of Lucknow, the airway beacon, and the WHP TV–tower. Which of these features is either located on or formed by the oldest rocks? Which is located on or formed by the youngest rocks?

Locknow is located on the oldest rock. Third Mountain is made of the youngest rock.

Analysis and Conclusions

1. Why is it impossible to determine if sedimentary rock layers have been overturned using only a topographic map?

The rock layers must be examined for such sedimentary features as ripple marks, cross-bedding, and mud cracks. Such features are not shown on topographic maps.

2. Using the Physical Map of the United States on pages 654 and 655 of your text, identify at least three eastern states (not including Pennsylvania) where folded rock layers would be expected to occur at Earth's surface. Why would folded rocks not be expected to occur in the Atlantic Coastal Plain?

Any state that contains the Appalachian Mountains would be expected to have folded layers. Virginia, West Virginia, Tennessee, and North Carolina are four examples. Folded layers would not be expected to occur on the Atlantic Coastal Plain because it is a passive continental margin.

NAME ______________________________

CLASS ______________ DATE ______________

Interpreting a Salinity Profile

Analysis and Conclusions

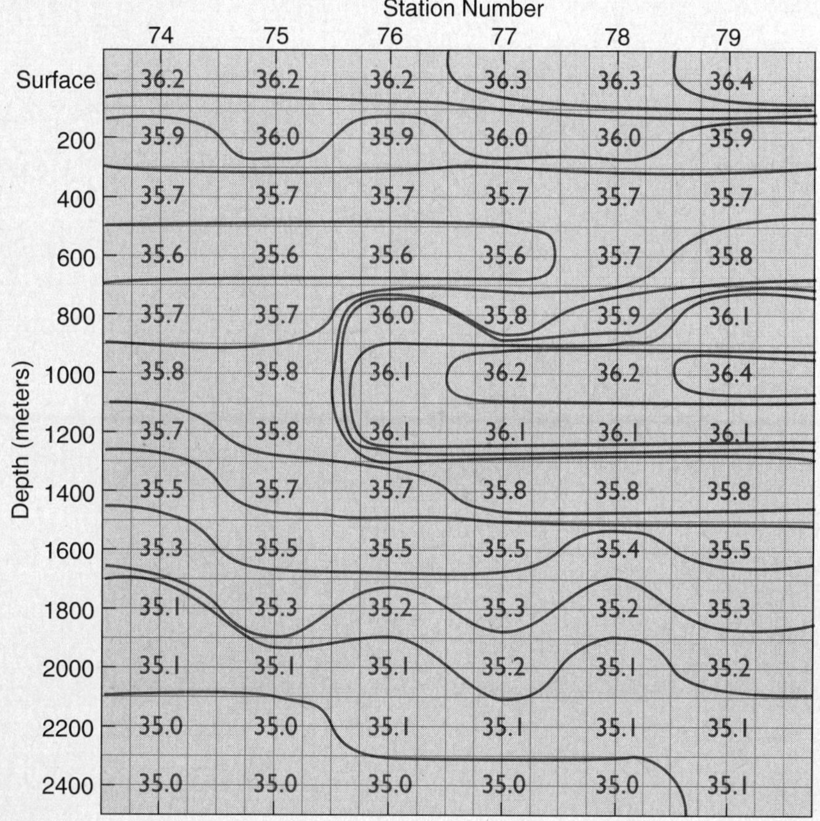

Figure 17.10 Grid for salinity profile

1. What is the average salinity of ocean water? In what area of your profile is this average value found?

Average salinity is 35‰. The average is found at 2200 and 2400 meters on the profile.

2. At which stations and depths are salinity values on your profile highest? At which stations and depths are salinity values lowest?

The highest values are located at station 79 at depths of 0 and 1000 meters. The lowest values are located at stations 74 and 75 at a depth of 2200 meters and at stations 74–78 at a depth of 2400 feet.

3. The cruise area from which these salinity values were taken is 36° N and 10°–20° W. Turn to the Earth's Climate map on page 644 of your text and locate the cruise area. Describe the climate of the land area nearest to the cruise area.

Hot, dry summers, and mild, rainy winters

4. How would you expect the climate in the cruise area to affect the salinity at the ocean surface? How would you expect the climate to affect the deeper ocean levels? Does your salinity profile support your answer?

A hot, dry climate would cause evaporation, increasing salinity at the surface but not affecting the salinity at deeper levels. High salinity at the surface of the profile and low salinity at the deepest levels supports this.

5. Describe the salinity profile at depths of 800–1200 meters. Can the characteristics of the profile be explained by the climate of the area?

Salinity increases from west to east with very high salinity at station 79. Such a profile would not directly be caused by climate.

6. Explain how the presence of the Mediterranean Sea east of the cruise area accounts for the salinity profile at 800–1200 meters.

The Mediterranean Sea has very high salinity. Water from the Mediterranean Sea is responsible for higher salinity in deeper levels.

7. Based on your answer to question 6, explain the likely depth and direction of ocean currents in the cruise area.

A current flows west from the Mediterranean Sea at a depth of 800–1200 meters.

8. In some parts of the world, ocean water with above average salinity values sinks to deeper levels. Is there any evidence for such vertical movements of water in your salinity profile? Explain your answer.

No; Except for depths of 800–1200 meters, the highest salinity is at the surface and lowest salinity at deepest levels.

NAME ______________________

CLASS ______________ DATE ______________

The Ocean Floor

Procedure

1. Deep sea trenches are long linear depressions of the ocean floor. Locate the ocean trenches on the Physical World map, on pages 656–657 of your text. Where do most ocean trenches occur in relation to landmasses?

Most trenches occur near the edges of continents or other landmasses.

2. Use the map to determine the name of the longest ocean trench. Where is this trench located?

The longest trench is the Peru-Chile Trench, which extends along the west coast of South America.

3. Look at the locations of the mid-ocean ridges that appear on the map. Where do most mid-ocean ridges occur in relation to landmasses?

Most mid-ocean ridges occur at a distance from landmasses.

4. On the map, long parallel lines cross the mid-ocean ridges. What do these lines represent?

The long parallel lines represent transform faults.

5. Use your finger to trace the blue line along the mid-ocean ridge. How would you describe the bend of the line? Look at the map, what is causing this shape?

The line along the mid-ocean ridge can be described as a jagged line with steplike features; the ridges are offset at the transform fault.

6. Look at Figure 18.15 on page 338 of your text. It is a diagram of a small section of the Pacific Ocean floor. What features appear on the ocean floor in this area? How are these features formed?

The features are trenches and seamounts. Trenches form when one plate subducts another plate. Seamounts are submerged underwater volcanoes.

 NAME ______________________ CLASS ______________________ DATE ______________________

Analysis and Conclusions

1. How are trenches related to plate boundaries? How are trenches explained by the theory of plate tectonics?

Trenches occur where one plate subducts below another plate. According to the plate tectonic theory, this occurs where two plates converge.

2. Locate the continental shelves on the east and west coasts of South America. Compare the shelves. Use the plate tectonic theory to help explain any of the differences that you see.

The shelf along the east coast is wider than the shelf along the west coast. The east coast is a passive margin; the west coast is an active margin.

3. Compare the shape of ocean trenches to the shape of the mid-ocean ridges. Why are they different?

Ocean trenches are smooth curves; mid-ocean ridges are jagged. The transform faults along the mid-ocean ridge are responsible for the differences.

4. Explain why Japan has numerous severe earthquakes while few occur in Australia.

Japan lies along a plate boundary where the movement causes earthquakes. Australia lies in the middle of a plate.

CHAPTER 18

LAB ACTIVITY

NAME ______________________

CLASS ____________ DATE ____________

Contour of the Ocean Floor

Analysis and Conclusions

Use the graph grid on the other side of this data sheet to construct your ocean floor profile.

1. Approximately how wide is the continental shelf at Cape May, New Jersey, and at Cape Roca, Portugal?

The shelf is about 160 km wide at Cape May and 40 km wide at Cape Roca.

2. Look at the Physical World: Continents and Oceans Floor map on pages 656–657 of your text. Compare the width of the continental shelf along the east coast of North America with the continental shelf of the west coast of Europe.

The continental shelf on the east coast of North America is approximately four times as wide as that of the west coast of Europe.

3. Continental slope is the steep drop from the edge of the continental shelf. The less-steep portion after the slope is the continental rise. The deepest portions of the ocean are the abyssal plains. Seamounts are peaks rising from the ocean floor that do not rise to the surface. Label all such points on your diagram.

4. Because of the vertical exaggeration of the diagram, the slopes look much greater than they really are. Calculate the actual slope of the continental slope in fathoms per kilometer at Cape May and Cape Roca. (Slope equals change in depth divided by change in distance.)

Slope at Cape May is

$$\frac{1000 \text{ fathoms} - 100 \text{ fathoms}}{200 \text{ kilometers} - 1600 \text{ kilometers}} = 22.5 \text{ fathoms/kilometer}$$

Slope at Cape Roca is

$$\frac{1000 \text{ fathoms} - 100 \text{ fathoms}}{5560 \text{ kilometers} - 5440 \text{ kilometers}} = 7.5 \text{ fathoms/kilometer}$$

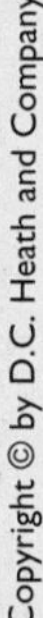

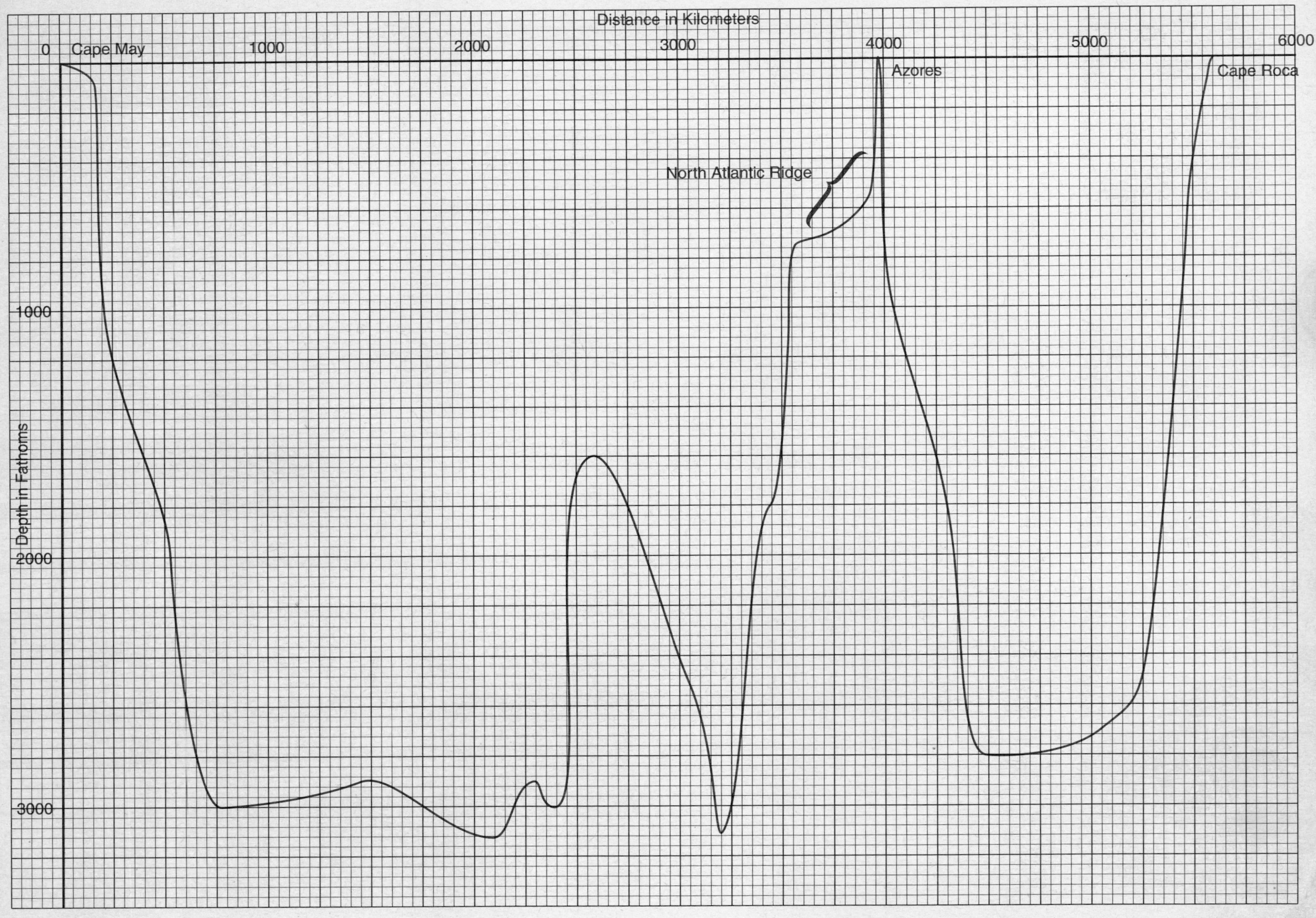

Distance in Kilometers
0
Cape May
1000
2000
3000
4000
5000
6000
Azores
Cape Roca
North Atlantic Ridge
Depth in Fathoms
1000
2000
3000

CHAPTER 19

MAP ACTIVITY

NAME ______

CLASS ______ DATE ______

World Ocean Currents

Procedure

Data Table

Name of Current	Ocean Basin	Location in Ocean Basin	General Temperature	Flow Direction Relative to Equator
Gulf Stream	Atlantic	west	warm	away
California	Pacific	east	cold	toward
Canary	Atlantic	east	cold	toward
Peru	Pacific	east	cold	toward
Brazil	Atlantic	west	warm	away
Kuroshio	Pacific	west	warm	away
W. Australia	Indian	east	cold	toward
E. Australia	Pacific	west	warm	away
Benguela	Atlantic	east	cold	toward
Agulhas	Indian	west	warm	away

Part A—Current Properties

2. Based on your data, what is the relationship between the temperature of the ocean current and the direction of current flow relative to the equator? Explain why this relationship occurs.

Warm currents flow away from the equator; cold currents flow toward the equator. The equator is warm, and therefore currents flowing from equatorial regions are warm. Currents flowing toward the equator originate in colder areas and are therefore cold.

3. What is the relationship between current temperature and the side of the ocean on which that current flows?

Warm ocean currents are found on the west sides of ocean basins, while cold ocean currents occur on the east sides.

Part B—Northern Hemisphere

4. Lay a sheet of tracing paper over the Surface Ocean Currents map on page 658 of your text so that it completely covers the western half of the map. With a sharp pencil, trace as much of the map border and equator as possible. Using a colored pencil, trace the four arrows showing the flow direction of the North Equatorial current in the Pacific Ocean. In what compass direction do the arrows point? West

5. Move the tracing paper to the Prevailing World Winds map on page 659 of your text and align the map border and the equator. With a different colored pencil, trace the three arrows representing the Northeast Trades in the Pacific Ocean. In what compass direction do these arrows point? (Note that winds are named for the direction *from* which they blow not the direction to which they blow.) Southwest

6. Turn your tracing paper so that the arrows for the Northeast Trades are, in general, pointing away from you. Do the arrows for the North Equatorial current point to your left or to your right? Right

7. Based upon your previous answer, what is the general relationship between ocean current direction and the winds that cause them in the Northern Hemisphere?

Ocean currents in the Northern Hemisphere flow to the right of the winds that cause them.

Part C—Southern Hemisphere

8. Once again, align your tracing paper with the Surface Ocean Currents map and trace the two South Equatorial arrows in the Pacific Ocean. In what compass direction do the arrows point? West

9. Move the tracing paper to the Prevailing World Winds map and trace the four Southeast Trades arrows in the Pacific Ocean. In what compass direction do the arrows point? Northwest

10. Turn your tracing paper so that the arrows for the Southeast Trades are, in general, pointing away from you. Do the arrows for the South Equatorial current point to your left or to your right? Left

11. Based upon your previous answer, what is the general relationship between ocean current direction and the winds that cause them in the Southern Hemisphere?

Ocean currents in the Southern Hemisphere flow to the left of the winds that cause them.

Analysis and Conclusions

Refer to the Surface Ocean Currents map on page 658 of your text to answer questions 1–4.

1. Compare the directions (clockwise or counterclockwise) of the major circulation patterns in the oceans of the Northern and Southern Hemispheres.

clockwise in Northern Hemisphere; counterclockwise in Southern Hemisphere

2. What is the general relationship between current temperature and direction of flow along the east coast of the continents? Along the west coast of the continents?

East coasts have warm currents flowing away from the equator (poleward) while west coasts have cold currents flowing toward the equator.

3. An ocean fog will occur when moist air blowing from a warm ocean current meets cold air over a cold ocean current (Chapter 19, Topic 5). Which Australian coast (N, S, E, or W) is most likely to experience such fogs? Explain your answer.

Fog is more likely to occur on the west coast where warm, moist air from the South Equatorial current meets the cold waters of the West Australia current.

4. Which current flows around Earth without interruption by land? Where does it flow?

The West Wind Drift flows around Antarctica.

CHAPTER 20
LAB
ACTIVITY

NAME ______

CLASS ______ DATE ______

TEXT
ACTIVITY
DATA
SHEET

The Simple Spectroscope

Analysis and Conclusions

In the spaces provided use colored pencils to draw the pattern you see for incandescent light, fluorescent light, daylight, and sodium chloride.

Incandescent Light

Fluorescent Light

Daylight

Sodium Chloride

 NAME ______ CLASS ______ DATE ______

1. Describe the spectrum for white light based on your observations of the incandescent bulb. What does the spectrum tell you about the composition of white light?

White light is composed of many individual colors.

2. Compare the spectra for the incandescent light, fluorescent light, and daylight. How are all three similar? How do they differ?

All three show a continuous spectrum composed of all colors from red through violet. The spectrum of the fluorescent light is continuous but shows distinct bright lines in the green and violet.

3. Describe the spectrum for sodium chloride. What type of spectrum is it? How do the colors differ from the other spectra you have seen?

It is a bright-line spectrum with two very bright yellow lines. Other spectra have been continuous with many colors.

4. Once again, observe the spectrum of daylight. If you look carefully, you should be able to see that some colors are missing. What do you think accounts for these missing colors?

The colors were absorbed by gases in the sun's atmosphere. Earth's atmosphere is also an absorber.

NAME ______

CLASS ______ DATE ______

Constellations and the Seasons

Procedure

Part A—Locating Stars

1. Turn to the star maps on pages 660–661 of your text. Does the position of Polaris relative to the northern horizon on each map change throughout the year?

No

2. Locate the Big Dipper on the Winter map. If a line connecting the Pointers in the Big Dipper is continued to the right, to which star does the line point? How can the Big Dipper be used to find direction in the Northern Hemisphere?

Polaris; The Big Dipper points toward Polaris, which is north.

3. If a line drawn through the three closely spaced stars in the middle of Orion is continued to the left, toward which constellation does it point? Canis

4. Name the constellation in which each of the following stars is located:

(a) Polaris Ursa Minor
(b) Antares Scorpius
(c) Vega Lyra
(d) Spica Virgo
(e) Betelgeuse Orion
(f) Rigel Orion
(g) Arcturus Bootes

Data Table

Constellation	Autumn	Winter	Spring	Summer
Bootes	not visible	not visible	overhead	W
Lyra	NW	not visible	NE	overhead
Orion	E	overhead	not visible	not visible
Pegasus	overhead	NW	not visible	E

Part B—Apparent Motion

7. Write *Map A* on the bottom of a sheet of tracing paper and trace the circular outline and compass directions from the Autumn map. Trace the outline of Gemini and label it *Autumn.* Move the tracing paper to the Winter map and line up the compass directions. Trace the position of Gemini on this map and label it *Winter.* Repeat for the Spring map. Note that Gemini does not appear on the Summer map. Draw arrows between the seasonal positions of Gemini to show its direction of movement. What is the general compass direction of movement of Gemini across the sky over the three seasons?

Gemini moves east to west (or northeast to northwest).

8. Write *Map B* on the bottom of a second sheet of tracing paper and trace the outline and compass directions from the Spring map. Mark the locations of the stars Vega, Deneb, and Altair. Connect the stars and label the triangle *Spring.* These three stars make up the *Summer Triangle.* Repeat this procedure for the Summer and Autumn maps. In what season does the Summer Triangle rise above the horizon, in what direction does it move across the sky, and in what season does it set?

spring; westward; autumn.

9. Write *Map C* on a third sheet of tracing paper and trace the outline and compass directions from the Spring map. Mark and label Polaris and the constellation Cassiopeia. Label the whole drawing *Position A.* Move Map C to the Summer map. Again trace Cassiopeia. Label this tracing *Position B.* Draw an arrow from Position A pointing toward Position B. In what direction (clockwise or counterclockwise) has Cassiopeia moved relative to Polaris between Position A and Position B? In what direction must other constellations move relative to Polaris from one season to another?

Cassiopeia moved counterclockwise relative to Polaris. Other constellations must move counterclockwise.

Analysis and Conclusions

1. Explain why the position of Polaris does not change relative to the northern horizon during the year. How does this fact help in finding direction?

Polaris is over Earth's northern axis of rotation. Polaris is always north.

2. Explain how stars and constellations can serve as landmarks for other stars and constellations.

Certain stars within constellations, such as the Pointer stars in the Big Dipper and the three stars in Orion's belt, can be used to locate other stars and constellations.

3. Look over the data you collected in the data table for procedure step 5. Which season provides the best viewing of each constellation? Explain.

The best viewing occurs when the constellations are directly overhead. In this way, haze on the horizon cannot obscure the view. This occurs for Bootes in spring, Lyra in summer, Orion in winter, and Pegasus in autumn.

4. Based upon the path plotted on Map A, where is Gemini in the summer? Explain why it does not appear on the Summer map.

In summer, Gemini is over the northern horizon and cannot be seen.

5. The three closely-spaced stars in the middle of Orion are located almost directly over Earth's equator. Thus, Orion can be seen in the Southern Hemisphere. For an observer at a mid-latitude location in South America, in what compass direction will Orion first appear above the horizon each year? If this observer is looking toward the point in the sky directly above the South Pole, will Orion move clockwise or counterclockwise with the seasons? Explain.

east; clockwise; Since the observer is facing in the opposite direction, toward the South Pole instead of the North Pole, the motion of the stars rising in the east and setting in the west will be clockwise around the point in the sky directly over the South Pole.

6. Map C shows Cassiopeia at two different times during the year. Cassiopeia will also be in these same two positions at two different times each day. If the four star maps represented the position of the stars during one rotation of Earth on its axis, how much time in hours would have passed between positions A and B? Explain.

Six hours; Since there are four maps for one year, the maps must be one fourth of a year apart in time. For one day, the maps must be one fourth of a day apart. One fourth of a 24 hour day is 6 hours.

CHAPTER 22

LAB ACTIVITY

NAME ______

CLASS ______ DATE ______

Ellipses and Eccentricity

Analysis and Conclusions

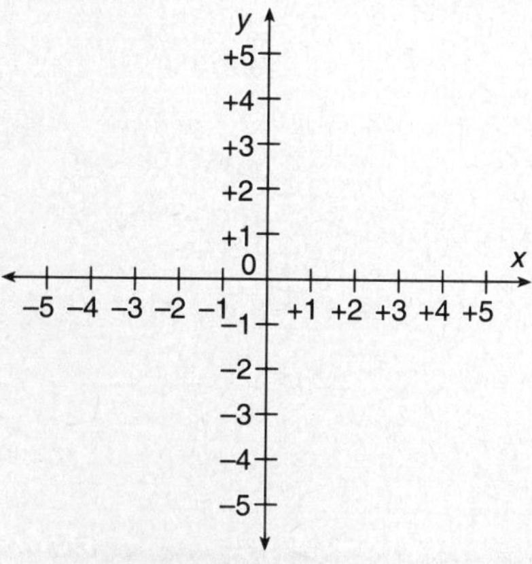

Data Table B						
	Ellipse 1	Ellipse 2	Ellipse 3	Ellipse 4	Ellipse 5	Ellipse 6
distance between foci (d)	9.0	6.0	3.0	6.0	3.0	1.8
length of major axis (L)	10.0	10.0	10.0	6.7	5.0	6.0
eccentricity (e = d/L)	0.9	0.6	0.3	0.9	0.6	0.3

1. Study the shapes of Ellipses 1, 2, and 3. Which ellipse appears to be the most circular? Which ellipse appears to be the least circular? What are the eccentricities of these ellipses?

Ellipse 3 appears most circular and has an eccentricity of 0.3. Ellipse 1 appears least circular and has an eccentricity of 0.9.

2. Describe the relationship between how circular an ellipse appears and its eccentricity.

As ellipses become more circular, the eccentricity decreases.

3. Which ellipse has the same eccentricity as Ellipse 1? How do the shapes of these two ellipses compare? Which ellipse has the same eccentricity as Ellipse 3? How do the shapes of these two ellipses compare?

Ellipse 4 has the same eccentricity and shape as Ellipse 1. Ellipse 6 has the same eccentricity and shape as Ellipse 3.

4. Which factors—distance between foci, length of the major axis, or eccentricity—have to be equal in order for two ellipses to have the same shape? Give evidence for your answer.

The eccentricity (e) must be the same if the ellipses are to have the same shape. Ellipses with the same focal length but different eccentricities, such as Ellipses 2 and 4, have different shapes. Ellipses with the same major axis length but different eccentricities, such as Ellipses 1, 2, and 3, have different shapes.

5. What geometric shape would result if both foci were located at point (0,0) of the graph? What would be the eccentricity of such an ellipse?

The shape would be a circle (e = 0).

6. Data Table C shows the orbital eccentricity of the planets. Compare the shapes of your ellipses with the shapes of the planets' orbits. Which ellipses are the best models for the shape of the planets' orbits? Explain your answer.

The eccentricities of Ellipses 3 and 6 (0.3) are closest to those of the planets' orbits.

7. Which planet has the most circular orbit? Which planet has the least circular orbit? Explain your answer.

The orbit of Venus has the lowest eccentricity and therefore has the most circular orbit. Pluto's orbit has the highest eccentricity and therefore has the least circular orbit.

8. Many comets have eccentricities of close to 1. Describe the shape of such an orbit. Which of your ellipses is most similar to the orbit of one of these comets?

The comet's orbit would be very elliptical. It would be most similar to Ellipses 1 and 4.

9. Mars has two moons, Phobos and Deimos. The orbit of Phobos has a major axis length of 18 800 km. The distance between the foci is 281 km. The orbit of Deimos has a major axis length of 46 918 km. The distance between foci is 23.4 km. Which moon has a more circular orbit? Explain your answer.

The orbit of Deimos has a lower eccentricity (0.0005) than the orbit of Phobos (0.015) and is therefore more circular.

10. The orbit of Mars has an eccentricity of 0.093. The distance between the two foci is 0.283 AU. The closest Mars gets to the sun is 1.38 AU. What is the farthest Mars gets from the sun? (Hint: Remember that the sun is located at one of the foci.)

$$\frac{d}{e} = L; \quad \frac{0.283}{0.093\text{ AU}} = 3.04\text{ AU}$$

$$3.04\text{ AU} - 1.38\text{ AU} = 1.66\text{ AU}$$

NAME ____________________

CLASS ____________ DATE ____________

CHAPTER 23

LAB ACTIVITY

TEXT ACTIVITY

DATA SHEET

Dimensions of the Solar System

Data Table A

Name of Planet	Distance from sun		Size of Planet		
	Actual (in million km)	On Model (in cm)	Actual Diameter (in thousand km)	Model Diameter (in cm)	Model Radius (in cm)
Mercury	58	1.2	4.9	0.2	0.1
Venus	108	2.2	12.1	0.6	0.3
Earth	150	3.0	12.8	0.6	0.3
Mars	228	4.6	6.9	0.3	0.2
Jupiter	778	15.6	142.8	6.5	3.3
Saturn	1427	28.5	120.0	5.5	2.8
Uranus	2870	57.4	51.8	2.4	1.2
Neptune	4497	89.9	49.5	2.3	1.2
Pluto	5900	118.0	2.4	0.1	0.1

Analysis and Conclusions

1. Based on your model, describe how the sizes of the inner planets compare to the sizes of the outer planets. Which planet is an exception to your answer?

The inner planets are much smaller than the outer planets. Pluto, which is the smallest planet in the solar system, is the exception.

2. Describe how the distances between the orbits of the inner planets compare to the distances between the orbits of the outer planets.

The distances between the orbits of the inner planets are much smaller than the distances between the orbits of the outer planets.

3. How is your model of the orbit of Pluto incorrect? (Refer to Chapter 23.)

Currently, Pluto is closer to the sun than Neptune.

4. How many times farther from the sun is the orbit of Pluto than the orbit of Earth?

Pluto is at an average distance of 5900 million km from the sun. Earth is at an average distance of 150 million km.

$$\frac{5900 \text{ million km}}{150 \text{ million km}} = 39.3 \text{ times farther}$$

5. How many times larger than Earth is the planet Uranus?

The diameter of Uranus is 51.8 thousand km. The diameter of Earth is 12.8 thousand km.

$$\frac{51.8 \text{ thousand km}}{12.8 \text{ thousand km}} = 4.0 \text{ times larger}$$

6. Calculate the orbit distance of Pluto using the same scale you used to calculate its diameter. Multiply Pluto's actual distance from the sun by 1000 and divide the answer by 22. Round off the answer to the nearest 1 cm. How long a strip of adding machine tape would you need to fit Pluto's orbit?

$$\frac{5900 \text{ million km}}{1} \times \frac{1 \text{ cm}}{2.2 \times 10^4 \text{km}} = 268\ 181.8 \text{ cm}$$

NAME ______________________

CLASS ______________ DATE ______________

Moon, Sun, and Seasons

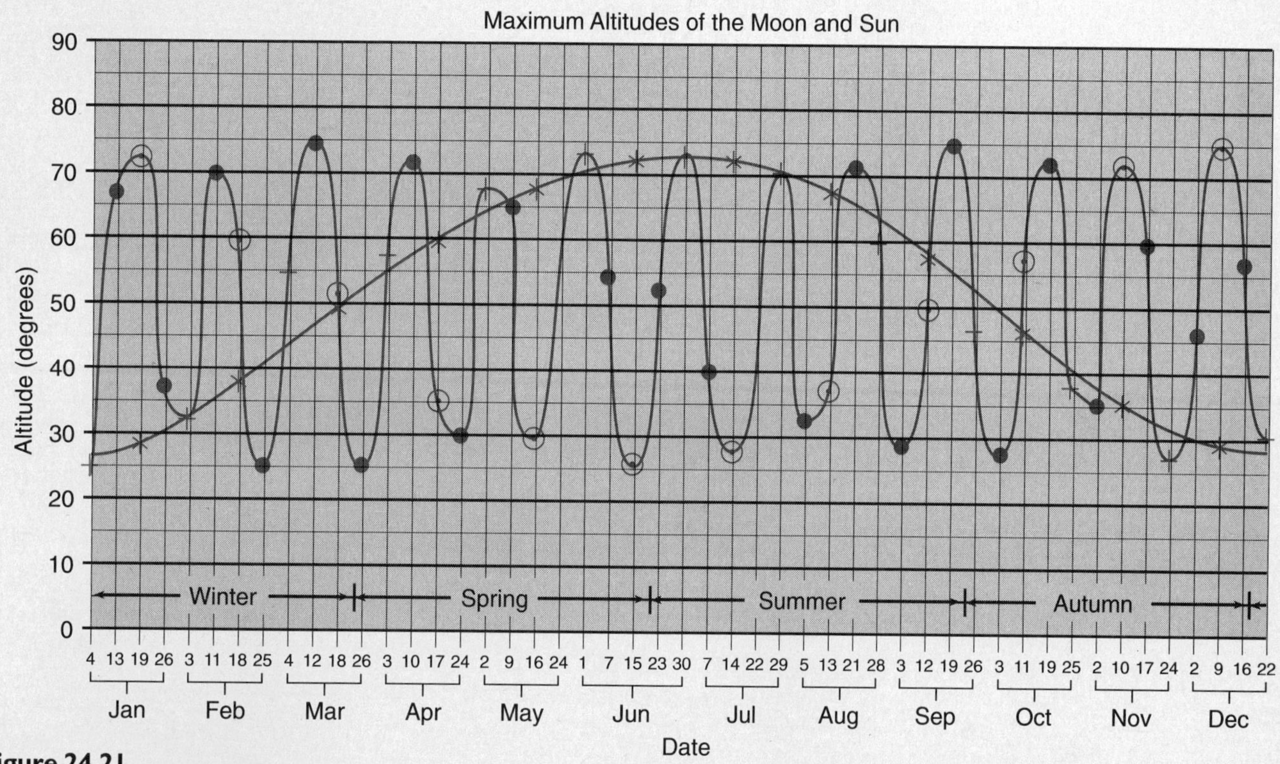

Figure 24.21

Analysis and Conclusions

1. Based upon the pattern on your graph, what is the most likely date of the first full moon in the next year? Explain your answer.

The first full moon would be January 8. With the exception of February, each full moon occurred one calendar day earlier than on the previous month.

2. On your graph, compare the new moon altitudes throughout the year to the curve connecting the sun's altitudes. Why do the new moon altitudes parallel the path of the sun all year?

The new moon is always on the same side of Earth as the sun. Therefore, the new moon's apparent location in the sky must always be near that of the sun. The variations in the altitudes of the sun and new moon over the course of the year will be the same.

3. (a) In which month is the sun highest in the sky? Lowest in the sky? (b) During which month is the full moon highest in the sky? Lowest in the sky? (c) From your observations, what is the relationship between the sun's noon altitude and the maximum altitude of the full moon?

(a) The sun is highest in June, lowest in December. (b) The moon is highest in December, lowest in June. (c) When the sun is at its highest altitude, the full moon is at its lowest altitude. When the sun is at its lowest altitude, the moon is at its highest altitude.

4. Recall that the full moon is always on the opposite side of Earth from the sun. In June, Earth's Northern Hemisphere is tipped toward the sun and away from the full moon. What effect does Earth's tip have on the altitudes of the sun and the full moon? How is this shown on your graph? What season begins in the Northern Hemisphere in June?

In June, the sun will be high in the sky, and the full moon will be low. On the graph, the sun is at its highest altitude in June when the moon is at its lowest altitude. Summer begins in the Northern Hemisphere in June.

5. Compare the altitudes of the sun and the full moon in December. Based on your results, predict how Earth's Northern Hemisphere is tipped relative to the sun and the full moon in December. What season begins in the Northern Hemisphere in December?

In December, the sun is low in the sky, and the full moon is high. The Northern Hemisphere is tipped away from the sun and toward the full moon. Winter begins in the Northern Hemisphere in December.

NAME ______________________________

CLASS ____________ DATE ____________

Apparent Size of the Sun

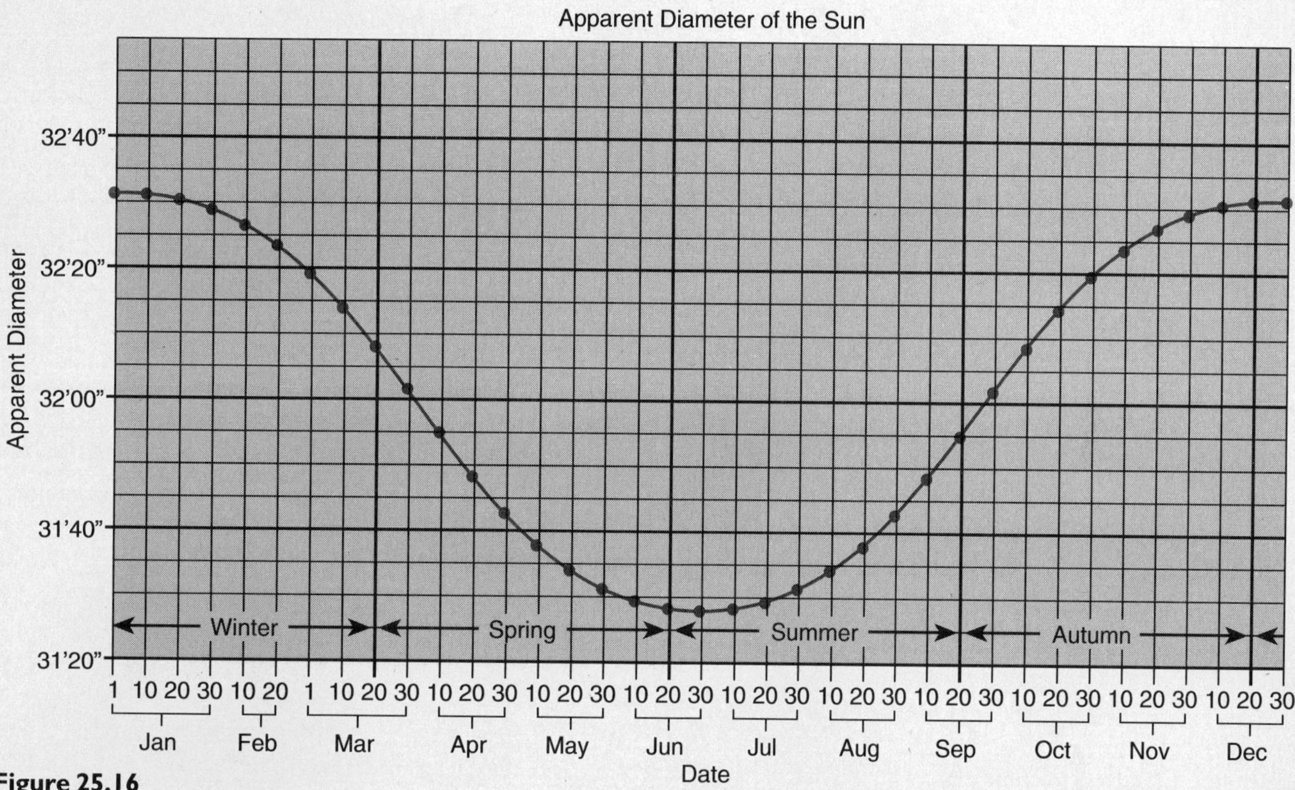

Figure 25.16

Analysis and Conclusions

1. In general, how is the apparent size of an object affected by its distance from an observer? Does an object appear larger when the observer is closer or farther away from it?

The object will appear larger when the observer is closer, smaller when the observer is farther away.

2. According to your graph, in which season is the sun's apparent diameter largest? Will Earth be closer to or farther from the sun at that time?

The sun's apparent diameter is largest in winter. Earth must be closer to the sun during the winter.

3. In which season is the sun's apparent diameter smallest? Will Earth be closer to or farther from the sun at that time?

The sun's apparent diameter is smallest in summer. Earth must be farther from the sun during the summer.

4. Based upon your answers to questions 1–3, explain how you know that distance from the sun is not a cause of seasons.

According to the answers to questions 1–3, Earth is farther from the sun during the summer and closer during the winter. If distance were a cause of seasons, the opposite relationship should be true.

5. What is *aphelion*? From your graph, determine between which dates Earth is at aphelion.

Aphelion is the point in the orbit of a planet at which it is farthest from the sun. According to the graph, aphelion occurs between June 30 and July 10.

6. What is *perihelion*? From your graph, determine between which dates Earth is at perihelion.

Perihelion is the point in a planet's orbit at which it is nearest to the sun. According to the graph, perihelion occurs between January 1 and January 10.

7. Compare your answers to questions 5 and 6 with the dates of aphelion and perihelion given on page 466. How do they compare?

The answers are consistent with the text. The text lists perihelion as occurring on or about January 2 and aphelion as occurring on or about July 4.

8. Using the values in the data table on page 470 of your text for the maximum and minimum apparent diameters, calculate the average apparent diameter of the sun. Show your work. Remember that 60 seconds is equivalent to 1 minute.

$$\text{average apparent diameter} = (32'32'' + 31'28'')\,/\,2 = 32'$$

9. Use the formula below to calculate the percent variation in the apparent size of the sun throughout the year. Based on your answer, what is the percent variation in Earth's distance from the sun?

$$\%\ \text{variation} = \frac{\text{average - minimum}}{\text{average value}} \times 100$$

$$\frac{32' - 31'\,28''}{32' \times (60''/1')} \times 100 = 1.7\%$$

The percent variation is the amount by which Earth's distance varies from the average. Thus, Earth's distance from the sun is 150 000 000 km ± 1.7%, or 150 000 000 km ± 2 550 000 km. Point out to students that this is a small percent change. Ask them to think about the variation in heating of the atmosphere that occurs throughout the year in their location. Most students will probably conclude that the heating variations are greater than ±1.7%.

CHAPTER 26

LAB ACTIVITY

NAME ______

CLASS ______ DATE ______

Temperature Inversion

Analysis and Conclusions

Graph 1

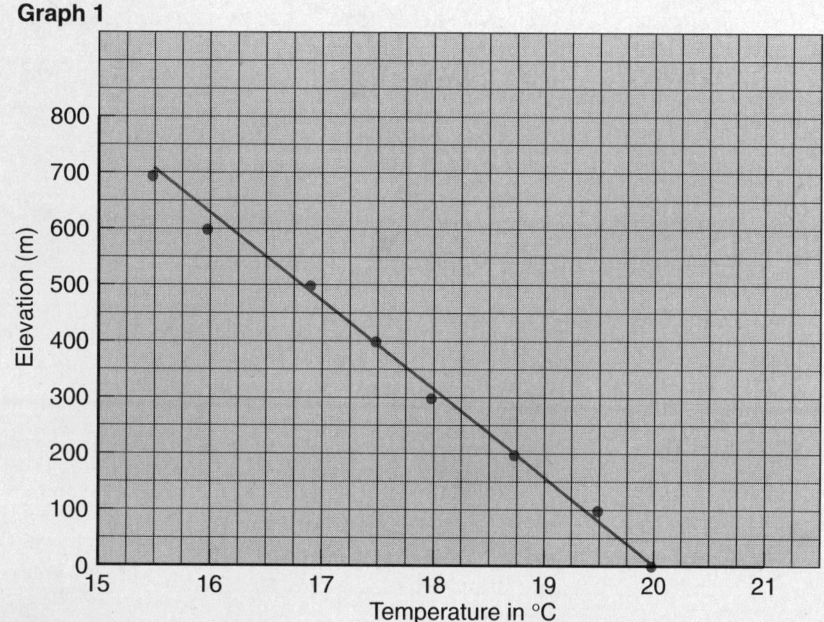

Graph 2

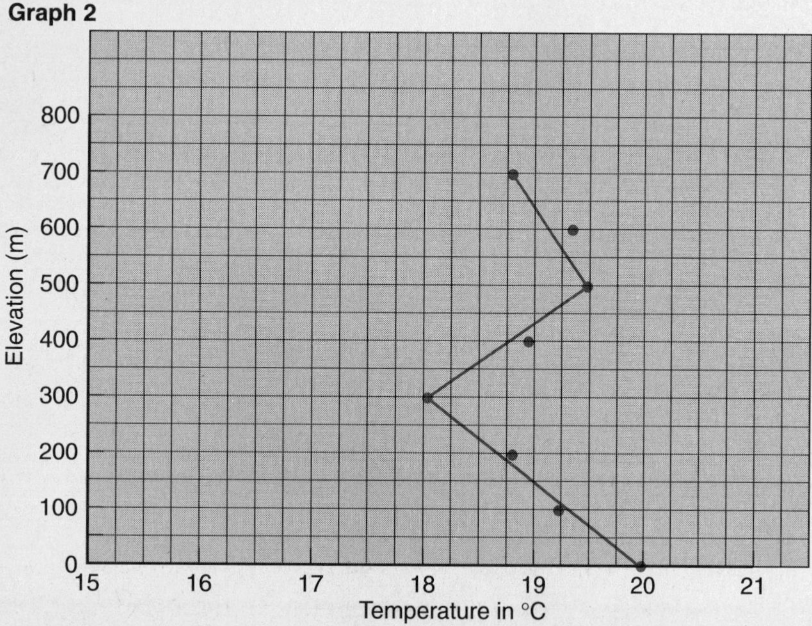

Figure 26.16

1. In Graph 1, does the temperature increase or decrease as altitude increases?

Temperature decreases as altitude increases.

2. In Graph 1, how many meters of elevation does it take for the temperature to change by 1°C? Does the rate at which the temperature decreases change as altitude increases?

Temperature changes 1°C per 160 meters. No, the rate at which temperature changes remains the same.

3. How does the rate of temperature change from 0–200 meters shown in Graph 1 compare with the rate of temperature change from 0–200 meters shown in Graph 2?

The rate of change in Graph 2 is about the same as the rate of change in Graph 1.

4. Describe the changes in temperature above 200 meters in Graph 2.

In Graph 2 above 200 meters, the temperature begins to rise.

5. Determine which of your graphs represents normal conditions and which represents a temperature inversion. Write these terms as titles on the appropriate graphs. Based on your graphs, explain what a temperature inversion is.

Graph 1 represents normal conditions; Graph 2 represents temperature inversion. Answers will vary but should include some description of temperature changes being upside down or the opposite of the normal lapse rate.

6. Since the addition of heat increases the distance between particles, volume also changes. Any slight changes in volume affect density because density is the mass of a substance divided by its volume. In Graph 2, how would the density of air from 200–500 meters compare with the density of air above 500 meters?

The air above 500 meters is denser than the air from 200 to 500 meters.

7. How would the density difference implied in Graph 2 affect the movement of air pollutants that are released at the surface? Why is it important to be aware of this effect?

Air pollutants would be trapped near the surface of the earth by a dense layer of air. Air quality would be much worse than usual during this time.

8. Strong winds can destroy or prevent temperature inversions from forming. Which city, Des Moines, Iowa or Denver, Colorado, is more likely to experience frequent temperature inversions? Explain your answer.

Denver, Colorado; Features of topography, such as mountains, can increase the frequency of temperature inversions by trapping the air.

NAME ____________________

CLASS ____________ DATE ____________

CHAPTER 27

LAB ACTIVITY

TEXT ACTIVITY DATA SHEET

Dew Point and Relative Humidity

Analysis and Conclusions

Data Table A—Dew Point Method	
1. Temperature of classroom air (°C)	____
2. Capacity of air at classroom air temperature (g/kg)	____
3. Dew Point from trial 1 (°C)	____
4. Dew point from trial 2 (°C)	____
5. Average dew point (°C)	____
6. Specific humidity (capacity at dew point) (g/kg)	____
7. Relative humidity = $\frac{\text{Specific humidity}}{\text{capacity}}$ (%)	____

Data Table B—Psychrometer Method	
1. Temperature of classroom air (dry-bulb temperature) (°C)	____
2. Wet-bulb temperature (°C)	____
3. Difference between dry- and wet-bulb temperatures (°C)	____
4. Relative humidity (%)	____

1. Compare the two relative humidity values for the classroom air from Data Tables A and B. Are the two values the same or different? If the values differ, which value do you think will be more accurate? Explain your answer.

Answers will vary. The first method is probably less accurate because the first appearance of dew may be missed.

2. Suppose you are looking at clouds that have just formed on a summer afternoon. What do you know about the relative humidity of the air at the bottom of the cloud?

The bottom of the cloud shows that the dew point has been reached.

3. Imagine that early one cool morning you use a psychrometer outdoors and discover that the wet-bulb and dry-bulb values are the same.

(a) What conclusion can you draw about evaporation from the wet-bulb thermometer in this case?

No evaporation is taking place.

(b) What conclusion can you draw about the relative humidity in this case?

Relative humidity is 100 percent.

(c) From your knowledge of relative humidity, would this be a good or bad day for hanging the laundry outdoors to dry? Explain your answer.

Clothes will not dry in air with 100 percent relative humidity.

CHAPTER 28

LAB

ACTIVITY

NAME ______________________________

CLASS ______________ DATE ______________

Recording and Correlating Weather Variables

Daily Weather Chart

Date/ Time	Temperature (°C)	Air Pressure (mb)	Wind Direction	Wind Speed (mb)	Relative Humidity (%)	Total Precipitation (cm)	State of Sky	Cloud type	Present Weather Conditions

Data Table A

Weather Conditions	**High Air Pressure**	**Low Air Pressure**
Range of temperatures (°C)		
Relative humidity range		
General weather conditions		
General state of sky		

28 NAME ____________ CLASS ____________ DATE ____________

Analysis and Conclusions

1. Is there a wind direction that usually brings cooler weather? Explain your answer.

North winds bring in cooler air because they come from colder latitudes.

2. Which wind direction usually brings warmer weather? Explain your answer.

South winds bring in warmer air because they come from warmer latitudes.

3. How is wind speed affected when air pressure changes rapidly? How is wind speed affected when air pressure holds steady?

Wind speed increases as air pressure changes. Winds remain light when the air pressure is steady.

4. According to your data, is high pressure associated with clear weather or stormy weather? Is low pressure associated with clear weather or stormy weather?

In general, high pressure is associated with clear weather, and low pressure is associated with stormy weather.

5. Is the state of the sky a good indicator of the next day's weather? Explain your answer.

Student answers will vary. The state of the sky is not a good indicator of the next day's weather.

6. Which cloud types are associated with precipitation? State your evidence, referring to data on your chart.

Nimbostratus and cumulonimbus

7. What is the relationship between relative humidity and weather? Explain your answer.

High humidity occurs with precipitation. Low humidity occurs with clear weather.

8. Do changes in relative humidity indicate changes in weather conditions? Explain the relationship, referring to data on your chart.

Decreasing humidity indicates clearing, and increasing humidity indicates precipitation.

9. On the basis of your data and conclusions, what weather conditions are the most useful for making your own local forecast?

Wind direction, air pressure, relative humidity, and cloud type are most useful.

10. Forecast the weather for the next two days and explain your prediction.

Answers will vary.

NAME ____________________

CLASS ____________ DATE ____________

CHAPTER 29
LAB ACTIVITY

TEXT ACTIVITY
DATA SHEET

Evaporation and the Windchill Factor

Data Table A	
Initial Room Temperature	
Final Room Temperature	
Water Temperature, Air Drying One Minute	
Water Temperature, Air Drying Two Minutes	

Data Table B			
		Temperature after Blow Drying	
Liquid	Initial Temperature	One Minute	Two Minutes
water			
glycerin			
alcohol			

Analysis and Conclusions

Point out to students that the reason wind increases the rate of evaporation is that it replaces the saturated air surrounding the moist surface with drier, non-saturated air.

1. Compare your temperature results from air drying water and blow drying water. In which case was there a greater change in temperature between the first and second minute?

Blow drying the water produced a greater temperature change.

2. What effect did the air from the blow dryer have on the liquids and the thermometer bulb?

It made the liquids evaporate at a greater rate. The evaporation removed heat from the thermometer and caused the temperature to fall.

3. Why did the change in temperature differ during blow drying for the different liquids?

The liquids did not evaporate at the same rate.

4. Which liquids had the most rapid and the least rapid evaporation rates?

The alcohol evaporated the fastest, and the glycerin evaporated the slowest.

5. Why was cloth fastened to the bulb of the thermometer?

The cloth holds more liquid than the surface of the bulb alone, allowing more evaporation to take place.

6. Why was it important to record the room temperature at the beginning and the end of the experiment?

If the room temperature varied during the experiment, the varied temperature would affect the accuracy of the results.

7. If the air in the room was saturated with water vapor, how would the temperatures of the three liquids be affected by blow drying? Explain your answer.

The temperature would not change because the saturated air would allow no more evaporation.

8. When you put a drop of water and a drop of alcohol on the back of your hand, which felt cooler? Why do you think people who have fevers are sponged with rubbing alcohol?

Alcohol feels cooler. Alcohol evaporates rapidly, drawing heat from a feverish patient.

9. How does the wind cool you on a hot summer day?

By continually blowing the moist air away from the body, wind speeds up the evaporation of perspiration from the skin.

10. What can a strong wind on a very cold day do to your exposed skin?

Wind can cool your skin below the air temperature. Frostbite can occur, depending on wind speed and air temperature.

11. Explain why windchill is *not* a factor for a car left outside on a cold, windy night.

The car's surface does not produce any moisture. Therefore, no evaporation takes place, and the car remains at the same temperature as the air.

12. Given that evaporation removes heat from the surroundings, predict the effect that condensation will have on the surroundings. How does condensation affect the weather in a low-pressure system? (See Topic 9, page 550.)

Condensation releases heat to the surroundings. As moisture condenses to form clouds in a low-pressure system, the air is heated, which in turn lowers the pressure further. The increased pressure gradient results in stronger winds.

NAME ______________________

CLASS ______________ DATE ______________

Reading Weather Maps

Procedure

1. Look at the weather maps on pages 662–663 of your text. Use the Physical United States map on pages 654–655 of your text as a reference and name the cities and states where weather stations, identified as station models, are located.

The fourteen cities are Atlanta, GA; Bismarck, ND; Boise, ID; Chicago, IL; Kansas City, MO; Miami, FL; Minneapolis/St. Paul, MN; New York, NY; Oklahoma City, OK; Phoenix, AZ; Portland, OR; Salt Lake City, UT; San Antonio, TX; and San Francisco, CA.

2. At each station, the station model displays temperature and three other weather variables. What are the three variables?

The variables are wind speed, wind direction, and percentage of sky cover.

3. Which city had the highest temperature over the four-day period? Which city had the lowest temperature?

The highest temperature was in Miami on January 31 at 61°F. The lowest temperature was in New York City on January 28 at –12°F.

4. Identify the city with the highest wind speed and the city with the lowest wind speed over the four-day period. Give the wind direction and date for each of these cities.

The station with the highest wind speed was Salt Lake City at 20 knots on January 28. The wind direction was SE. The station with the lowest wind speed was Boise on January 30. There was no wind.

5. Look at the January 28 weather map. List four cities with 100 percent cloud cover and four cities with no cloud cover.

The four cities with 100 percent sky cover were Boise, Salt Lake City, Minneapolis/St. Paul, and Chicago. The four cities with clear skies were Kansas City, Oklahoma City, Atlanta, and Miami.

6. On many simplified weather maps, the centers of high-pressure systems are symbolized by an H with a circle around it, and the centers of low-pressure systems are symbolized by an L with a circle around it. Look at the January 31 weather map. Name two states where high-pressure systems are centered and two states where low-pressure systems are centered.

High-pressure systems were centered in Idaho and Mississippi. Low-pressure systems were centered in Arizona and New Mexico.

7. What type of front extended through the western states on January 30? Describe where the front had moved on January 31.

The front was a cold front. It moved halfway between Phoenix and San Antonio.

8. What type of precipitation was falling in (a) Ohio on January 28, (b) North Dakota on January 29, and (c) North Carolina on January 30? Refer to page 514 of your text, Figure 27.15.

(a) rain (b) snow (c) drizzle

Analysis and Conclusions

1. In what general direction do weather systems move across the continental United States? Use evidence from the maps to support your answer.

The weather systems move from west to east.

2. Use the four weather variables on your maps to summarize the weather conditions in Atlanta on January 29, 30, and 31. (Suggestion: Construct a data table with the dates across the top of the table and the four weather conditions down the left side.)

Data Table

Variable	Jan. 29	Jan. 30	Jan. 31
Temperature °F	32	59	34
Percent Sky Cover	10	100	10
Wind Speed (knots)	1–2	8–12	3–7
Wind Direction	SE	SW	NW

3. Explain what factors led to the changes in weather conditions in Atlanta between January 29 and 30 and between January 30 and 31.

A warm front followed by a cold front crossed Atlanta.

4. Predict how weather conditions in Miami will change between January 31 and February 1. Explain the reasons for your prediction.

The temperatures in Miami will decrease because a cold front will pass through the city.

NAME ______________________________

CLASS ______________ DATE ______________

Forecasting Severe Storms

Procedure

1. Identify the weather variables shown on the map.

The weather variables are wind speed, wind direction, cloud cover, temperature, dew point, and precipitation.

2. What are the dew points in Indianapolis, Louisville, and Chattanooga? What are the temperatures in these three cities?

Indianapolis has a dew point of 43°F and a temperature of 52°F, Louisville has a dew point of 52°F and a temperature of 64°F, and Chattanooga has a dew point of 59°F and a temperature of 70°F.

3. Using the map on page 571 of your text (Figure 30.13), identify the types of fronts present at locations A, B, and C. In which direction are the fronts moving?

Front A is a cold front moving east. Front B is a warm front moving north. Front C is an occluded front moving north.

Analysis and Conclusions

1. Explain how the low-pressure system centered over southeastern Iowa influences the movement of the fronts.

Winds move counterclockwise around low-pressure systems. Therefore, the cold front extending south is pushed east, and the warm front extending to the east is pushed north.

2. If the wind direction remains the same, predict how the dew point in Indianapolis will change. Explain your answer.

The dew point increases from north to south. Because the wind is coming from the south, moist air should be pushed north, increasing the dew point over Indianapolis.

3. Give two reasons why you would expect the temperature in Indianapolis to rise over the course of the day.

South winds push warmer air from the south. The temperature should also increase due to heat from the sun.

4. The dot-dash line extending from Mississippi up to Illinois represents a line of thunderstorms called a squall line. What are the weather conditions that caused the squall line to form?

Cool, dry air from the west is pushed over warm, moist air from the south, causing unstable conditions.

5. Explain why the winds in Memphis are stronger than the winds in any other city on the map.

The squall line is located directly over Memphis.

6. Based on your answers for questions 2 and 3, explain why conditions favor the formation of very severe storms.

Winds from the south cause the lower levels of air to become warmer and more moist. Therefore, there is a larger differential in temperature and dew point between the bottom layer of warm air from the south and the top layer of cool air from the west.

CHAPTER 31

MAP

ACTIVITY

NAME ______________________

CLASS ____________ DATE ____________

World Climates

Procedure

Part A—Using an Earth's Climates Map

1. For each of the cities listed below use the Earth's Climates map to estimate the city's latitude and to determine the city's climate.

Data Table			
City	**Latitude**	**Climate**	**Climate Characteristics**
Manaus, Brazil	4°S	Wet Tropical	hot and very rainy all year
Bombay, India	19°N	Wet-and-Dry Tropical	hot all year with wet and dry seasons
Mexico City, Mexico	20°N	Highland Climate	temperature and precipitation vary greatly
Houston, Texas	30°N	Humid Subtropical	hot, humid summers and mild winters
Cairo, Egypt	25°N	Arid	desert climate with very little rain
Rome, Italy	42°N	Mediterranean Subtropical	hot, dry summers and mild, rainy winters
Chicago, Illinois	42°N	Humid Continental	warm summers and cold, snowy winters
Yakutsk, Russia	62°N	Subarctic	short summers and long, cold, winters

2. Compare the climates for cities in your data table with latitudes within 5° of one another. Is latitude the only factor that determines climate? Explain your answer.

No, other factors affect climate besides latitude. Students can compare the climate for Bombay and Mexico City, Houston and Cairo, or Rome and Chicago.

Part B—Interpreting an Earth's Climates Map

4. Which climate is found most often in the belt between 5°N and 5°S? Between 55°N and 65°N? Of the six climate controls listed in the introduction, which is primarily responsible for the differences?

5°N–5°S, wet tropical; 55°N–65°N, subarctic; latitude

5. Which three continents do *not* have subarctic, subpolar, or polar climates? Why?

South America, Africa, and Australia.

6. Locate Johannesburg and Cape Town on the continent of Africa. Near which city would a farmer needing rain year-round prefer to live? Explain your answer.

Johannesburg; The climate there is mild and rainy all year.

7. Locate the cities of Sydney and Perth in Australia. Which city is likely to have lower humidity in December? Explain your answer.

Perth; December is summer in Australia. In summer, Perth is hot and dry.

8. The average annual range of surface air temperatures is 56° for Yakutsk, Russia, and 46° for Edmonton in Alberta, Canada. Which climate control is responsible for the difference in temperature ranges between the two cities?

Since Asia is a larger continent, its climate is less tempered by oceans. Therefore, Yakutsk has greater seasonal temperature variations than Edmonton.

9. Compare the climates of St. Petersburg, Russia, and Nairobi, Kenya. Predict which city has a larger annual temperature range. Explain your answer.

The climate in Nairobi is hot all year. St. Petersburg has a change from warm in summer to cold in winter, resulting in a larger temperature range.

10. Locate Phoenix, Arizona, and Jacksonville, Florida, and imagine a straight line between the two cities. List the climates that occur from west to east along the line. What does this mean about rainfall and humidity from west to east along the line? By latitude or location, give one example of this same kind of climate change from another continent.

arid, semiarid, and humid subtropical; Rainfall and humidity must increase from west to east. The pattern can be seen in Australia, southern South America and southern Africa. The pattern from dry to wet can also be seen from west to east across Asia.

11. Recall that air rising in the doldrums forms a low-pressure belt around the equator. In the horse latitudes, sinking air forms high-pressure belts at 30°N and 30°S. Use the Climates map to determine with which kinds of climates these two wind belts are generally associated.

The horse latitudes are associated with the dry climates, while the doldrums are associated with humid tropical climates.

Part C—Correlating Data from Two Maps

13. Turn to the Patterns of Annual Precipitation map (page 582 of your text). Compare the areas that have under 10 inches of annual precipitation with the same areas on the Earth's Climates map. With which climates are these areas associated?

arid, semiarid, subarctic, subpolar, and polar

14. Locate the coastal regions of the Atlantic Ocean above 50°N latitude on both the Earth's Climate map and on the Surface Ocean Currents map. What climate occurs at 50°N on the west side of the Atlantic Ocean? At 50°N on the east side? What causes these climates?

West side has polar and subpolar climates due to cold air from the Labrador and East Greenland currents. The east side has a temperate marine climate due to warm air from the Gulf Stream and North Atlantic.

15. Use the Earth's Climates map to name the continents on which Highland Climates occur and the Physical World map to determine which features coincide with these climates. Which climate control is responsible for the location of Highland Climates?

North America (Rockies), South America (Andes), Africa (Ahmar Mountains, not on map), and Asia (Himalayas). Altitude is the significant climate control.

Analysis and Conclusions

1. How would the Earth's Climate map appear if latitude were the only controlling factor?

Climate zones would occur in horizontal bands parallel to lines of latitude.

2. Monsoons are seasonal winds that bring rain. Which kind of climate is associated with monsoons? How do you know this?

wet-and-dry tropical climates; Since monsoons are seasonal, areas that experience monsoons alternate between rainy seasons and dry seasons.

3. Growers of citrus fruits in Florida sometimes lose their crops to bitter cold winter air masses from Canada. Why are citrus growers in California much less likely to suffer damage from these same air masses?

The Rocky Mountains protect California from cold Canadian air.

NAME ____________________

CLASS ____________ DATE ____________

Interpreting Geologic History

Procedure

1. Using the Physical Map of the United States on pages 654–655 of your text, locate Utah, Wyoming, the Rocky Mountains, the Uinta Mountains, and the Green River. In what mountain range does the Green River begin? The Green River is a tributary of what larger river? Record your answers.

The Green River begins in the Rocky Mountains and is a tributary of the Colorado River.

2. Now look at the Flaming Gorge geologic map on page 653 of your text. Notice the compass direction shown in the lower part of the map. Which edge of the map is the north edge? In which compass direction is the top edge of the map?

The right side is the north edge; the top edge is east.

3. Use the map scale to calculate the approximate area shown in the map.

The map is about 2.5 miles by 2.9 miles. Based upon that data, the area is 7.25 or 7.3 (to the nearest tenth) square miles.

4. The relief of an area is the difference between the highest and lowest points of elevation in the area. Using the cross-section, determine the approximate relief of the map area.

The total relief is about 1400 ft.

5. How does the cement of a calcareous sandstone differ from that of a quartzitic sandstone? Identify rock units from Figure 32.16 of your text that have these two cement types. How could the acid test (page 51) be used to distinguish the two cements?

The calcareous sandstone is cemented with calcite, while the quartzitic sandstone is cemented with quartz. The Weber and Morgan formations both have calcareous sandstones, while the Navajo and Uinta Mountains are quartzitic sandstones. Rocks with calcite cement should bubble in acid.

6. Using the Geologic Timetable on pages 600–601 of your text, determine which of the rock units listed in Figure 32.16 were formed during the Paleozoic Era. Which were formed during the Mesozoic Era?

Morgan, Weber, and Park City are Paleozoic; Dinwoody, Moenkopi, Shinarump, Chinle, Navajo, and Carmel are Mesozoic.

7. Locate the Dinwoody Formation in the cross-section below the map. Name the younger rock unit that is in contact with the Dinwoody. Name the older rock unit that is in contact with the Dinwoody. If you were standing on the Dinwoody Formation on the line of the cross-section, in what direction would you walk along the line of the cross-section to reach the younger formation? In what direction would you walk to find the older rocks?

The Moenkopi is the next younger rock unit; the Park City is next older. You would walk north (or NNW) to reach the younger formation (the Moenkopi) and south (or SSE) to reach the older (the Park City).

8. Assuming the rocks have not been turned over, what is the youngest rock shown in the cross-section? How do you know? Which rule for interpreting relative time (Chapter 32, Topic 2) did you use to determine your answer?

The Navajo Sandstone is the youngest because it is at the top; law of superposition.

9. Locate the fault on both the map and the cross-section. This is the Uinta Fault. Identify two rock units in contact with the Uinta Fault.

the Uinta Mountain Group and the Morgan Formation

What is the age of the fault relative to these rock units? How do you know?

The fault is younger than either rock unit because it cuts across both.

What rule for interpreting relative time did you use to determine your answer?

the law of cross-cutting relationships

10. The Shinarump Formation was deposited on the eroded surface of the Moenkopi Formation. What is such an erosional surface in the rock record called? Describe the steps needed to form this surface. Refer to the names Shinarump and Moenkopi.

Such surfaces are unconformities. The Moenkopi was raised above sea level, eroded, and then buried under Shinarump sediments.

11. Which rock unit forms the rim of Horseshoe Canyon? What does that indicate about the resistance to erosion of that unit compared to the rocks above it?

The Park City Formation forms the rim of the canyon. It must be more resistant to erosion than the units above it.

Analysis and Conclusions

1. The Shinarump Formation is a coarse-grained sandstone that resembles a conglomerate. How does the age of the sand grains in the sandstone compare with the age of the sandstone itself? Explain your answer using the correct rule for relative time.

The large sand grains are older than the sandstone; the law of included fragments states that pieces of one rock in another rock must be older.

2. The geologic map symbol ⊥ indicates the strike of the rock layers (see page 295 of your text). The number with the symbol is the measurement of the angle at which the layers dip underground. Locate the Dinwoody and Morgan Formations on the map. Note the dip angle of each. Which formation dips more steeply? Does the cross-section verify your answer? Explain.

The Morgan at 45° has a steeper dip than the Dinwoody at 19°. This difference is also shown in the cross-section where the Morgan dip increases toward the surface.

3. Along the line of the cross-section, how does the dip direction of the Uinta Mountain Group compare with that of the Uinta Fault?

The two dip in opposite directions. The Uinta Mountain Group has a generally northern dip, while the Uinta Fault dips toward the south.

4. Examine the Park City Formation on both the map and the cross-section. In the cross-section, the Park City Formation is one of the thinner units. Why does it cover so much of the map area?

The dip of the Park City is nearly horizontal. The unit does not disappear underground until surface elevations rise above it into younger rocks.

CHAPTER 33

LAB ACTIVITY

NAME ______________________________

CLASS ____________________ DATE ____________________

Analysis of Brachiopod Fossils

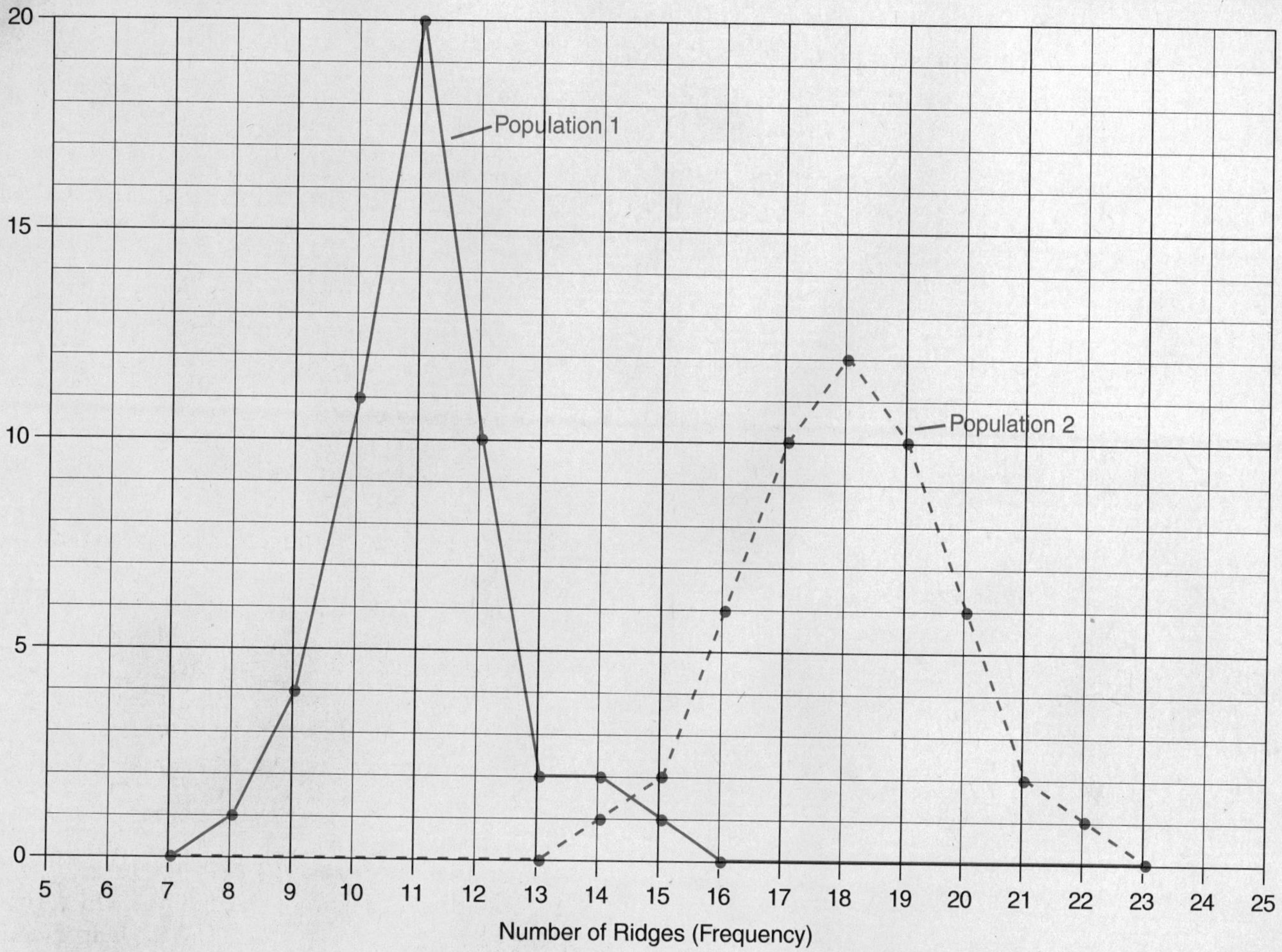

Population 1

Population 2

Number of Ridges (Frequency)

Analysis and Conclusions

1. What are the modes for each population? Are the modes for each population the same as the medians?

Both the modes and the medians of population 1 and 2 are 11 and 18 respectively.

2. Based on your graph, do you conclude that there are distinct differences between the two populations? Explain your answer.

There is very little overlap between the two graphs. The modes and medians of the two graphs are also different. One can conclude that the two populations are distinct.

3. Counting the number of ridges on the brachiopod shells is just one way to analyze the brachiopod population. What are some other ways?

Measure the dimensions of the shells—length or width or thickness.

Data Table B		
Number of Ridges (Frequency)	Population 1	Population 2
7	0	0
8	1	0
9	3	0
10	11	0
11	20	0
12	10	0
13	2	0
14	2	1
15	1	2
16	0	6
17	0	10
18	0	12
19	0	10
20	0	6
21	0	2
22	0	1
23	0	0
Total	50	50

4. You are given three brachiopod fossils that were collected at the same location as Population 1 or 2. You do not know where these samples were collected. Two shells have 9 ridges, and one shell has 11 ridges. Based on your data, can you determine to which population they belong? Explain your answer.

The number of ridges most closely matches the number of ridges in Population 1.

5. You are brought three more brachiopod fossils. Two have 14 ridges and one has 15 ridges. Can you determine to which population these brachiopod fossils belong? Explain your answer.

Because brachiopods with 14 and 15 ridges were found in both populations, one cannot determine to which population these new fossils belong based on the number of ridges.

6. You return to the site where the Population 2 fossils were collected. You find 50 more brachiopod fossils in a layer of younger rocks. You count the number of ridges on each shell and determine that the mode is 23 ridges and the median is 21 fossils. How would the shape of the graph for these fossils differ from the shape of the graph for the older fossils?

The graph would be skewed to the right.

7. Based on these new Population 2 fossils, what would you conclude about the evolution of brachiopods at that location?

The number of ridges increased over time.

NAME ______________________

CLASS ______________ DATE ______________

How Big Was That Dinosaur?

Data Table	
Kind of dinosaur	
Model mass	g
Model length or height	cm
Actual dimension of real dinosaur	m
Actual dimension of real dinosaur	cm
Scale	
Scale cubed	
Mass of actual dinosaur	g
Mass of actual dinosaur	kg
Your weight from bathroom scale	lbs
Weight of student 2	lbs
Weight of student 3	lbs
Weight of student 4	lbs
Weight of student 5	lbs
Weight of an average student	lbs
Mass of average student	kg
Number of students equal in mass to one dinosaur	students

Dinosaur Size Data	
Name	Dimensions
Tyrannosaurus	6 meters high, 15 meters long
Stegosaurus	8 meters long
Triceratops	9 meters long
Trachodon	5 meters high, 9 meters long
Apatosaurus	70 meters long

 NAME ______________ CLASS ______________ DATE ______________

Analysis and Conclusions

1. Consider your value for the number of students equal in mass to one dinosaur. Do you think that the value is reasonable and logical? Explain.

This question is designed to make students think about their final answer. Students who do not arrive at reasonable, logical answers should be encouraged to recheck their measurements and arithmetic.

2. Is the volume of your classroom more or less than the volume of your dinosaur? List the specific steps to take to find out. (Note: Only list the steps. Do not perform the calculation unless you wish.)

Basically, this question involves two steps: (1) determining the volume of the dinosaur; and (2) determining the volume of the classroom. There are several methods by which the volume of the dinosaur can be found, including using the model's scale or displacing an equal volume of water. The assumption about a dinosaur having a density of 1 g/cm^3 can be used with the dinosaur mass already determined. The volume of the room can be determined by measuring the dimensions and multiplying. Other methods, such as measuring the amount of water needed to fill the room, may also be accepted, even if they are impractical.

3. *Tyrannosaurus rex* had a huge head with teeth that measured up to 18 centimeters long. If *Tyrannosaurus* were around today, could it swallow a human whole? Based upon the scaling methods used in this lab, propose a method of finding out. (Note: Again, only explain how you would determine the answer. Do not do the calculation unless you wish.)

Scale is the key to this question. Compare the 18 centimeter long *Tyrannosaurus* tooth to the length of a human tooth. Based upon the size of the human mouth, compare the size of the dinosaur's mouth to the size of a human's mouth. *Tyrannosaurus* probably could have swallowed a human whole.